WARSHIP 1995

WARSHIP 1995

Edited by John Roberts

CONWAY
MARITIME PRESS

Frontispiece: The main control top of the battleship Dreadnought *in 1907, at the head of the forward tripod mast, aft of the first funnel. The development of fire control positions in British dreadnoughts is detailed in John Robert's article* The Mast and Funnel Question (p.40). (Courtesy John Roberts)

© Brassey's (UK) Ltd 1995

First published in Great Britain 1995 by
Conway Maritime Press,
An imprint of Brassey's (UK) Ltd
33 John Street
London WC1N 2AT

British Library Cataloguing in Publication Data
Warship . .
  1995
  1. Warships
  623.825

ISBN 0–85177–654–X

Design, typesetting and page make-up by
Books Unlimited (Nottm), Pleasley, Nottinghamshire, NG19 7QZ
Printed and bound in Great Britain by
Butler & Tanner Ltd, Frome

CONTENTS

EDITORIAL

By its nature *Warship* has a tendency to reflect the current state of the recording of naval technical history. The latter has evolved substantially over the past twenty-five years, during which period the technical content to be found in warship publications generally has become both more extensive and more accurate. At the same time, many of the facts and figures that were once the almost exclusive preserve of naval architects, officers and administrators have become much more widely known and, what is more important, understood. In addition the authors of such works, at one time almost entirely made up of enthusiasts, now come from a much wider range of disciplines, although they still, in general, write on naval matters because of a strong personal interest in the subject.

Like many others, I began my study of warships by collecting information in much the same way as people collect stamps. This was largely concerned with the simple process of grouping ships into their classes, gathering basic particulars and histories and recording variations in appearance. Today it is comparatively easy to obtain such information; *Conway's All the World's Fighting Ships* series, for example, provides basic particulars of all but minor craft back to 1860 and there are beginning to emerge similar works to cover earlier periods. As always, however, there are still gaps to be filled, and examples of this can be found within these pages. The article by Donald Canney on the vessels of the Union Navy during the American Civil War gives details of many river vessels which have not previously been given the coverage allocated to their contemporaries in the regular navy, while Pierre Hervieux's article on German auxiliary patrol vessels of the Second World War adds to the available information on operational matters, in which there are still many areas of detail where information is incorrect or incomplete.

The recording of basic reference material provides the ground work for the next stage of naval research which focuses on more limited subjects, both technical and operational, in greater detail. For many years this category has been the mainstay of naval technical history in general and *Warship* in particular. Hence, the accompanying pages have several such articles that cover the origins, particulars and histories of individual ship classes. Three of these articles are concerned with all of these aspects and are typical of this type of in-depth study – Erwin Sieche on the Austro-Hungarian navy's *Franz Joseph I* class of the 1890s, John Jordan on the French cruisers of the *La Galissonniere* class of the 1930s and Richard Wright on the Royal Navy *Dragonfly* class river gunboats, also of the 1930s. Two others are of a more specialised nature with Thomas Lynch concentrating mainly on the operational history of the Canadian carriers *Warrior* and *Magnificent*, while George Moore describes the design history of the British Type 42 frigate of the 1950s. The latter cannot

of course describe anything but the design history, as these ships were never built. Again this is an area in which interest has grown steadily over the last quarter of a century, recognising that the continuity of warship design history is incomplete without them as they often provide the link between the designs of those ships that *were* built.

These items introduce something new to the straightforward assemblage of information as they become concerned with the 'why' as well as the 'what' of naval history. This is a critical step as it adds understanding to knowledge and begins to provide a more complete picture of past events. It also opens up the route to more detailed questions, not simply of ships and their histories, but to their background. This background can be of a general nature, covering such things as policy and politics or go into matters of detail, such as the development of naval equipment or the effects of individual personalities. In the latter category David Brown's article on Sir Rowland Baker is a welcome addition to these pages in providing details of the effect of one man on the development of both Royal Navy and Canadian Navy ships. This is a rarity for, while there are many biographies of naval officers, there are very few for naval architects. This is unfortunate because personal records can add substantially to understanding of how warship designs have developed, providing details that would not be available from official documents. To some extent the effects of personalities are also to be found in Richard Layman's discussion article on the dubious aspects of some accounts of General 'Billy' Mitchell's test bombing of the German battleship *Ostfriesland* in 1921 – a clear demonstration of the ill effects of badly recorded history. Mitchell was certainly a character and certainly had an effect – principally on aircraft enthusiasts, who read more into the results of these tests than was justified. Also in the 'discussion' class, but on a broader base, is Keith McBride's article on the state of dreadnought development in 1914 – who was building what and why, and where it seemed to be leading. This includes some detail of ship designs both speculative and intended (but not built) which, as mentioned previously, provide links between earlier and later designs – one can only wonder, and speculate, as to what might have happened had war not broken out in August 1914.

Finally there are two articles concentrating on the detail and development of equipment – John Campbell's article on British heavy coast defence guns, and John Brook's article on the evolution of fire control positions in British dreadnoughts prior to the First World War. Although land based, the coast defence guns in question were naval weapons which for the most part were intended for use against naval targets. In the case of Singapore, this was taken a little too literally and the inability of her heavy guns to fire inland proved something of an embarrassment.

The article on fire-control is an example of one of the most recent trends in naval technical history. It describes in detail a particular aspect of naval technological development that, although only a small part of a much larger story (both in the development of ships and fire-control), had a substantial effect on the evolution of the British dreadnought and its potential in time of war. Despite its importance, this subject, and many others with a similar claim, have been covered only superficially until quite recently. In the last few years books have appeared on naval engineering, fire-control, radar and Asdic/Sonar, which cover their subjects in substantial detail. All of these areas are complex and will no doubt take some time to establish themselves as part of the enthusiasts essential reference/reading material. Fire-control is a particularly difficult subject to tackle, although, once one has established an understanding of the terminology and the basic principals upon which it works, it becomes less formidable than it would at first appear. The more recent work on this subject – represented by the research of Professor Jon Sumida and now that of John Brooks – has concerned itself with the British navy prior to and during the First World War. No doubt, in time this will extend to cover developments in other navies and other periods. Bearing in mind the potential, and that there are other subjects similarly waiting to be researched in-depth, it is obvious that there is still vast scope for original and valuable work. However, as important and exciting as this work may be, it is worth remembering that it has evolved from the basic research produced by many people over many years. This work should not be underestimated, it provides the information from which new enthusiasts establish their interest, is the foundation upon which the majority of later research has been built and gives us all our basic works of reference.

John Roberts

Akizuki class article
We have been asked to point out that the drawings reproduced on page 153 of Warship 1993 were drawn by Mr Talao Ishibashi and were his copyright. We apologise to Mr Ishibashi for omitting the credit line making this clear.

THE UNION NAVY

during the Civil War, 1861–65

The war vessels of the United States Navy in the Civil War were an astonishingly diverse assortment of vessels – from technologically advanced turret ironclads, to converted river boats and harbour ferries, and obsolete wooden frigates. Donald L Canney, who is working on a book about the Civil War Union Navy, surveys this seemingly confused fleet of vessels, which was generated from the various operational roles required by the conflict and the uncertain state of naval technology at the time.

The tasks required of the Union Navy's vessels during the Civil War included the blockade of Southern coasts, close infantry fire-support in shallow inland streams, blue water cruising in search of Confederate commerce raiders, countering enemy ironclads and operations against coastal fortifications. Each of these required different types of vessels which did not necessarily coincide with those available in the prewar navy. The upshot was a vast acquisition programme, including the construction of both ironclads and conventional ships and the purchase of more or less suitable merchant vessels for conversion to naval use.

The technological flux of the mid-nineteenth century also made uniformity in naval forces nearly non-existent. The sailing warship was by now obsolete but the 1861 naval establishment still retained many of these vessels – the last pure sailing frigate had been commissioned as late as 1854. Also obsolete, but still in the inventory, were the paddle steamers built in the 1840s and 1850s, with their huge paddle boxes and vulnerable machinery. Yet more variety came from the introduction of iron armour – casemate and turret systems were tried, plus some one-off experiments. On the western rivers, conventional steamboats were converted into sometimes bizarre looking armour-clads with amazingly light draughts. The following is an attempt to systematise the warships of the Union Navy during the conflict; first, however, the state of naval technology in the US Navy must be presented.

Steam power, though now the primary propulsion system, had not yet progressed beyond the uneconomical, simple expansion engine, making a sailing rig mandatory for extended cruising at sea. The naval cruiser, unlike merchant steamers on closed circuits, could ill afford to be a slave to the amount of coal in her bunkers. The typical steam screw-sloop was propelled by a two-cylinder engine with which she could manage a speed of 7kts. By the war's end, newer vessels, with larger engines and leaner hulls, improved on this by 4 to 5kts. Unfortunately, screw propulsion machinery was complicated and breakdowns were frequent. On the other hand, the paddle steamer had simpler engines and was usually faster. Consequently the navy-built screw steamer, though well armed, was no match for a blockade runner powered by paddle wheels. Another factor in the blockade was the requirement that the blockader remain on station for weeks at a time, whereas the runner simply made a quick point-to-point run with as much cargo as possible.

Of course the Civil War was also played out on numerous inland waterways, resulting in a genus of vessels unique to this conflict. These shallow draught, converted riverboats could go – said the hyperbole – where there was a heavy dew. Indeed, it was not unknown for a side wheeler to 'walk' itself to a navigable depth of water. Even the river ironclads were often radical conversions from merchant steamers. These long, relatively flimsy, river boats featured 'hog chains' – for-and-aft iron trusses which literally held up the boat's ends and prevented the hull buckling upward amidships. Of course, the obvious distinction between these and blue water vessels was the ability of the former to simply tie-up to the nearest tree and send the crew foraging for fuel. These vessels were specific to this internal conflict and were immediately discarded when the war ended.

The majority of the ships were built of wood in the traditional manner and the use of iron was limited to fittings – the navy had no facilities for iron shipbuilding. In larger ships, diagonal hull-strapping was employed to prevent hogging, tough live oak was the favoured material but supplies of this dwindled and various other varieties found their way into later vessels.

Ironclads had been used in the Crimea and the American adversaries quickly applied this new technology. The North, despite its industrial base, had not the capacity to roll iron more than $2\frac{1}{2}$in thick. This, with the limited number of shops capable of building iron vessels, were factors in the number and quality of such vessels in the Union Navy. Various attempts were made to layer the available thicknesses into shot resistant casemates or turrets.

The monitors used eight or more layers of 1in iron to good effect. The machinery of the typical screw ironclad was, again, generally unable to produce over 7kts. On the rivers, the barge like hull lines and swift currents made for slow and exceedingly unwieldy vessels.

The majority of the purchased vessels were intended for the blockade. Here presence was emphasised rather than armament: an internationally recognised blockade was determined not by the efficiency of the vessels but by their existence on station. Therefore, the navy department caught considerable public criticism when it appeared that they would purchase anything that would float, including New York Harbour ferry boats. Indeed, some of the purchased vessels proved ill-suited to navy usage. The ferries, however, made good gun platforms for joint army operations on the rivers. Conversion of merchant vessels for naval use typically involved strengthening gun decks, removal of superfluous cabins, installation of ammunition storage spaces and, often, adding protective sheet iron over pilot houses and other vulnerable spaces.

Finally, the state of the navy in 1861 is pertinent here. Though there were ninety vessels on the register, some fifty were sailing vessels, of which ten were active. Of forty steamers, five were unserviceable, one was on the Great Lakes and two were tugs. There were thirty-two useful steamers, including eight in ordinary. What follows is a description of the major classes or categories of Union war vessels.

The '90 day' Gunboats were the smallest of the wartime new construction – 158ft long and 671 tons, carrying one large pivot and a pair of broadside guns. All but one survived the war. This photograph of an unidentified member of the class was probably taken on the James River.

Conventional Steam Warships

The mid-nineteenth century steam sloop formed the bulk of the US Navy at the outbreak of hostilities. The majority of the wartime navy-yard built ships were based on pre-war designs ranging in size from the '90-day' gunboats upward. The typical steam sloop or gunboat had a single gundeck with weaponry built around one or two large smoothbore pivot guns and two or more broadside carriage guns. Their rig ranged from two-masted schooners to full square-rigged ships and their machinery was usually a two-cylinder simple-expansion unit typically yielding a 7kt cruising speed, though some of the larger sloops bested this with larger engines and the advantage of length. Note that the first line steam frigates such as *Colorado* were too deep to be used in many operations in the deep south.

Unadilla Class: The so-called '90-day' gunboats were built for the blockade and their origin can be traced to within a month of Lincoln's proclamation of this policy. Their general arrangement, size (158ft pp x 28ft x 10ft = 671 tons) and armament (single large pivot gun and two broadside guns) were based on an early gunboat, the *Pocahontas*, of the 1850s. Twenty-three were built, all by non-navy builders; the '90-day' appellation came about from a delivery date contract stipulation for four of the vessels. In fact, the shortest time from contract to commission was the *Unadilla*, at 93 days.

Their hulls were usually white oak framing and yellow pine plank, with diagonal iron-strapping for longitudinal strength. Engines were simple expansion units of the back-acting (return connecting rods in British parlance) variety with two 30in cylinders and two boilers, yielding 400hp and a maximum speed of 10kts. They had forced draught fans, surface condensers and bunkers for 112 tons of coal. The screw could be disconnected to reduce drag when under sail alone. Though designed as fore topsail schooners, operating in ports and rivers for most of the time

The Mohican *class (*Wyoming *or* Tuscarora *is seen in this view) were well armed, strongly built and versatile – capable of blue water cruising and coastal work. Their armament was built around big Dahlgren pivot guns rather than broadside weapons. The* Kearsarge, *famous for her action with* Alabama, *was a variation on this theme.* (Naval Historical Center)

resulted in their dispensing with the sails entirely. The complement of these vessels ranged from 65 to 100.

Their midships pivot gun was usually an 11in Dahlgren smoothbore or a 100pdr Parrott rifle on circular pivot rails allowing its use on either side, with a 16ft segment of each bulwark built to unship allowing a considerable field of fire. Two 24pdr carriage guns, plus a 20pdr boat howitzer completed their armament. The performance of these vessels was not spectacular but was more than adequate, considering their hasty genesis and construction. The constant steaming required on the blockade detracted materially from their early 10kt capability.

The '90-day' gunboats were all in commission by 8 March 1862, with four participating in the attack on Port Royal in November 1861. All save one were in commission at the close of the war. Only one, the *Scotia*, had been sunk and that twice: once in a collision and a second time as the victim of a mine. Ten were with Farragut at New Orleans. The *Cayuga* had been the vulnerable lead ship in that operation and came away with forty-two hits. They racked up 146 blockade captures. The last (*Unadilla*) was sold in November 1869, in Hong Kong. The '90-day' gunboats of the *Unadilla* class were: *Aroostook, Cayuga, Chippewa, Chocura, Huron, Itasca, Kanawha, Katahdin, Kennebec, Kineo, Marblehead, Ottawa, Owasco, Pembina, Penobscot, Pinola, Sagamore, Sciota, Seneca, Tahoma, Unadilla, Winona* and *Wissahickon*.

Kansas Class Sloops: These eight vessels were to rectify some of the '90-day' ships' shortcomings. Additional length and larger engines were to enhance speed and added beam was to provide a steadier gun platform, resulting measurements being 171 to 179ft × 30ft beam. A variety of engines was tried, some yielding good speed, but the unusual machinery generally created maintenance problems. All retained two-masted rigs until the postwar years when the remaining ships received a third mast. All were armed with single pivot guns amidships and four broadside weapons, usually 32pdrs or 9in Dahlgrens.

The vessels proved to be significantly faster than the '90-day' ships and a cruising speed of 10kts is probably a fair generalisation for the group. Only two were in commis-

sion as early as 1863 but five participated in the operations against Fort Fisher in late 1864–early 1865. Two (*Maumee* and *Pequot*) were decommissioned at the end of the war and all but *Yantic* were out of service by 1883. The *Yantic* served in various auxiliary roles until as late as 1929 by which time she was disintegrating from age. The *Kansas* class consisted of *Kansas, Maumee, Nipsic, Nyack, Pequot, Saco, Shawmut* and *Yantic*.

Mohican and Class: These screw sloops were among the most useful and long lasting vessels of this era. Of ten included in the class, six saw over twenty years service each, and three, over thirty years. The group included the *Kearsarge*, which made herself a legend with the defeat of the Confederate cruiser *Alabama* in 1864.

The class included six built in 1859 and four more added as a wartime measure in 1861. They were built to six plans, two at 188ft and the remainder at 198ft in length. Below are their names arranged according to their respective designs:

1. *Mohican* ('59), *Kearsarge* ('61).
2. *Tuscarora* ('59), *Wyoming* ('61).
3. *Iroquois* ('59), *Oneida* and *Wachusett* ('61).
4. *Dacotah* ('59).
5. *Seminole* ('59).
6. *Narragansett* ('59).

Congress authorised the original ships in 1858, noting the need for steamers capable of coastal work, both in home waters and in response to the continuing troubles in China (the T'ai P'ing rebellion). They were to be 'full power' steamers, as opposed to the earlier frigates, such as *Merrimack*, which were officially auxiliary steamers.

In terms of weaponry and its relation to hull design,

these ships were a significant break from the past. The *Mohican* and class were the first major war vessels designed without emphasis on broadside guns. By 1855 John Dahlgren's 11in gun (capable of throwing shell as well as shot) had completed trials, making it theoretically possible to replace no less than four 32pdrs with a single weapon throwing a 132lb projectile. That logic was the genesis of these vessels: ships for which no precedent has been found.

The upshot of this was a class wherein a 200ft gundeck supported as few as six cannon. For comparison, the 1854 *Constellation* had batteries of twenty to twenty-four guns. The size and weight (10 tons including carriage) of the 11in gun precluded broadside use and conventional carriages. Pivot rails (racers) allowed the use of the guns on either broadside. The ultimate extension of these principles would be seen in the *Monongahela* of 1863, which had a total battery of three pivot guns.

There were two major varieties in this group. *Narragansett* and *Seminole* were shorter by 10ft, narrower by 2ft and, at 1043 tons and 1230 tons respectively, significantly smaller than their companions. Each carried a single 11in pivot gun, while the others were designed to mount two 11in. All carried four 32pdrs in broadside. All the 1859 vessels began their careers with such batteries. However, in the 1861 vessels, and in later refits of the 1859 ships, there was considerable variety. Rifled 100pdr Parrotts were often substituted for the Dahlgrens (*Mohican* carried one on forecastle pivot rails) and an additional pair of broadside guns was sometimes fitted. Several had 30pdr or 50pdr rifles mounted on the topgallant forecastle.

The vessels were designed to draw 13ft or less (*Narragansett* and *Seminole* drew 10ft) and their hull construction was unremarkable. However, the concentration of fewer weapons amidships allowed for the use of quite sharp hull lines in the pursuit of speed. Decks and internal arrange-

ments were simple, with a long unbroken gundeck and berth deck interrupted by machinery spaces. In the postwar era, forecastle and quarter decks proliferated, with the former sometimes extending to the foremast. Their original rig reflected reliance on steam: topmasts and topsails only and no square sails on the mizzen. In postwar years, economy moves brought re-emphasis on sailing rig and resulted in greater sail area.

All had two-cylinder machinery, usually back- or direct-acting, with two or three boilers, producing 700 to 873hp. They managed 11 to 12kts early in their service lives and *Dacotah* recorded 13.2kts on trials.

The careers of these screw sloops involved more extended cruising at sea than for any other class of wartime steamers. All, save *Narragansett* and *Seminole*, made cruises in search of various Confederate raiders and the *Tuscarora* was instrumental in forcing the abandonment of CSS *Sumter* in 1862. The *Wyoming* was employed upholding trading privileges in Japan – and sank a Japanese warship in the process. The *Kearsarge*'s war record was uneventful until the sinking of the *Alabama* in 1864. The *Wachusett* gained notoriety when her commanding officer rammed her 'accidentally' into the Confederate cruiser *Florida* in neutral waters. The *Tuscarora*, *Mohican*, *Oneida*, *Iroquois* and *Seminole* saw action in various coastal campaigns, from Northern Virginia to Mobile Bay.

The shortest post war career belonged to *Oneida*, sunk in a collision in 1870, and *Seminole* and *Mohican* were out of service by 1872. The *Kearsarge* was lost in the Caribbean in 1894, though the guns with which she downed *Alabama* had long since been enshrined ashore. The last of this noteworthy class was *Iroquois*, sold in 1910.

Ossipee and Sacramento Classes: These ten vessels were essentially enlargements of the *Mohican*s; with increased beam for steadiness and increased length for speed. They retained the big pivot-gun battery as applied to the *Mohican*s but in the *Sacramento*s a third 11in smoothbore or 150pdr Parrott was mounted forward. As noted previously, *Monongahela* became the apotheosis of Dahlgren's 'all big gun' ideas, arriving for duty on the Mississippi River armed only with three big pivot-guns. Farragut, concerned with rate of fire and vulnerability in

Lackawanna of the Sacramento class, carried the centre-line pivot gun to its limit – mounting three, with four 9in and one 50pdr. This view shows her lofty, post war ship rig – substantially larger than her original bark arrangement (much like that shown in the photograph of the Mohican class vessel). (Naval Historical Center)

the river campaigns, immediately added six broadside guns. Typically, therefore, they were armed with two 11in, one 150pdr rifle and four 32pdrs or four 9in smoothbores. The *Ossipee* class had dimensions of 205ft × 38ft × 16ft 9in = 1934 tons and consisted of *Ossipee, Juniata, Adirondack* and *Housatonic*. The *Sacramento* class had dimensions of 225–232ft × 37ft 6in–38ft × 16ft 10in–17ft 7in = 2030–2526 tons and consisted of *Sacramento, Shenandoah, Ticonderoga, Monongahela, Lackawanna* and *Canandaigua*.

Their back-acting machinery was designed by chief engineer B F Isherwood and they typically cruised at 12kts. Originally all had rather sparse barque rigs and, in some cases, neither bowsprits nor cutwater knees. Loftier masting, additional yards, cutwater knees and bowsprits were postwar additions. The *Monongahela* and *Lackawanna* had improvised iron cutwater plating for use in ramming the Confederate ironclad *Tennessee* at the battle of Mobile Bay.

All went into service between August 1862 and June 1863. The *Lackawanna, Monongahela* and *Ossipee*, were at Mobile Bay and *Juniata, Shenandoah* and *Ticonderoga* took part in the Fort Fisher operations. The *Adirondack* was wrecked during her first cruise in August 1862. The *Housatonic* made history as a victim: the first warship to be sunk by an enemy submersible (the *H L Hunley*), off Charleston in 1864.

Their postwar careers were generally long, with the exception of *Sacramento* which was lost in 1867, and five were active into the 1880s. A tidal wave washed *Monongahela* ashore at St Croix in 1867 but she was refloated and finished her career as a sail training ship, burning at Guantanamo Bay in 1908. Her remains can still be seen there.

Hartford Class Steam Sloops: These five sloops, authorised in 1857, were essentially replacements for the sailing sloops, which mounted some twenty guns on a single open gun deck, with pivot guns on forecastle and poop. The new ships were comparable to the British corvettes *Cadmus* and *Pearl* of 1856, and were to have a draught of about 18ft, enabling them to operate in southern ports. Four were constructed at navy yards and the fifth, *Brooklyn*, was contracted to Jacob Westervelt, a prominent builder of clipper ships. The ships and their dimensions were as follows:

Hartford (225ft × 44ft × 23ft 3in = 2550 tons)
Richmond (225ft × 42ft × 20ft 8in = 2604 tons)
Brooklyn (223ft × 43ft × 22ft 8in = 2532 tons)
Pensacola (230ft 8in × 44ft 6in × ? = 3000 tons)
Lancaster (235ft 8in × 46ft × 22ft 3in = 3290 tons)

The unique vessel of the group was *Lancaster*, with significantly greater dimensions and displacement. She mounted twenty-four broadside 9in guns, plus two pivots, and was the only vessel to have a complete spar deck throughout her career. The broadside battery of *Richmond* and *Brooklyn* was sixteen guns and that of the remaining pair twenty each – with some career variations. In the postwar years several had 8in rifles (conversions from Dahlgren smoothbores) mounted abaft the foremast on pivot rails.

They were powered by two-cylinder back acting or di-

The Richmond, *a sister ship to* Hartford, *although of slightly differing dimensions. The heavy armament and moderate draught of these vessels made them particularly useful for operations against coastal fortifications. This post war view shows a wide port for an additional pivot gun – an 8in rifle.* (Naval Historical Center)

USS Colorado *at Woosung, China, c1871. Though mounting a powerful battery of forty-six 9in pivot guns,* Colorado *and others of her class were too deep for many southern harbours which limited their wartime use. Two,* Roanoke *and* Merrimack, *were converted to ironclads in attempts to make better use of their large hulls.* (Naval Historical Center)

rect acting machinery. The *Pensacola*'s machinery was an experiment in the steam expansion controversy and was an unmitigated failure: weighing twice that of the *Lancaster*'s for instance, and proving significantly less efficient – they were soon replaced. The class was not noted for speed: with sail, for example, *Hartford* could attain 11kts and most cruised under steam at 8 to 9kts.

Hull construction and design was conventional. Live oak and iron diagonal-strapping contributed to their longevity. They were ship rigged and *Hartford* made use of rigging screws (turnbuckles) rather than deadeyes (as early as 1864). The *Lancaster* was rebuilt with a ram bow in the 1870s, along with a heroic eagle figurehead, which still exists today.

All went into commission in 1859 or 1860. The wartime careers of these ships were action filled (excepting *Lancaster*, stationed in the Pacific), with their significant firepower and moderate draught making them naturals for operations against coastal fortifications. The *Hartford*, *Richmond*, *Brooklyn* and *Pensacola* were at New Orleans and all but the latter were also at Mobile Bay in 1864.

Each exceeded 30 years of active service, with *Brooklyn* first to go, in 1891. The other four served into the next century, with *Hartford*, having become a venerated icon as Farragut's flagship, surviving until 1956.

Merrimack Class Steam Frigates: Six frigates were authorised in 1854, the first screw propelled class in the US Navy. In the tradition set down so vividly by *Constitution* of 1797, these ships were to be larger than their counterparts in other navies, and faster than more heavily armed enemies. Five of these were 'double banked' frigates with a main gun deck carrying from twenty-four to twenty-eight of the new 9in Dahlgren smoothbore shell guns and the upper deck originally armed with 8in shell guns in broadside and a 10in Dahlgren on the forecastle. The sixth ship, *Niagara*, was unique and is discussed below. The group and their dimensions were:

Merrimack (256ft 10$\frac{1}{2}$in × 50ft 2in × 26ft 2$\frac{1}{2}$in = 4635 tons)
Wabash (262ft 4in × 50ft 2in × 26ft 2in = 4774 tons)
Minnesota (264ft 8$\frac{1}{2}$in × 50ft 2in × 26ft 2in = 4833 tons)
Roanoke and *Colorado* (263ft 8$\frac{1}{4}$in × 51ft 4in × 26ft 2in = 4772 tons)

There were four hull designs: essentially enlarged sailing frigate configurations with more widely spaced ports for the Dahlgren shell guns and additional machinery spaces. Hull construction was principally oak with two sets of diagonal iron-strapping.

Two 72in cylinders propelled *Merrimack* and *Wabash*, while *Minnesota*, *Roanoake* and *Colorado* had trunk engines, with larger piston diameters but similar cubic capacity to the other vessels'. All had telescopic funnels and hoisting screws.

The ships drew considerable attention, particularly overseas, where their battery was considered quite formidable. Unfortunately, they proved to be quite slow: not likely to exceed 8kts under steam. In any case, the Royal Navy built two classes of screw frigates (eleven vessels) in response.

These frigates, drawing some 23ft, had limited use in the War between the States as they could not enter the majority of the southern ports. The *Wabash* participated in the Port Royal expedition in 1862 and she, and *Minnesota* and *Colorado*, took part in the bombardment of Fort Fisher late in

The Niagara *was designed by George Steers, famous for fast vessels, such as clipper ships and the yacht* America. *She had exceedingly sharp lines and a lofty rig but was given only a dozen spar-deck 11in guns. When twenty 11in were added to her gun deck her ports became dangerously low and she soon reverted to twelve guns.* (Courtesy Peabody Museum of Salem)

the war. The *Merrimack* of course was burned at Gosport (Norfolk) in 1861 and reappeared as the ironclad *Virginia*. *Roanoke* was converted to a useless ironclad (see below). The *Colorado* participated in the 1871 Korean punitive expedition and was sold in 1885. The *Minnesota* was sold in 1901 and the *Wabash* in 1912.

The preceding classes comprised the majority of the navy-built screw propelled unarmoured war vessels during the war. Three other prewar ships round out the total: *San Jacinto*, *Pawnee* and *Niagara*. The first of these was built in 1851. She was armed with six 8in shell guns, was 210ft long and weighed 2200 tons. Her claim to fame was in stopping the steamer *Trent* and taking prisoner the Confederate diplomats, Mason and Slidell.

The *Pawnee* was built contemporaneously with the *Mohican* class, by contract with John Griffiths of New York. To achieve 10ft draught he designed a beamy hull with concavity at the stern and twin screws. She was first given four 11in Dahlgrens, all on pivot rails, but was later rearmed with broadside 9in guns, eventually carrying twelve of these, plus two large rifles. She was exceedingly useful in river fire support operations but was excessively leewardly at sea and had a short postwar career.

The *Niagara* was contracted to George Steers, famous for his yacht *America* and other fast vessels. He attempted to combine sharp clipper hull lines with a frigate's weaponry, apparently intending to have her carry a battery comparable to the *Merrimack et al*. This was only possible by making her significantly larger than the other five and, at 328ft(pp) in length and weighing 5540 tons, she was the largest vessel to be built in the US up to that time.

Despite her commodious gundeck, she was only given spar deck weapons: twelve 11in Dahlgrens, on pivot rails. With a 3-cylinder engine she attained 10 to 11kts, but exceeded 16kts under sail. She laid the first Atlantic Cable with HMS *Agamemnon* in 1857. In 1863 she was given a full complement of twenty 11in guns along with the dozen spar deck guns. This enormous battery brought her ports dan-

gerously low and she reverted to her dozen guns (now 150pdrs) shortly thereafter. Later, in European waters, her commander refused combat with the rebel ironclad *Stonewall*. She was sold in the 1880s.

Finally, there were six screw steamers which had been purchased in the 1850s. These, *Mohawk*, *Crusader*, *Pocahontas*, *Mystic*, *Sumter* and *Wyandotte*, were 157ft to 169ft in length, 450 to 750 tons, and carried four to seven guns. *Sumter* was sunk in 1863, *Mohawk* was sold in 1864 and the rest served through the war.

Paddle Wheel Vessels

The last major American paddle wheel warships were the *Susquehanna* and *Powhatan*, of the early 1850s. At 3824 and 3865 tons respectively, they carried no less than fourteen 9in or larger guns. Both these veterans of Commodore Perry's Japan expedition continued to be useful during the conflict, particularly in the coastal campaigns, and survived long after the war. The third major paddle steamer was the *Mississippi* of 1841. At 3220 tons and mounting twenty guns of 9in or larger calibre, this reliable vessel was with Farragut on the Mississippi River until lost at the battle of Port Hudson in 1863. Smaller prewar side-wheelers were the *Water Witch* (255 tons), *Saranac* and *Saginaw*. The latter two remained on the west coast through the war. Another, the ex-Revenue cutter *Harriet Lane* (600 tons, four guns) was a useful addition until captured in 1863. The navy's only prewar iron ship, the side-wheeler *Michi-*

The 250ft, 3600 ton side-wheeler, Powhatan *was part of Commodore Perry's Japan expedition and was the Navy's last major side-wheel ship. She carried up to twenty large guns during the war.*

gan of 1841, was on the Great Lakes.

The double ended gunboats complete the inventory of navy-built conventional steamers. Thirty-nine of these, in three classes, saw wartime service. They were intended specifically for river work: with light draught of 6 to 7ft and rudders at each end. Paddle wheels were less likely to foul river obstructions than screws and provided for reliable, speedy operation: the machinery was invariably a single-cylinder directly connected to the paddle wheel shaft. Their batteries featured a large pivot gun at each end and four broadside guns. Most were built in civilian yards.

The *Octorara* and class numbered twelve, built to nine designs ranging from 730 to 1120 tons, and 207ft to 232ft in length. All went into service in early 1862. The *Sassacus* class, of twenty-eight vessels, were all 1173 tons and 236ft long. Twenty-seven of these entered service during the war. The *Wateree* was iron hulled. The *Mohongo* class numbered seven but only the *Muscoota* and *Suwannee* were commissioned before the surrender at Appomattox. These were iron-hulled (255ft long, 1173 tons) versions of the *Sassacus* class. All were contract-built and were the first American class of iron vessels (excepting the ironclads themselves).

Ironclad Vessels

The ironclad navy can be subdivided into monitors (revolving turret, low freeboard vessels) and casemated ships, with the preponderance going heavily to the former. Sixty

monitor type vessels were begun during the war, with thirty-seven completed by the end of 1865. There were nineteen non-turret vessels, of which fifteen were for river service. Only two broadside armoured vessels saw wartime service – *Galena* and *New Ironsides*.

Already twenty years in construction, the Stevens Battery was far from complete in 1861. She had an iron hull and 6in armour, but would have drawn over 20ft – far too deep for the southern coast. Her designer, inventor Robert Stevens, had intended her to defend New York Harbour. The navy rejected her and eventually she was turned over to the state of New Jersey. Though predating the Crimean ironclads, this experiment had little influence on Civil War armoured vessels.

John Ericsson's original *Monitor* was less a ship than a motorised floating gun platform. She was built to combat the Confederate ironclads – not to decimate fortifications or fight at sea. Her two 11in smoothbore Dahlgrens sat behind eight layers of 1in iron, bent into a turret 20ft in diameter. Two layers of $\frac{1}{2}$in plates covered horizontal oak beams forming the upper deck of the ship, which in itself was protected by vertical side armouring – 5in of iron over 25in of oak. At the time of her encounter with *Virginia* (ex-*Merrimack*), the turret and a pilot house were the only parts of the ship higher than her 18in freeboard.

Her machinery was also Ericsson designed: two pistons in a single cylinder, operating 'vibrating levers' connected to the propeller shaft, with which she attained 6kts. Independent auxiliary engines operated the turret (at $2\frac{1}{2}$ turns per minute) and ventilation blowers.

Finally, the iron hull itself was unique. She was flat bottomed with bilges at 35deg from the horizontal, angling up to the shelf which held her vertical iron and wood side armour. Ericsson made no attempt to give her more than a simple curve fore and aft, rather than ship like lines. Shal-

Mendota, *one of the* Sassacus *class double-enders. Built for narrow rivers with midship paddles, twin rudders and identical hull lines for and aft, these vessels were also quite fast – 12 to 14kts.*

Cross section of the original – John Ericsson's USS Monitor *– first of 60 monitors begun during the war. Though iron-hulled, her deck beams and armour backing were oak. In the later monitors ship-like lines replaced the flat bottom and angular bilges but the turret and low freeboard (18in) remained little changed. (Naval Historical Center)*

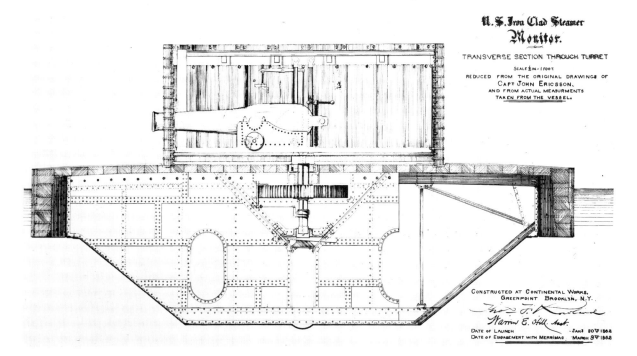

U.S. Iron Clad Steamer
Monitor.
TRANSVERSE SECTION THROUGH TURRET
SCALE ½IN · 1 FOOT
REDUCED FROM THE ORIGINAL DRAWINGS OF
CAPT JOHN ERICSSON,
AND FROM ACTUAL MEASUREMENTS
TAKEN FROM THE VESSEL.

CONSTRUCTED AT CONTINENTAL WORKS,
GREENPOINT, BROOKLYN, N.Y.

DATE OF LAUNCH · JAN? 30Ŧ 1862
DATE OF ENGAGEMENT WITH MERRIMAC · MARCH 9Ŧ 1862

low draught was one of the government's requirements and she drew only 10ft 5in when complete and loaded.

As completed, the ship had dimensions of 179ft × 41ft 6in and displaced 987 tons. Her complement was 49. She had been laid down on 25 October 1861 and commissioned on 25 February – some twelve days before ending the rampage of the CSS *Virginia* at Hampton Roads. It is noteworthy that, because of concerns about concussion within the turret, her 11in guns were limited to 15lb of powder – less than half their standard charge. The *Monitor*'s later career was relatively uneventful, though a few modifications were made: including increased protection for the pilot house and a more conventional funnel. She sank in a gale on 31 December 1862.

The *Monitor* was not the first ironclad, the Crimean War batteries at Kinburn have this distinction. However, the *Monitor*'s turret was the first to be operational and her clash with *Virginia* (ex-*Merrimack*) was the first battle between ironclad vessels.

Passaic Class Monitors: Ten *Passaic* class monitors were built, with their authorisation coming less than a week after the battle at Hampton Roads. Major improvements were the mounting of the pilot house above the turret, giving the hull faired ship-like lines (and a sheer), 11in turret armour and provision for two 15in smoothbore Dahlgrens (though a shortage of these limited the wartime batteries to one 15in and 11in gun each). The 15in gun was the largest available during the war, firing a 440lb projectile. The ships of the class were: *Camanche, Catskill, Lehigh, Montauk, Nahant, Nantucket, Passaic, Patapsco, Sangamon* and *Weehawken*.

The number and type of changes over the original *Monitor* made the *Passaics* vastly different vessels, as they only retained the general configuration of the original ship. All were built by contract as the navy had no facilities for building iron vessels. The *Passaic* was commissioned in December 1862, eight others by April 1863 and *Camanche*, assembled on the West Coast in May 1865.

The USS Tippecanoe *of the* Canonicus *class. The vessels of the class carried two 15in Dahlgren guns, firing a 440lb projectile – the largest naval gun then in use. She is shown at about the time of the Spanish-American war and was sold in 1899. (USN)*

All were 200ft × 45ft and of 1335 tons displacement and drew 11ft 6in – deeper than the original *Monitor*. Seven were involved in the 7 April 1862 attack on Charleston, SC, which proved a debacle for the Union Navy. They proved unwieldy and slow (maximum speed about 7kts, or 4kts in current) and they were vulnerable to hits at the turret's juncture with the deck which had the effect of jamming the turret. Their rate of fire was slow – one round every 5 to 7 minutes for the 15in – and aiming the turret was somewhat haphazard. Later, a protective ring was placed around the turret base and extra protection was given to the vulnerable pilot house.

Though these ships were inappropriate against fortifications, *Weehawken* encountered the ironclad *Atlanta* in 1863 and, as her 15in shot penetrated 4in of iron and 18in of wood, brought her surrender with five shots. The *Patapsco* was mined in January 1865 and *Weehawken* sank in a storm in 1863. The remainder had major postwar rebuilds, replacing their wood deck beams with iron, and remained in the inventory for decades (though infrequently in full commission). Several were commissioned during the Spanish American war (1898) and the last were sold in 1904.

Canonicus Class: The *Canonicus* class numbered nine vessels, *Canonicus, Catawba, Mahopac, Manayunk, Manhattan, Oneota, Saugus, Tecumseh* and *Tippecanoe*, built incorporating the improvements added to the *Passaic*s after the assault on Charleston in April 1862. Externally, the most obvious change was increased length and sharper bows, features which, along with larger engines and more boiler power, were to add speed. Further, all had twin 15in guns in the turrets, with their barrels turned down to allow them to protrude through the gunports. They measured about 225ft × 43ft and displaced 2100 tons. Sponsons were added to lessen the drag produced by the armoured overhang, and they attained 8kts.

The *Saugus* was the first in commission (7 April 1864), two (*Catawba* and *Oneota*) were sold to Peru before commissioning and *Tippecanoe* was completed after hostilities ended. The *Tecumseh* was the most famous of this class – mined at Mobile Bay in August 1864, and sinking with most of her crew, she remains there to this day. Postwar the first to be sold was *Saugus*, in 1891; the last, *Canonicus*, in 1908.

Dictator: Other than the original *Monitor*, plus members of the *Passaic* and *Canonicus* classes, the *Dictator* was the only other single turret Ericsson-designed monitor to see service during the war. (The light draught monitors, reviewed below, were not entirely Ericsson designed).

John Ericsson intended the *Dictator*, and a never completed companion – *Puritan*, to be ocean-going craft attaining 16kts. At 314ft × 50ft and 4438 tons, *Dictator* was one of the largest iron vessels built in the US to date. Her side armour was 6in iron over wood backing and the turret plating was 15in thick. She was armed with two 15in Dahlgren smoothbores on specially designed carriages and was powered by engines with 100in diameter cylinders. Though commissioned before the war's end, problems with her machinery and boilers prevented her participation in combat. She eventually proved capable of a speed of 10kts. She was decommissioned in 1877. The *Puritan*, which was to have 20in guns and was over 340ft long, was never completed; a new vessel took the name in the 1870s.

Casco Class Light Draught Monitors: The original Ericsson design for these twenty-three vessels was significantly re-worked by Alban Stimers of the navy's ironclad office, with ballast tanks worked into their hulls to allow reducing their profile in combat. This and other added weights resulted in a 3in freeboard (without stores, etc) on the first ships launched. Major modifications, including deletion of the Ericsson turret and the addition of a spar torpedo, did little to rectify their problems. They had been intended for very light draught river work but in the end did well to remain afloat at all. All were broken up or sold by 1875.

Double Turret Monitors: Five twin-turret monitors were completed in 1864–5: *Onondaga, Monadnock, Miantonomoh, Tonawanda* and *Agamenticus*. Only the first two saw wartime service. The *Onondaga* was designed by G W Quintard with Ericsson turrets, carrying two 15in smoothbores and two 8in rifles. She was iron hulled (226ft × 49ft 3in, 2592 tons) and had 11³/₄in armour on turrets and 5¹/₂in on her sides. With her twin screws she could make 7kts. She was commissioned in March 1864 and was active with the James River flotilla, easily penetrating the 6in iron of the Confederate *Virginia II* at Trent's Reach in early 1865. Postwar she was sold to France; she was broken up in 1903.

The Onondaga *is shown here after her postwar sale to France and refitting with new guns. Her original 15in guns had made quick work of the 6in iron with wooden backing of the Confederate* Virginia II *in 1865. Each turret also carried a 150pdr rifle.* (Naval Historical Center)

The *Monadnock* was wooden hulled, enabling her construction at Portsmouth Navy Yard, New Hampshire. She carried four 15in guns, in Ericsson turrets with 10in plating; side plating was 5in at the sheer. Twin screws drove the vessel, powered by two Ericsson engines. She measured 250ft × 53ft 8in and 3295 tons and was capable of a speed of 7 to 8kts. She participated in the attacks on Fort Fisher late in the war. In 1865 she rounded Cape Horn to San Francisco, taking heavy weather in her stride – though fitted with a substantial breakwater to protect the forward turret. She was broken up in 1874 and a new iron hulled vessel obtained her name. The other three double turret monitors were variations on *Monadnock*.

Roanoke: The Triple Turret Monitor: *Roanoke* was more a product of 'monitor fever' than of a calculated plan. The 1854 steam frigate was cut down and saddled with three Ericsson turrets (with 11in armour) along with 4¹/₂in of side armour and a ram bow. She carried two 15in and two 11in Dahlgrens and two 150pdr rifles on her 278ft wooden hull. She may have been of more use as a steam frigate – she was too deep for river work and rolled too dangerously to be safe at sea. She was guard ship on the James River from June 1863 to the end of the war and was broken up in 1883.

Casemate Ironclads: *New Ironsides, Galena, Keokuk*. The first two were contemporaries of *Monitor*, intended as possible alternatives to that vessel. The *Galena* (180ft, 738 tons) employed interlocking iron armour (about 3in thick) over 18in of wood on an otherwise conventional wooden hull. She carried four 9in Dahlgrens and two 100pdr rifles. With Ericsson engines she made 8kts maximum and rolled heavily at sea. Her armour proved totally inadequate against Drewry's Bluff in 1862: she was penetrated repeatedly with significant losses. She was later dis-armoured and served until 1869.

The *New Ironsides* was given 4¹/₂in of forged iron over some 15in of wood. She was 232ft(pp) in length, over 57ft

The Roanoke, *a former steam frigate converted to carry three Ericsson turrets, 4¹/₂in armour and a formidable ram. The weight and the high centre of gravity made her dangerous at sea and her deep draught made her useless on rivers.* (Naval Historical Center)

in beam and weighed 3486 tons; with armour only extending over the length of the battery of fourteen 11in Dahlgrens and two 150pdr rifles. Athwartships iron and wood bulkheads completed the battery 'box'. She was built by Merrick and Cramp and bark rigged. Though underpowered and leewardly at sea she proved nearly impregnable to shot, particularly in the protracted actions at Charleston in 1864. Had it not been for 'monitor fever' *New Ironsides* might have become the pattern for later Union ironclads. She was accidentally destroyed shortly after the war.

The *Keokuk* used another experimental armour scheme:

New Ironsides, *the Union Navy's only successful broadside ironclad. Her fourteen 11in and two 150pdr guns yielded a 1200lb plus broadside but she was far overshadowed by the drama of Hampton Roads and the technology of monitors.* (Naval Historical Center)

iron and wood sandwiched vertically under ⁷/₁₆in boiler iron. She was 159ft long and 677 tons with two stationary 'turrets' each carrying an 11in Dahlgren. She was delivered in February 1863 and was sunk at Charleston in April, completely riddled by enemy shot.

Sailing Vessels

The US Navy had seven ships of the line at the war's beginning. Two, including the 120-gun *Pennsylvania*, were lost by fire at Norfolk Navy Yard. None of the remainder were in active roles. Of thirteen frigates, seven were in active service. There were fourteen active sloops including the 1854, 20-gun *Constellation*. Two brigs rounded out the sailing fleet.

Acquired Vessels

Rather than individually detailing the acquired wartime vessels, the following is a survey of these vessels, by size, propulsion, mode of acquisition and, in some instances, specialisation. These are approximate numbers, based primarily on Paul Silverstone's *Warships of the Civil War Navies*. Note that the Mississippi River squadron is dealt with separately.

About 345 vessels of all types were acquired by purchase and/or capture by the navy during the conflict, including 251 steamers and ninety-three sailing ships. Of the total, eighty-four were captured of which fifty-five were steamers. Seven were brought from other government agencies, namely the Revenue Service and US Coast Survey. Note that the total number of captured vessels is much larger than the number taken for navy use.

Some thirty-four large (over 200ft) steam paddle wheel vessels were acquired for combat roles, sixteen by purchase and eighteen by capture. (Note that captured merchant vessels were technically purchased via prize courts). The largest was the *Vanderbilt*, at 340ft and 3360 tons, donated for $1 by Cornelius Vanderbilt. Eleven large screw steamers were purchased and four captured. Of the purchased screw steamers five were sister ships acquired before their completion and armed with eight to ten heavy guns – *Proteus, Nereus, Neptune, Glaucus* and *Galatea*. Medium sized steamers (over 100ft) numbered sixty, forty of them screw vessels. Nineteen of the total were captures, plus *Harriet Lane* from the Revenue Service and *Hetzel* from Coast Survey. Small steamers – less than 100ft – numbered thirty-two, four of them captured. Additionally, eighteen harbour ferries were purchased.

A rare prewar photograph of a US sailing warship, possibly the frigate Congress. *Though obsolete, sailing vessels continued to be employed in secondary roles throughout the war – usually on foreign stations.*

Auxiliary vessels (not armed for combat) numbered twenty-seven, of which eight were captures. Eighty-one tugs were acquired, including two by capture, and one from another agency. Additionally, the navy had four tugs built. Of the sailing vessels, there were thirteen full rigged ships, eighteen barques, two brigs and thirty-eight schooners and sloops, in addition to twenty-two purchased mortar schooners. Of the total, three were from other agencies and twenty-eight were captures. One was found – the yacht *America* raised from a river bed in Florida. None of these figures include the 'stone fleet' – sailing vessels purchased and sunk at the entrances of various southern ports in an attempt to block access to these ports.

The Mississippi River Fleet

This flotilla was originally under the War Department but was transferred to the navy in August 1862 – other vessels being transferred as completed. Twenty-four ironclads were built, with two of these incomplete by the war's end. The first three vessels of the fleet were 'timberclads' and nine were turreted. Eight ironclads were massive rebuild-

The converted ferry boat USS Commodore Perry. *These ungainly vessels proved invaluable as gun platforms for riverine warfare – eighteen were purchased.* (Naval Historical Center)

ings of merchant steamboats. There were twelve rams, structurally strengthened conventional steamers with little ordnance, intended for close combat – specifically, *Vindicator* and *Avenger*, which supposedly reached over 15mph.

There were some seventy-six 'tinclads' – converted merchant steamers with light iron plating. Other modifications included lowering of machinery into the holds, strengthening the decks for ordnance and the removal of passenger accommodations. Forty-nine were stern wheelers and twenty-three were side wheel vessels. The largest of the latter were *Black Hawk* and *Oachita*, at over 230ft long each, carrying ten and twenty-three guns respectively. Stern wheel vessels were of particular use in narrow waterways and side wheelers were more manoeuvrable. The tinclads typically measured 150ft to 175ft in length and carried six to eight guns.

The three timberclads were converted in 1861 by direction of Captain John Rodgers of the navy and then detailed to the army to assist in river operations. The *Conestoga*, *Lexington* and *Tyler* had their cabins removed and 5in oak planking installed. Timber strengthening was added and their boilers lowered into the holds. The first carried six guns, *Lexington* nine and *Tyler* thirteen. Though of 'ex-

ceedingly rough' construction, they served well throughout the war. The *Conestoga* was lost in 1864.

The first ironclads were the City class – seven vessels built by James B Eads, a well known civil engineer, and designed by S M Pook of the navy. These 'Pook Turtles' were 175ft × 50ft with paddle wheels recessed into the stern. They had $2\frac{1}{2}$in of iron on the forward casemate, 60ft down the sides and on the pilot house and oak backing 24in thick forward and 12in on the sides. They carried thirteen guns each, usually a mix of 32pdrs, 8in (64pdrs) and 30pdr–100pdr rifles – three across the bow, four on each broadside and two at the stern. Their hulls were basic scows – flat bottoms with angled bilges. Their two-cylinder engines and five boilers yielded a tentative $5\frac{1}{2}$kts.

They were the first ironclads in US service (the *Carondelet* was commissioned January 1862) and all were active through the western river campaigns. Their armour was not impenetrable and was often supplemented by their commanders. Three, *Cairo*, *Baron de Kalb* and *Cincinnati*, were sunk (two by mines) but the latter was raised for further service. The *Cairo* was recovered from the Yazoo River in 1962 and her remains are at Vicksburg Military

The blockade runner Robert E Lee, *as USS* Fort Donelson *in 1864. Built on the Clyde, this iron vessel made twenty-one runs through the Union lines before capture. Her oscillating engines and paddle wheels gave her a speed of up to 13.5kts.*

Park. Other class vessels were *Mound City, Cincinnati, Louisville* and *Pittsburgh*.

Other early casemate vessels were *Essex* and *Benton*, both radical conversions, the former from a stern wheel ferry, the latter from a catamaran snag boat. The *Essex* had a huge two-deck casemate, dimensions of 205ft × 60ft and carried eight heavy guns. Her armour was $1^3/_4$in iron and 30in of wood. In adverse current, she was towed. The

The Rattler, *a typical stern wheel riverboat converted to a 'tinclad' by adding light plating and strengthening the gun decks. Note the angled face of the casemate, forward. She carried six 24pdr and two 30pdr rifles.*

The 'Timberclad' Conestoga *of the Western Rivers fleet. Early riverboat conversion used 5in oak planking and heavier deck beams to support six guns.* (Naval Historical Center)

Benton was 187ft × 75ft and carried sixteen heavy guns – four of them across her wide bow – making her the most powerful of the 'riverclads'. Her plating was $2^1/_2$in forward and $5/_8$in aft with 20in to 30in backing. She also was a stern wheel ship and was as underpowered as others of her ilk, making $2^1/_2$kts against the current and 5kts in slack water. Both vessels served successfully throughout the war.

The *Chillicothe, Tuscumbia* and *Indianola* were purpose-built casemate vessels, commissioned between September

Cairo, *one of the City class ironclads, which preceded* Ericsson's Monitor *both in commission and in action – in February 1862. Note the transverse step in the battery side, which denotes the forward end of the 2.5in side armour, between the second and third gun ports. The ships of the class each carried 13 guns – including two in the stern. The remains of* Cairo *can now be seen at the Vicksburg Historical Park in Mississippi.* (Naval Historical Center)

River warfare emphasised forward fire and the ironclad Tuscumbia *carried three 11in Dahlgrens athwartships in the forward casemate. Hog chains, to prevent sagging at the ends, can be seen running longitudinally above her deck. Note also the mortar boat in the foreground and the 'tinclad' No10 in the background.* (Naval Historical Center)

1862 and early 1863. The first had side paddle wheels mounted on her quarters and a forward casemate housing two 11in Dahlgrens. Her forward plating was 3in, with 2in on the hull sides. Temporary cabins were built between the casemate and stern wheel housings. She made 9mph upstream – one of the few such steamers to exceed expectations. Her longitudinal strength was lacking, requiring added strapping to prevent hogging, but she served throughout the war.

The *Tuscumbia* was a broader version (72ft) of the *Chillicothe*, with three 11in guns in the athwartship casemate. She was 176ft long and powered by four cylinders – two for the paddle wheels and two for a pair of screw propellers. A stern casemate was given two 9in guns and her great width required cross-wise, in addition to lengthwise, hog chains. She was exceedingly poorly constructed and spent much time in refit.

The *Indianola* was identical in power plant to *Tuscumbia* but carried two forward 11in smoothbores plus two stern 9in guns. She was 175ft × 52ft and had a chequered career: forced aground and captured, blown up by the Confederates and repossessed by the Union.

The *Lafayette*, *Choctaw* and *Eastport* all had similar

Removal of the entire riverboat cabin structure and the addition of iron (and, experimentally, rubber) armour resulted in USS Choctaw, *one of the more bizarre looking vessels of war. Though 270ft long with a 69ft beam, she carried only eight guns and was slow – she was, however, useful.* (Naval Historical Center)

rebuilds, based on merchant steamer hulls and machinery. They were huge but carried relatively little ordnance. The *Lafayette* was 292ft × 66ft, carrying a pair of 11in Dahlgrens, two 100pdr rifles and, for a short time, two 9in. The *Choctaw*, at 270ft × 69ft, had three 9in, one 100pdr, two 30pdrs and two 24pdrs. The *Eastport*, 280ft × c57ft, carried four 9in smoothbores and a pair each of 50pdr and 100pdr. The first could make 4kts and *Choctaw* made 2kts upstream. The *Lafayette*'s armour was $2\frac{1}{2}$in, plus a layer of rubber, then wood backing – the rubber merely rotted away and proved a useless experiment in protection. The *Choctaw* had 1in plating on the casemate plus 30in of wood, with a layer of rubber between them. The *Eastport* was captured while under construction and has left little documentation. Although the armour of these boats was inadequate their size was an asset – they could take many hits in non-critical areas. The *Eastport* was blown up to prevent capture during the Red River (Louisiana) expedition in 1864.

Seven turreted vessels were completed for river warfare. The *Osage* and *Neosho* were an unusual combination of

The stern wheel, light draught, turreted Osage. *Stern wheels were less likely to foul on river snags and required less depth –* Osage *drew no more than 4ft, hence the need for a high deck crown.* (Naval Historical Center)

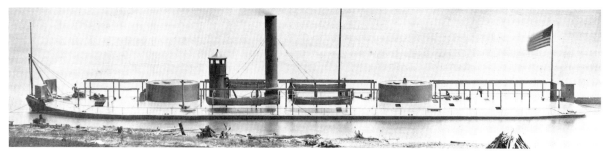

A Milwaukee class ironclad with both an Ericsson and an Eads turret. The latter were technologically advanced – steam power lowered the gun platform for elevation and for loading in the hold. The ships of the class were strongly built and one, the Chickasaw, *survived until 1944 as a ferry boat.* (US Military Academy, Poe Collection)

stern paddle wheels and turret while the *Ozark* and the *Milwaukee* class had quadruple screws.

The *Osage* and *Neosho* carried a single Ericsson turret, each with two 11in Dahlgrens and 6in plating, and $1^{1}/_{2}$in plating on the steeply crowned decks. It was only this crown that allowed habitation of the hull as they drew no more than 4ft of water (26in at launch). They were credited with 12mph but cruised at $7^{1}/_{2}$mph and measured 160ft × 45ft. The *Osage* was attacked by Confederate cavalry in 1864 – one of the more bizarre episodes of the war – and she was mined in March 1865.

The *Ozark* had a single Ericsson turret, identical to *Osage* and *Neosho*, and measured 160ft × 50ft with a $4^{1}/_{2}$ft draught. Though criticised for 'structural weakness' she had three 9in and one 10in guns added – exposed – on her deck. Her plating was about 2in on the sides and 1in on the deck. Four cylinders operated her four 7ft propellers, yielding 6mph and devouring more fuel than a steam frigate. She participated in the Red River Expedition (1864).

James B Eads designed the *Milwaukee* class – each with two turrets (and four 11in guns) and four propellers. Three received an Eads-designed forward turret, incorporating Coles type ball bearings around the perimeter, and a steam mechanism to lower the gun platforms into the hold for loading. Turret armour was 8in thick and the side armour 3in thick with wood backing. The deck plating on *Chickasaw* and *Kickapoo* was $^{3}/_{4}$in, twice that on *Milwaukee* and *Winnebago*. Their machinery, similar to *Ozark*'s, yielded 9mph maximum. Their iron hulls, measuring 220ft × 56ft and drawing 6ft of water, had both transverse and longitudinal bulkheads. The *Winnebago* and *Chickasaw* were at Mobile Bay, and *Milwaukee* was mined in 1865 – her bulkheads significantly delaying her sinking. The *Chickasaw* existed until 1944 as a river ferry.

Conclusion

The preceding has enumerated the major part of the Union Navy in commission during the war. Miscellaneous other vessels included captured warships, such as the Confederate ironclads *Atlanta* and *Tennessee*, an unsuccessful submersible (*Alligator*), an experimental spar torpedo boat, small boats such as Lt Cushing's torpedo launch which sank the ram *Albemarle*, and the 'Stone Fleet', which numbered forty-five vessels.

Finally, the vessels under construction should be mentioned. Some forty-five wooden steam sloops and frigates, ranging from 1100 to 4200 tons were begun in 1863 to counter any possible foreign intervention. These included vessels such as the 17kt *Wampanoag*, which was aimed at raiding enemy commerce (completed in 1867). Also unfinished was the monitor *Puritan*, the *Kalamazoo* class of twin-turret monitors (four vessels), two river monitors (*Marietta* and *Sandusky*) and the 15kt casemate ironclad *Dunderberg*. The latter, at over 7000 tons, was one of the largest wooden ships ever built – she was sold to France in 1867. Of course, the ironclad 'Stevens Battery' – begun in 1842 – remained undone and was finally broken up in the 1880s.

In summary, the Civil War navy was a massive undertaking. By war's end some 690 vessels had been in service – compared to around fifty available in 1861. Of the total, about 160 were navy-built vessels. There were around 140 in the Mississippi River fleet. These figures must all be taken as approximates – many vessels served in support roles and were not officially commissioned and no small boats are included (nor the 'Stone Fleet'). Further, this is an aggregate number – a running total of all vessels utilised during the war, rather than a single total at one particular time. Also, no other government agencies are represented – for instance, the army's own transport and gunboat fleet and Revenue Service vessels.

In any case, the US Navy of the Civil War was the largest it would be until the Second World War and, at least in raw numbers, was amongst the largest in the world. Both in terms of ships and the administrative and personnel aspects, it was a prodigious effort.

Bibliography

Sources other than my own two volumes (*The Old Steam Navy* published by the Naval Institute Press) include Paul Silverstone's *Warships of the Civil War Navies*; K Jack Bauer and Stephen S Roberts' *Register of Ships of the US Navy, 1775–1990*, *Official Records of the Union and Confederate Navy in the War of the Rebellion*; J R Soley's *Blockade and the Cruisers*; Charles Boynton's *History of the Navy during the Rebellion* (1868); F M Bennett's *The Steam Navy of the United States*; and official documents, including the *Annual Reports of the Secretary of the Navy* of the war years.

The Kaiser Franz Joseph I. Class Torpedo-rams

of the Austro-Hungarian Navy

In the 1880s the anti-big ship theories of the French 'jeune école' were looked upon with great favour by the naval authorities of the Austro-Hungarian Empire. This was in large part due to the fact that throughout its existence the Habsburg monarchy had attempted to limit its naval expenditure and these new principles of naval warfare promised a substantial reduction in the cost of maintaining a fleet. Erwin F Sieche examines the effects of this change in policy on the fleet of the 1890s, with particular reference to the development of the torpedo-ram cruiser.

The 'jeune école' was initiated by the French minister of the navy, Vice Admiral Théophile Aube, who declared that the day of the battleship had passed and that the future lay with large numbers of smaller, faster craft, whose principal weapon was to be the torpedo. Not only did the adoption of this approach offer economic advantages but, in the 1880s when the theories became popular, it also seemed very logical. For Austria-Hungary there was the added advantage that located within her territory was one of the principal elements required for this new tactical development: the torpedo factory of Robert Whitehead, who had steadily built up a world monopoly of the production of this striking new weapon.[1]

In theory, by following the teachings of the 'jeune école' Austria-Hungary had only to build cheap torpedo craft and their supporting vessels in order to effectively defend her long Dalmatian coast against intruders. This was intended as a defensive strategy and at the same time the possibility of employing offensive battlefleet tactics in the Adriatic was effectively abandoned.

The Origin of the Torpedo-ram

Although the ideas, on which Austria-Hungary was to base her future naval policy, were French, the cruising ships which were to lead the new hierarchy of torpedo vessels[2] into battle were of British origin. In about 1880 George Rendel[3] designed for Armstrongs at Elswick a new type of

cruiser – the Chilean *Esmeralda* – which featured a protective deck and an armament of two heavy and six medium calibre guns. Like the 'jeune école' Armstrongs promoted the development of cruisers and torpedo craft and, in succeeding years, many more of these 'Elswick cruisers' were constructed for foreign navies, each design featuring a steady improvement in protection and other features on the one before.[4] Among these ships were two vessels built in 1884–86 for Austria-Hungary, *Panther* and *Leopard*, small protected cruisers officially classified as 'ram cruisers'. At the same time, Austria-Hungary herself entered the field of naval arms export: the chief designer of the Stabilimento Tecnico Triestino,[5] Theodor von Schunk,[6] designing an austere ram-cruiser for Argentina – the *Patagonia*. This vessel, launched in 1885 at the company's San Rocco yard,[7] provided valuable experience in the construction of vessels of this type. Shortly afterwards von Schunk began work on two larger ram-cruisers, the *Kaiser Franz Joseph I* and *Kaiserin Elisabeth* – the first of what were to become the leading ships of a new 'jeune école' fleet.

The Austro-Hungarian Torpedo-rams

Following the construction of the two barbette ships *Kronprinzessin Erzherzogin Stefanie* and *Kronprinz Erzherzog Rudolf* in the years 1884–89, Austro-Hungarian capital ship construction entered a hiatus. The principal reason for this was the poor financial state of the Habsburg monar-

Admiral Maximilian Freiherr Daublebsky von Sterneck zu Ehrenstein (born Klagenfurt, Carinthia 14 February 1829, died Vienna 5 December 1897). For some unknown reason, even in contemporary literature, he was always referred to as 'Sterneck' despite the fact that his true family name was Daublebsky. His service career was one of a steady rise to prominence. At the Battle of Lissa he was commander of Tegetthoff's flagship, the armoured frigate Erzherzog Ferdinand Max, *and during the action rammed three Italian vessels, including the* Ré d'Italia *which sank – this may well be one of the reasons why he favoured the idea of the 'torpedo-ramcruiser' when he later became C-in-C of the navy. When Tegetthoff became C-in-C of the Austrian Navy in March 1868, Sterneck became his adjutant. From 17 November 1883 until his death Sterneck was C-in-C of the then Austro-Hungarian Navy. On 22 December his rank of nobility was raised from 'Ritter' to 'Freiherr'. He was buried in the crypt of the former Austro-Hungarian Navy church 'Madonna del mare' at Pola (now Gospa od mora, Pula, Croatia). His heart is buried by the garden wall of the chapel of his family castle – Schloss Krastowitz, Carinthia (now an agricultural school).*

chy, but there was also a desire to wait for the trend in the future development of warships to become clearer. In any case the head of the navy, Admiral Maximilian Freiherr Daublebsky von Sterneck, who held this post from 17 November 1883 until his death in 1897, wished to remodel the fleet in accordance with the ideas of the 'jeune école' and it was this that controlled the development of the fleet until the mid 1890s.

The principal vessel of this new fleet was to be the torpedo-ram cruiser whose primary functions were: to act as a command ship for the torpedo flotillas and to carry the squadron's staff officers; to engage an enemy fleet with long range gunfire in support of attacks by the torpedo flotilla and its withdrawal; if necessary, to attack an enemy with the ram in defence of a withdrawing flotilla; to replenish the torpedo boats for further attacks by supplying them with torpedoes, boiler water, coal and personnel; and to recover damaged torpedo boats and assist them in returning to base. In certain circumstances it was envisaged that the ship would engage enemy battleships with her heavy guns and repel counterattacks by enemy light forces with her medium calibre guns. To defend herself in a melee with enemy torpedo boats she was to carry a number of light QF guns with as high a command as possible.[8] All of these requirements were to be accommodated in a ship of very limited dimensions.

The first of these vessels, *Kaiser Franz Joseph I*, was planned as a replacement for the obsolete casemate ship *Lissa*, built in 1867–69. The new vessel, initially designated 'torpedo-ram cruiser A', was designed by von Schunk as a 4000 tonnes ship with the classic Elswick cruiser layout of two heavy and six medium calibre guns. She was protected by coal bunkers abreast the boiler rooms, a horizontal waterline cofferdam (filled with cellulose pulp) and a protective deck of only 38mm thickness. In the decade before the introduction of case hardened steel armour, the cofferdam system was state-of-the-art defence for 'protective deck' ships. The basic principle was similar to that used in modern self-sealing fuel tanks for aircraft and racing cars. When a shell passed through the cofferdam, the cellulose pulp (actually very hard plates of pressed cocoa fibre) was intended to close the penetration hole – partly by recovery and partly because it would swell-up in sea water.[9] The shell in the meantime was expected to have been brought to a stop by the surrounding coal bunkers, the coal in which was also to have cushioned its detonation.

At this time the gun manufacturing facilities of Austria-Hungary were not fully developed and it was necessary to purchase the ship's guns and mountings abroad. The heavy and medium calibre weapons were ordered from F Krupp at Essen and the Hotchkiss QF guns from Armstrongs in England. The main armament of two 24cm/35cal, Mod1886, guns were carried fore and aft on single mountings consisting of a rotating platform covered by a thin steel, hemispherical shield. These were operated by a complicated and cumbersome hydraulic system driven by two independent steam pumps located below the armoured deck, close to each turret. Each pump served its own turret via a distribution box but, for back-up purposes, they were cross-connected through longitudinal pipes running under the armoured deck. The guns' trunnions were situated forward of the centre of gravity. Elevation was by means of a hydraulic ram which gave a maximum elevation of 13.5deg – which was also the fixed loading angle. The loading position was also fixed in training and the guns had to be brought back to the fore-and-aft line for this purpose. At maximum elevation the 215kg shell had a range of about 10,000m.[10]

The secondary armament consisted of six 15cm/35cal, Mod 1886, guns fitted in single manually operated mountings, also protected by hemispherical shields. At a maximum elevation of 16deg the 21kg projectile had the same range as the main armament – 10,000m.[11]

Sterneck's 'jeune école' Fleet

The primary justification for the construction of the two ram-cruisers was cost which, as predicted by the 'jeune école', was remarkably low. Whereas a barbette ship like the *Kronprinz Erzherzog Rudolf* had cost 18 million

crowns, each ram cruiser had been constructed for only 5 million – making it possible to build three cruisers for the price of one battleship. The torpedo-ram soon became an essential part of Sterneck's plan for a 'jeune école' fleet. In 1891 he proposed a fleet strength of four divisions, each consisting of a torpedo-ram cruiser, a torpedo ship, a torpedo vessel and six torpedo boats. This proposal was approved by the Emperor on 18 August 1891 and was then submitted to the board of ministers who, after extensive debate on the military value of the plan and the financial limitations of the dual monarchy (particularly the Hungarian half), imposed severe cutbacks on the 1891 budget.[12]

In addition to these problems, technical changes had begun to erode the efficacy of Sterneck's proposed fleet. The development of the medium calibre QF gun, first introduced in the Elswick cruiser *Piemonte* constructed for Italy during 1887–89, soon rendered existing cruisers armed with slower firing guns obsolete. At the same time the development of case-hardened steel armour had made the construction of armoured cruisers a much more acceptable

Kaiserin Elisabeth *on 8 December 1892, in tropical white paint and about to leave on the world cruise with the Austro-Hungarian heir to the throne – Archduke Ferdinand d'Este. Note the stern torpedo tube and the sponsons for QF guns at the stern.*

Kaiser Franz Joseph I, *moored off the distinctive construction sheds of the naval arsenal at Pola. The cruiser is painted in the Victorian colour scheme of the period – black hull and gun cupolas, white superstructure and funnels, and yellow masts. Note the forward 24cm gun in its loading position and the 37mm/33cal Hotchkiss mitrailleuses in the fighting tops. From the top of the foremast to a special gaff can be seen a string of five lamps – these were part of the 'Sellner apparatus' a system of signalling by code with different coloured lights developed by Rear Admiral Leopold Sellner.*

Kaiser Franz Joseph I, *1890–1905*. (Drawn by the author)

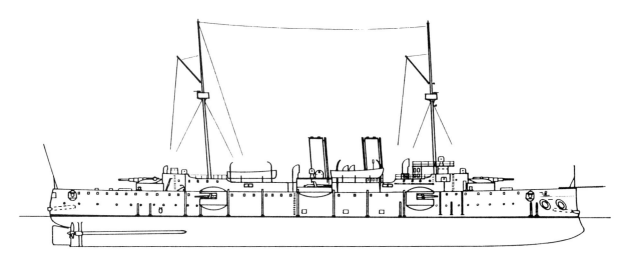

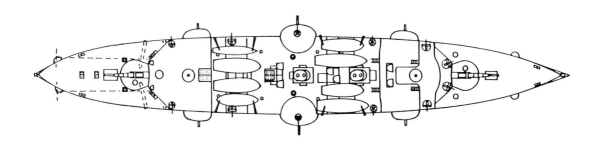

The after 24cm/36cal, C/86 Krupp gun of the Kaiserin Elisabeth. *The barrel, including the breech-block, weighed 26,900kg and, when fired, recoiled a distance of 102cm. Note the 24cm practice shell, in its carrying tray, on the deck by the two sailors.*

proposition and during the first half of the 1890s there was a general move away from protected cruisers. As a direct result of the latter the third principal ship of Sterneck's plan, 'torpedo-ram cruiser C', was redesigned with side armour, an additional pair of medium calibre guns and more powerful machinery which, at the cost of over 1000 tons displacement, produced the first armoured cruiser of the Austro-Hungarian Navy – *Kaiserin und Koenigin Maria Theresia*. The fourth torpedo ship (light cruiser) –

which may have been named *Puma* – had been postponed pending reports on the Italian cruiser *Giovanni Bausan* but was never restarted. When the second torpedo ram, *Kaiserin Elisabeth*, was commissioned on 24 January 1892, the Italians, the Habsburgs' most likely opponent at sea, had already outbuilt Austria-Hungary in this class of ves-

Kaiserin Elisabeth, *1892–1905*. (Drawn by the author)

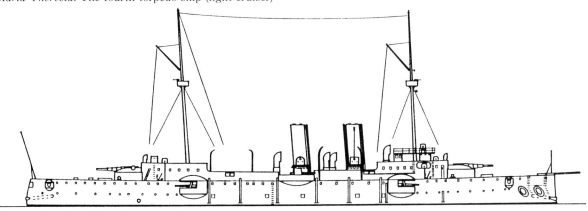

sel having commissioned seven – *Giovanni Bausan*, four ships of the *Etna* class, *Dogali* and *Piemonte*.

Nevertheless, Sterneck stubbornly continued to fight for his proposals but first technical developments and finally, Sterneck's death on 5 December 1897 brought the process to an end – the support for his 'jeune école' fleet faded away and Austria-Hungary returned to capital ship construction with the building of the *Habsburg* class battleships, the first of which was laid down in 1899.

The torpedo-ram cruisers became obsolete very quickly, being unarmoured, too slow and armed with outdated slow-firing guns – to the officers of the Austro-Hungarian Navy they were 'Sterneck's tin cans'. Nevertheless, they were found useful employment on overseas services and during 1905–06 their value was enhanced by improvements in their armament. The latter involved replacing the 24cm Krupp guns with modern 15cm/40cal Skoda guns and refitting the 15cm/35cal guns on the upper deck where they were dryer and had a better command – their original positions, in casemates on the main deck, having been found unsatisfactory in anything other than calm weather due to their close proximity to the water-line. In 1908 the two ships were reclassified as 2nd class cruisers and in 1911 as small cruisers.

Conclusion

The torpedo-ram cruiser and the armoured cruiser, although seen as state-of-art technology in their own time, were both short lived, surviving for only a decade before being superseded by other types. Low budget 'jeune école' navies, such as those of Austria-Hungary or South America, were quickly superseded by the rapidly developing technologies of the time. This resulted in fleet construction programmes that were outdated before they could be properly implemented and, in consequence, effectively negated the value of the money invested in them. This was particu-

A superb view of the fore end of Kaiser Franz Joseph I. *Just visible, on the fore side of the superstructure, is the ship's name in brass lettering, confirming the accepted spelling of the ship's name – as opposed to the use of* 'Josef' *which was also often employed.*

larly serious for the navies involved as these were of a type that expected a substantial lifespan from their ships and could not contemplate the scrapping of vessels after so short a period as ten years. Although Austria-Hungary attempted to improve her torpedo-ram cruisers by rearming them they remained substantially obsolete and the only serious employment that could be found for them was in training and overseas service. During the First World War they were virtually worthless as fighting ships and only *Kaiserin Elisabeth*, being trapped in the Far East, saw action – as a floating battery engaged in shore bombardments.

Service Careers

SMS Kaiser Franz Joseph I
1890: with the barbette ships *Kronprinz Erzherzog Rudolf* (flag Rear Admiral Hinke) and *Kronprinzessin Erzherzogin Stephanie* and the cruiser *Tiger*, took part in a cruise of the North Sea and Baltic. During 5–11 August the squadron visited Spithead, being reviewed on the 11th by Queen Victoria and the Prince of Wales at Cowes. On 3 September the ship was visited by Emperor Wilhelm II at Kiel – the second of four European monarchs to inspect the squadron; the other two being the kings of Denmark and Portugal.[13]
1892: took part in the Columbus celebrations at Genoa and Huelva, visiting Valletta harbour, Malta, on 23–26 October during her return journey.
1895: with her sister ship and the armoured cruiser *Maria*

The Kaiserin Elisabeth *dry-docked and under repair at the German yard in Tsingtau during 3–18 May 1909 as a result of damage received in the Woosung River (now Huang Pu River), east of Shanghai, on 23–24 March 1909. Unforeseen tidal currents had moved her from her night anchorage during dense fog and she had run aground, taking on a heavy list to starboard. During the subsequent salvage operations five Austrian sailors were killed when their boat capsized. As a result of this incident, her commander – FrgKpt Maximilian Herzberg, was immediately relieved of his command and was retired from the service on 1 November 1909 (during the First World War Herzberg attempted to restore his honour by becoming a successful naval aviator). Note the distinctive ram bow and the forward torpedo tube above it.*

Table 1: *TORPEDO-RAMS OF THE 1882–89 PERIOD*

	Esmeralda	Giovanni Bausan	Naniwa	Dogali	Patagonia	Piemonte	K Franz Joseph I
Construction date:	1881–83	1882–83	1884–85	1885	1885	1888–89	1888–89
Deep displacement (tons):	3000	3277	3650	2200	1485	2780	4332
Dimensions (m):	82.3wl × 12.8 × 5.56max	89.32wl × 12.85 × 5.98max	91.4wl × 14 × 6.1max	76.3wl × 12.8 × 3.91max	64.9wl × 9.88 × 3.91max	97.8 × 11.6 × 5.19max	102.6wl × 14.7 × 5.9max
ihp = speed(kts) max:	6803 = 18.28	6470 = 17.4	7000 = 18.5	7197 = 19.66	2370 = 14	12,000 = 22	8743 = 19
No of screws:	2	2	3	2		2	2
Armament:	2 × 25.4cm/30, 6 × 15.2cm/26, 2 × 57mm, 3 × 35.6cm torp tubes	2 × 25.4cm/20, 6 × 15.2cm/33, 2 × 57mm, 2 × 35.6cm torp tubes	2 × 26cm, 6 × 15cm, 2 × 57mm, 4 × 35.6cm torp tubes	6 × 15.2cm/40, 9 × 57mm/40, 2 × 37mm, 4 × 35.6cm torp tubes	1 × 25.4cm, 3 × 15.2cm, 4 × 7cm	6 × 15.2cm, 6 × 12cm, 10 × 57mm, 2 × 35.6cm torp tubes	2 × 24cm/35, 6 × 15cm/35, 5 × 47mm/40, 447mm/33, 4 × 40cm torp tubes
Protective deck(mm):	25	38	76	51	32	76	38–76
Complement:	296	295	325	247	210	247	399

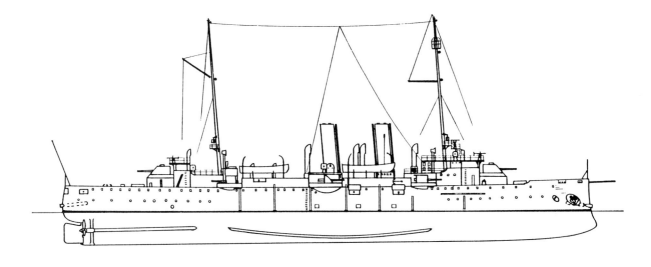

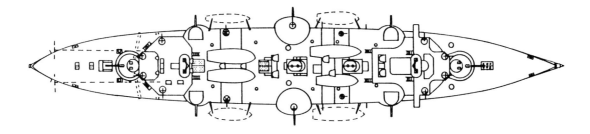

Theresia took part in the celebrations at the opening of the Kiel canal.

1897: transferred to the Far East but returned to form part of international demonstration fleet off Crete.

1898: took part in Vasco da Gama celebrations at Lisbon.

1903 and 1904: training cruises in the Mediterranean.

1905: rearmed.

1905–13: station ship in Far East.

1914–18: during First World War based in Bocche di Cattaro (Boka Kotorska).

1914 and 1916: carried out bombardments of Mount Lovcen.

Kaiser Franz Joseph I, *1905–1918*. (Drawn by the author)

1918: remained neutral during naval mutiny at Cattaro 1–3 February; reduced to nucleus crew on 7 February and became an accommodation ship at Bocche di Cattaro – all 15cm/35cal guns landed; at the armistice at Teodo (Tivat).

1919: employed as ammunition ship under French control – moored in Bay of Zanjica outside Boka Kotorska; capsized in heavy Bora gale on 17 October as a result of top-heavy condition produced by a combination of the ship in light condition but with a heavy load of ammunition and open hatches.

Kaiserin Elisabeth, *1906–1914*. (Drawn by the author)

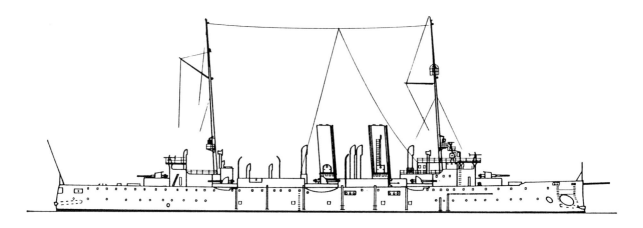

1922: wreck located by a Dutch sponsored salvage company and some deck fittings, such as the cranes, recovered.[14]

1967: some parts of the wreck salvaged by the Yugoslavian salvage company Brodospas.[15]

SMS Kaiserin Elisabeth

1892–3: special world cruise with the Austro-Hungarian heir to the throne, Archduke Franz Ferdinand.[16]

1895: with Austro-Hungarian squadron at the opening of the Kiel Canal, followed by a fleet review in the Levant.

1896: cruise to the Levant.

1899: special mission to the Far East.[17]

1900–02: stationed in Far East. Part of international squadron during Boxer rebellion in China.

1904–05: stationship in Far East.

1906: rearmed.

1906, 1907 and 1908: training cruises in the Mediterranean.

1908–10: stationship in Far East.[18]

1911 and 1912: training cruises in the Mediterranean.

1913: became stationship in the Levant as a result of the Balkan war.

1. Cofferdam filled with cellulose
2. Armoured deck
3. Coal bunker
4. Coal bunker

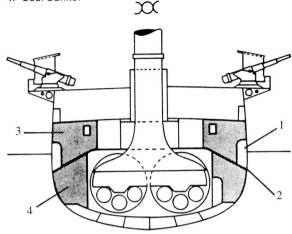

Transverse section of Kaiser Franz Joseph I. (Drawn by the author)

Profile and transverse section of the Krupp 24cm/35cal gun mounting.

1. Rangefinder cupola
2. Rangefinder
3. Cupola
4. Barbette ring
5. Turntable
6. Telescopic rammer
7. Elevator
8. Pivot
9. Piston
10. Trunnion

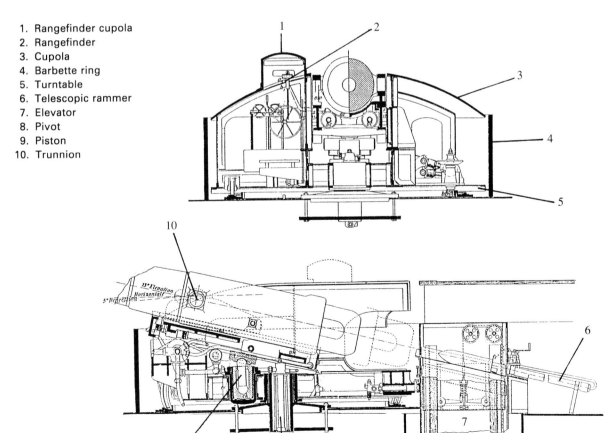

The Kaiser Franz Joseph I *after her 1905 refit when the original Krupp 24cm guns were replaced with 15cm Skoda weapons. The casting of the conical shaped turrets of these mountings posed some problems for Skoda, hence* Kaiserin Elisabeth *received her new guns a year later and in open shields of a simpler design.* The Kaiser Franz Joseph I. *after her 1905 refit when the original Krupp 24cm guns were replaced with 15cm Skoda weapons. The casting of the conical shaped turrets of these mountings posed some problems for Skoda, hence* Kaiserin Elisabeth *received her new guns a year later and in open shields of a simpler design.*

1913–14: stationship in Far East.
1914: moved to the German colony of Tsingtau (now Qingdao) on 22 July with the intention of operating with the German East Asiatic Squadron under Von Spee but this idea was rejected because of the ship's low speed. On 24 August she was ordered to decommission and send her crew to neutral Tientsin (now Tianjin) but two days later this was countermanded by an order to help the Germans defend Tsingtau ('Kaiserin Elisabeth mitkaempfen!' – 'Kaiserin Elisabeth to fight alongside the Germans'). The bow and stern guns were removed ashore to serve as perimeter defence guns. After carrying out various shore bombardments which consumed all the ship's ammunition she was moved out to the deepest part of the bay and scuttled on 22 November.[19] Following the fall of Tsingtau the Austrians, together with their German comrades, became Japanese POWs – the last members of the crew of *Kaiserin Elisabeth* were to return home in 1920.

Lead of hydraulic pipes for the 24cm gun mountings of Kaiser Franz Joseph I *and* Kaiserin Elisabeth.

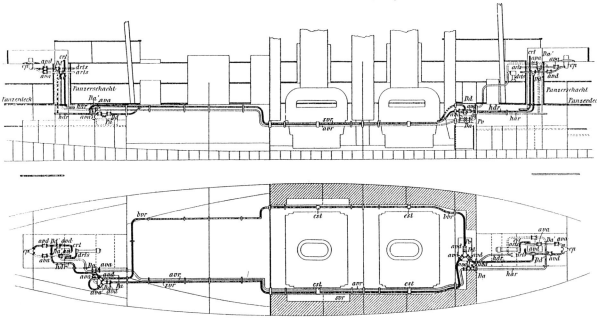

Notes

[1] Full details of the Whitehead story are given in *Sotto i mari del Mondo – La Whitehead 1875–1990* by Antonia Casali and Marina Cattaruzza, Editori Laterza (Bari, 1990).

[2] See Lawrence Sondhaus *Strategy, Tactics and the Politics of Penury: The Austro-Hungarian Navy and the Jeune école; The Journal of Military History*, Vol 56, No 4, October 1992, Society for Military History, Virginia Military Institute (Virginia, 1992).

[3] George Wightwick Rendel (1803–1902), civil engineer and partner in the Armstrong Ordnance Company; designer of hydraulic gun mountings and developer of the intermediate type cruiser; professional Civil Lord of the Admiralty (1882–85); founder of the Armstrong Pozzuoli Company. Mr David Topliss is preparing a book on Rendel designed cruisers.

[4] Rendel was followed as chief designer at Elswick first by William White in 1883 and then Phillip Watts in 1886, both men continued Rendel's work with the development of the Elswick cruiser and became Director of Naval Construction at the Admiralty when they left Armstrongs.

[5] In 1847 Giorgio Simeone Strudthoff founded the Stabilimento Tecnico Strudthoff at Trieste, San Andrea. Three years later his five sons purchased some land from the city of Muggia where they constructed the San Rocco Yard – named after a small chapel in the vicinity. On 27 April 1857 the remaining four sons and the children of the fifth combined with the Banca Triestino Reyer and Schlick to found the joint holding company Stabilimento Tecnico Triestino – commonly abbreviated to STT. After an extended period of financial development the STT was purchased in 1897 by the Rothschild dominated Viennese banking house K k Privat Kreditanstalt fuer Handel und Gewerbe. This brought fresh money and rapid modernisation and, on 3 April 1897, STT purchased the area of San Marco for the construction of a new shipyard which was to take over all capital ship construction for the company, the last large Austro-Hungarian warship built at San Rocco being the armoured cruiser *Kaiser Karl VI*. It is worth noting that the Kreditanstalt was also a major stockholder of the Bohemian gun plant – the Skoda Werke AG – and of the armour manufacturers Witkowitzer Eisenhuetten Gewerkuschaft AG, giving the Rothschild group control of the three principal suppliers for Austro-Hungarian capital ship construction. See Ernesto Gellner and Paolo Valenti, *San Rocco – Storia di un*

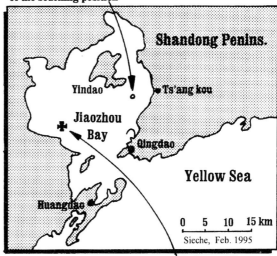

The second possibility of the scuttling position

Probably the scuttling spot of the 'Kaiserin Elisabeth'

Map of Jiaozhou Bay showing the two possible positions in which Kaiserin Elisabeth *was scuttled. (Drawn by the author)*

cantiere navale (Trieste, 1990); and Eduard Maerz, *Oesterreichische Bankpolitik in der Zeit der grossen Wende 1913–1923 – am Beispiel der Creditanstalt fuer Handel und Gewerbe* (Vienna, 1981).

Table 2: *ADMIRAL STERNECK'S FLEET PROGRAMME OF 1891*

Torpedo-ram cruiser	Torpedo ship	Torpedo vessel	Torpedo boats
Kaiser Franz Joseph I (May 1889)	*Panther* (Jun 1885)	*Meteor* (Jun 1887)	Six 1st Class of *Sperber/Habicht* type (1886–92)
Kaiserin Elisabeth (Sep 1890)	*Leopard* (Sep 1885)	*Blitz* (Jul 1888)	Six 1st class of *Sperber/Habicht* type (1886–92)
Torpedo-ram cruiser C* (Apr 1893)	*Tiger* (Jun 1887)	*Komet* (Aug 1888)	Six 1st class of *Sperber/Habicht* type (1886–92)
Torpedo-ram cruiser D* (Oct 1898)	(*Puma* ?)	*Planet* (Jun 1889)	Six 1st class, *Viper*, *Natter* and *Cobra* Class (1895–99)

Notes:

Dates in parenthesis are dates of launch.

*In the official budget forecasts these two vessels continued to be referred to as torpedo-ram cruisers after it was decided to complete them as armoured cruisers. Cruiser 'C' became the intermediate type, *Maria Theresia*, and cruiser 'D' the first true armoured cruiser of the fleet, *Kaiser Karl VI*.

Table 3: *PARTICULARS OF* KAISER FRANZ
JOSEPH I

Builder:	Stabilimento Tecnico Triestino, San Rocco Yard
Construction cost:	5,146,884 crowns
Laid down:	3 Jan 1888
Launched:	18 May 1889
Completed:	2 Jun 1890
Displacement:	4031 tonnes (3967.52 tons) as designed; 4332.7 tonnes (4267.47 tons) deep
Dimensions:	97.905m (pp), 102.56m (wl), 103.7m (oa) × 14.72m (max) × 5.985m (mean deep)
Submersion:	10.442 tonnes/cm
Machinery:	Built by STT's Andrea plant 1889; 4 double ended boilers with 24 furnaces; 2 horizontal, 3cyl, triple-expansion engines of 8000ihp; two 3-bladed Griffiths screws of 4.42m dia; 800ihp nominal, 8743ihp = 19.17kts on trials (20 May 1890), 18.86kts normal max
Fuel:	614 tonnes pit-coal or 632 tonnes pressed coal
Protection:	38mm deck (flat); 57mm deck (slope); 90mm barbettes; 40mm shields (24cm guns); 40mm casemates; 40–60mm shields (15cm guns); 45–50mm CT
Armament:	As built: 2 × 24cm/35cal Krupp C/86; 6 × 15cm/35cal Krupp C/86; 5 × 47mm/44cal Hotchkiss QF; 4 × 47mm/33cal Hotchkiss QF; 2 × 37mm/33cal Hotchkiss QF; 2 × 7cm/15cal field guns; 4 × 40cm torpedo tubes After 1905 refit: 2 × 15cm/40cal Skoda; 6 × 15cm/35cal Krupp C/86 14 × 47mm/44cal Skoda QF; 2 × 47mm/33cal Skoda QF; 1 × 8mm M01 MG; 4 × 40cm torpedo tubes; (a second 8mm MG, on an AA tripod mount – possibly captured from the Serbians – was added during the First World War)
Ammunition stowage:	As built: 24cm – 50Ap, 20 HE per gun; 15cm – 72 AP, 72 HE, 18 shrapnel, 18 segmented shrapnel per gun; 47mm/44 cal – 1400 HE, 700 steel shells total; 47mm/33cal – 700 HE, 200 steel shells total; 37mm/33cal – 900 HE total; 7cm – 70 HE, 30 shrapnel total for field guns. (After 1905 refit ammunition stowage was probably as that for *Kaiserin Elisabeth*)
Searchlights:	4 × 60cm, 3.25kW Schuckert projectors; 1 × 35cm, 1.625kW Schuckert boat projector
Complement:	339

[6] Theodor Schunk was born in Erlangen, Bavaria in 1829 and joined the Austrian Navy in 1849. In 1860 he was promoted to the rank of *Schiffbau Oberingenieur* but in June 1868 left the navy as a result of serious disagreements with his superior, chief naval designer Josef Ritter von Romako. Schunk signed a contract with the STT and served as the director of their San Rocco yard from 15 November 1885 until 1890. Schunk's files are held by the Oesterreichisches Staatsarchiv/Kriegsarchiv – qualification list 212/5160.

[7] See Gellner and Valenti, ibid, p33.

[8] See Josef Ritter von Lehnert, *Rueckblicke auf die Entwicklung der k.k. Flotten* in *Organ der Militaerwissenschaftlichen Vereine, Vol XXXV, 1887* p233.

[9] The Austro-Hungarian Navy published a semi-official monthly periodical, *Mitteilungen aus dem Gebiete des Seewesens,* a large section of which was a German summary of articles in foreign naval periodicals intended to keep the officers of the Austro-Hungarian Navy informed on the latest technical and tactical developments. The use of cellulose was widely discussed in contemporary naval literature and a good two dozen references are given in *Mitteilungen* – eg, No V and VI/1888, 'Cellulose trials at Toulon'; No I/1892 'Description of the French gun tests against cofferdams and the reasons why the French Navy dropped the system'; No VI and VII/1892, 'Use of Cellulose in the US warships *New York* and *Brooklyn*'; No IX/1894, Life gunnery tests against the cofferdam of the Danish cruiser *Hekla*'.

[10] *Unterricht fuer das 24cm Geschuetz L/35 C/86 auf hydraulischer Turmlafette,* K.u.k. Kriegsmarine (Pola, 1902). Twenty-four of these guns were installed in the eight German coast defence ships of the *Siegfried* class and a further six in the Austro-Hungarian casemate ship *Tegetthoff* during an 1893 refit which, including those mounted in the three ram cruisers, gives a total of thirty-six such guns in existence.

[11] *Unterricht fuer das 15cm Geschuetz L/35 C/86 apt,* K.u.k. Kriegsmarine (Pola, 1902). In all the Austro-Hungarian Navy purchased thirty-nine of these Krupp guns – twelve for the first two ram-cruisers, eight for the *Maria Theresia*, two for the torpedoship *Lussin*, five for the casemate ship *Tegetthoff* and six each for the barbette ships *Kronprinz Erzherzog Rudolf* and *Kronprinzessin Erzherzogin Stephanie*. It was this lucrative market that drove the home gun manufacturers toward making greater efforts to produce modern weapons.

[12] See Leo Reiter, *Die Entwicklung der k.u.k. Flotte und die Delegationen des Reichsrates,* (Vienna, 1949), p91.

[13] The *Kaiser Franz Joseph I* was commanded by Archduke Karl Stephan, one of the few Habsburgs to make a full time success of a naval career. To date no photographic record of the naval review at Cowes has come to light. Source – Official reports 'Vorfallenheitsberichte' OK/MS 1890 V–3/17 in the Oesterreichisches Staatsarchiv/Kriegsarchiv, Vienna.

[14] See *Marine – Gestern, Heute, No 1/1987,* p12; according to this article a Dutch broker named van Wienen purchased the salvage concession – his local agent was the ex Austro-Hungarian frigate-captain Milan von Millinkovic. Research by Mr Anthonie van Dijk has failed to find any record of van Wienen and none of the major Dutch salvage companies appear to have been involved. It would seem it was a locally organised enterprise which may explain the poor results – having been carried out by men of limited experience and lacking in professional salvage equipment.

[15] Brodospas is a combination of two Croatian words – 'brod' (ship) and 'spas' (salvage). See the 40-year jubilee monograph of the company – *Brodospas, Spasavanje na Jadranu* (Salvage

in the Adriatic), (Split, 1987), p180.

[16] As was usual at this time, the publicity minded Archduke Franz Ferdinand published a record of his experiences in a two volume illustrated book – *Tagebuch meiner Reise um die Erde 1892–1893*, (Vienna, 1896). In Franz Ferdinand's castle in Austria, Schloss Artstaetten, there is an exhibition of memorabilia from his world cruise. In his memoirs, Admiral Koudelka reveals that he served as ghost writer for the crown prince's book. See Lothar Baumgartner (Ed), *Denn Oesterreich lag einst am Meer – Das Leben des Admirals Alfred von Koudelka*, (Graz, 1987), p50.

[17] The secret purpose of this mission was to explore possible locations for an Austrian colony based on the German model. Prospective places examined included Namquan (now Nam-King or Namkwan) and Nimrod Sound, Sanmun Bay and Lotsun Bay but none were regarded as suitable. See Lothar Baumgartner (Ed), *Koudelka*, ibid, p67.

[18] During this deployment the cruiser left Pusan, Korea, on 22 August 1910 to go to the assistance of the British cruiser *Bedford* which was stranded on the Samarang Rock, south west of Quelpart Island. A British squadron was already on the scene when *Kaiserin Elisabeth* arrived and her help was not required but the Austrians received the thanks of the senior British officer, Vice Admiral Winsloe. Source: Official reports 'Vorfallenheitsberichte', OK/MS 1910, V–6/18 file No 2699, Oesterreichisches Staatsarchiv/Kriegsarchiv, Vienna.

[19] There are actually two possible positions for the wreck – either in Tsangkou deep (in fact a river bed in the Bay of Jiazhou) or in the actual deepest point of the Bay on the opposite side. To date no clear information has been available from the local authorities as to the exact location of the wreck.

Table 4: *PARTICULARS OF* KAISERIN ELISABETH

Builder:	Austro-Hungarian Naval Yard, Pola
Construction cost:	5,593,564 crowns
Laid down:	Jul 1888
Launched:	25 Sep 1890
Completed:	24 Jan 1892
Displacement:	4063.7 tonnes (3999.7 tons) as designed; (displ volume = 3960.7m³)
Dimensions:	97.905m (pp), 102.564m (wl), 103.678m (oa) × 14.748m (max) × 5.707m (design mean)
Submersion:	10.44 tonnes/cm
Machinery:	Built by STT's Andrea plant 1889–91; 4 double ended boilers with 24 furnaces; 2 horizontal, 3cyl, triple-expansion engines of 8000ihp; two 3-bladed Griffiths srews of 4.42m dia; 8000ihp nominal, 5947ihp = 16.9kts on trials (14 Aug 1913)
Fuel:	709 tonnes pit-coal or 584.7 tonnes pressed coal, bunker capacity 835m³
Protection:	38mm deck (flat); 56mm deck (slope); 90mm barbettes; 40mm shields (24cm guns); 40mm casemates; 40–60mm shields (15cm guns); 50mm CT (after 1905/06 refit the 15cm/40 guns had 90/50/25mm shields)
Armament:	As built: 2 × 24cm/35cal Krupp C/86; 6 × 15cm/35cal Krupp C/86; 11 × 47mm/44cal Skoda QF; 2 × 47mm/33cal Skoda QF; 2 × 37mm/23cal Skoda QF in spotting tops; 4 × 37mm Vickers Mitrailleuses C/1900; 2 × 7cm/15cal field guns; 4 × 40cm torpedo tubes
	After 1905/06 refit: 2 × 15cm/40cal Skoda; 6 × 15cm/35cal Krupp C/86; 12 × 47mm/44cal Skoda QF; 4 × 47mm/33cal Skoda QF; 2 × 7cm/15cal field guns; 4 × 40cm torpedo tubes
Ammunition stowage:	As built: Probably as *Kaiser Franz Joseph I*
	After 1905–06 refit: 15cm/40 – 20 AP, 130 HE per gun; 15cm/35 – 30 AP, 80 HE, 30 shrapnel per gun; 47mm/44cal – 300 HE, 100 steel shells per gun; 47mm/33cal – 464 HE per gun; 5 40cm torpedoes + 3 exercise torpedoes
Searchlights:	4 × 60cm, 3.25kW Schuckert projectors; 1 × 35cm, 1.625kW Schuckert boat projector
Complement:	4.26

THE MAST AND FUNNEL QUESTION

Fire-control positions in British dreadnoughts

1905–1915

The development of long-range gunnery which accompanied the introduction and development of British dreadnought battleships required the provision of a fire-control system which depended on well-sited control positions. Opinions fluctuated on the best locations for the different components of this system and it was often difficult for ship designers to reconcile the more familiar problems of top-weight, deck space[1] and day-to-day boat handling with the rapidly changing demands of gunnery officers. In this article John Brooks examines how successfully these issues were resolved in the series of classes that began with the *Dreadnought* and ended with the fully developed fire-control positions of the *Queen Elizabeth* class.

The all-big-gun armament of HMS *Dreadnought* and the even more radical *Invincibles* was intended to enable these revolutionary ships to hit harder and more often at longer ranges than any contemporary battleship or armoured cruiser. To do so, they depended on an effective system of fire-control which in turn required suitable fire-control positions for observational instruments and personnel. From these elevated positions, protected (as far as possible) from enemy fire, an unobstructed view of the distant enemy was essential, unimpeded by sea spray, the smoke from the guns and funnels of the firing ship and the splashes and smoke from bursting shell.

After *Dreadnought*, the Royal Navy constructed a series of battleship and battlecruiser classes which, 'after many strange changes in silhouette', culminated in the *Queen Elizabeth* class of fast battleships which 'must be given pride of place as the most perfect example of the naval constructor's art as yet put afloat'.[2] At the same time, the individual instruments first brought together in *Dreadnought* were further developed while new devices were introduced; all were integrated into an increasingly elaborate fire-control system which evolved throughout this period and eventually became centred on one of the various marks of Dreyer fire control table.[3]

Dreadnought *to* Neptune *and* Indefatigable

The *Dreadnought* should be recognised not just as a revolutionary ship but as a revolutionary gunnery system; when she entered service in 1907, she was the first ship provided with all the fire-control instruments necessary for the centralised control of effective long-range fire. Her fire-control top was equipped with the new Barr and Stroud 9ft rangefinder which was accurate out to the then long ranges of 7000–10,000yds; the instrument was carried on a traversing mounting to give it an all-round view.[4] The top was also provided with a pair of Dumaresqs; these ingenious and versatile instruments were a mechanical analogue of the simultaneous differential equations which describe the rates-of-change of enemy range and bearing due to the relative motions of the firing and target ships. The instrument was set initially with the known values for the firing ship's speed and the target bearing together with estimated values of the enemy's speed and the angle between courses. It then indicated both the rate-of-change of range (or range rate) and the deflection and these essential data were automatically maintained so long as the vane of the Dumaresq was kept pointing at the enemy ship.

On her first experimental cruise, the latest values of range, range rate and deflection were conveyed by voicepipes and navyphones to the *Dreadnought's* TS (transmitting station); step-by-step transmitters and receivers were fitted later. In the TS, she was provided with no less than four Vickers clocks. Before it was started, each clock was set with the latest range and range rate. As it ran, the clock rate was adjusted periodically to match the rate indicated by the Dumaresq; it then gave a continuous indication of the target range as it changed with the changing positions of the two ships. In the TS, the range and deflection received from the control top were also corrected to allow for such factors as wind, drift, air density and propellant temperature. The corrected values were then transmitted, by further step-by-step instruments to the turrets. Here the sight setters transferred the values displayed on the electric receivers to the gun sights 'which, in *Dreadnought*, were of a new and more accurate direct-action pattern'.[5]

Before opening fire, the range rate could be corrected by clock 'tuning', *ie* correcting the clock rate if its predicted ranges diverged from those being received from the rangefinder. Then, once the first salvoes were fired, the spotting officer in the control top corrected deflection and then range by observing the fall of shot. As soon as corrected values of range rate and deflection had been obtained, the setting of the Dumaresq could be adjusted in order that its further predictions of range rate and deflection were more precise.[6] Hence *Dreadnought* was equipped with a complete set of instruments which together provided the means of long range fire-control centred on the personnel in the fire-control top. This top was in an elevated though largely unprotected position, which was intended to give a clear view of the target so that the ship's principal rangefinder

The battleship Dreadnought, *seen here in the summer of 1907, had three fire-control positions aloft – the main control top at the head of the tripod mast, a secondary main armament control platform on the roof of the signal tower (just forward of the second funnel) and a control position for the after groups of the anti torpedo-boat armament in the main top.* (Courtesy J Roberts)

could obtain the ranges: the Dumaresq could predict the rates: and the spotting officer could close the control loop to correct fire by spotting the fall of shot.

As a rigid support for the fire-control top, *Dreadnought* was given a heavy tripod foremast.[7] In order that it could also support the main boat derrick, the mast was stepped abaft the fore funnel but this proved unsatisfactory since, in a head wind, the hot funnel gases made the passage through the mast to the top unpleasantly hot;[8] even worse, a following wind could result in funnel smoke being blown around the top, interfering with range-taking and spotting. This arrangement was not repeated in the *Invincible* class battlecruisers which had two tripods of equal height, the foremast being stepped ahead of the fore funnel. Control tops were erected on both masts, each top carrying a 9ft rangefinder on a circular track.[9] This same basic arrangement was then repeated in the next three classes of battleship (the *Bellerophon*s, *St Vincent*s and HMS *Neptune*) and in the *Indefatigable* class battlecruisers: although the position of the mainmast varied from class to class. The duplication of the fire-control aloft was also repeated below, the ships completed after *Dreadnought* having a second, after, TS and the necessary switch gear so that fire could be controlled from either TS working with either control top.[10]

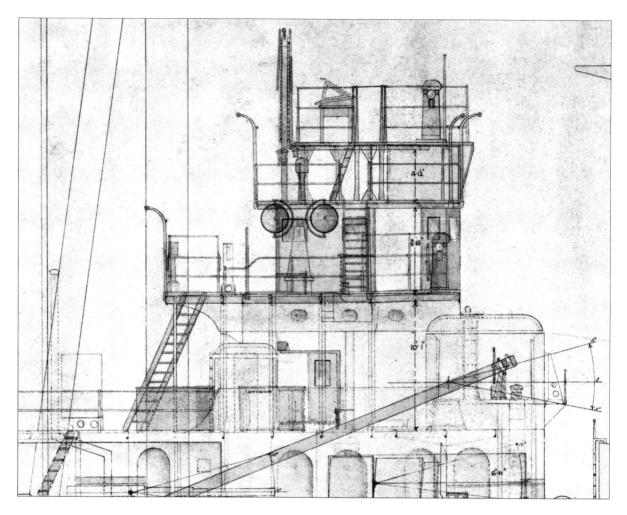

Part of the official as-fitted profile of the Indefatigable *showing the spotting and signal tower located beneath the bridge between the foremast and the conning tower. It is most unlikely that this position, with its severely restricted lines of sight, was ever used in action.* (NMM, NPB4359)

It must be doubted whether the control tops on the main-masts were ever of much use; Parkes published a photo-graph of *Invincible* working up to full speed at the Battle of the Falklands in which the mainmast is barely visible in the clouds of dense coal smoke. In any case, in the same year that the *Invincible*s were completed (though after the *St Vincent*s had been laid down) the C-in-C Home Fleet, Vice Admiral Sir Francis Bridgeman, questioned the whole principle of erecting 'heavy and conspicuous masts' to support an elevated fire-control position. His views and the correspondence it provoked are preserved in the Ships' Cover for *Hercules* and *Colossus* in a series of minutes under the heading 'Mastless Ships from a Gunnery Point of View'.[11] In his minute of 3 October 1908, Bridgeman stated that 'There is undoubtedly a growing opinion among offi-cers that the heavy mast is an avoidable danger ... Many ... would prefer to enter an action with their control lower down preferring to accept a possible lower percentage of accuracy'. On 14 October, Reginald Bacon, the DNO, re-

plied that 'a mast is chiefly of use to lift the range-finder and spotter above the smoke of the ship's guns and the enemy's bursting shell. The tripod masts of the *Dread-nought* type are very rigid and afford a really excellent position for working a range-finder'. He then continued:

The 'approach' and 'general action' form two dis-tinct periods as far as gunnery is concerned. The period of 'approach' being all important to obtain the change-of-range of the enemy and the correc-tions necessary to ensure early hitting while the 'general action' will probably be a period of control of fire by the bursting of shell mainly without the assistance of the range-finder.

It is during the 'approach' that an aloft position above the smoke for a range-finder is so valuable [but] the importance of a Lower Control is fully concurred in. An armoured position close to and in communication with the conning tower would be most valuable... So far as the gunnery requirements of the new battleships are concerned, the second mast is unnecessary.

On the 17th, the DNC (Sir Philip Watts) asked the DNO to state the approximate size of the proposed armoured con-trol-position close to the conning tower and 'whether [the] view from it is important, also whether it would be desired to work a rangefinder through a hole in the roof'. On 4 November, the DNO replied that an all-round view would be very important but that 'it would not be required to work a rangefinder through a hole in the roof[12] ... the foremast should be the mast retained to support a control position as the main is usually obscured by smoke'. He proposed that accommodation should be provided for the spotter and two assistants by, in effect, wrapping 6in armour around the front and sides of the conning tower. On 9 November, the DNC responded that 'a heavy addition as proposed by DNO cannot be accepted ... The most that can be done is to enlarge the present signal tower ... keeping the wall 3in'. Finally on 25 November, Jellicoe, the Controller, concluded the exchanges stating 'I do not consider 3in protection would be sufficient. No alteration is therefore to be made in K2 design [*Neptune*] to provide a spotting tower. The question of the removal of the main mast is to be considered for next year's battleships in association with a spotting tower not less than 6in thick'.

This sequence of minutes has been quoted at length since it provides at once insights into contemporary opinions on fire-control: how important issues were debated and decisions reached within the Admiralty hierarchy: and why *Hercules* and *Colossus* had very different fire-control arrangements from their predecessor. The *Neptune* was the last dreadnought battleship with two large tripod masts. She retained a fore conning tower of 11in armour but the 8in after conning tower was abolished and replaced by a 'light steel protected position [1 to 1½in] for the Director for the stern tube ... of the character now fitted to the *King Edward VII*.[13] When laid down in January 1909, her fire-control tops were the same as those of *St Vincent*. However, by the time Bacon handed over as DNO to Moore in November 1909, the decision had already been taken to fit her with the first complete director,[14] which was installed in December 1910[15] just beneath the control top on the foremast; in this respect, she provided an important indication of developments to come.

All three ships of the *Indefatigable* class were also given two tripod masts. The *Indefatigable* herself represented a first step towards the new fire-control arrangements discussed at the end of 1908. She had a separate signal and spotting tower situated between the conning tower and the forefunnel, protected by 4in armour. Its long axis was athwartship and each of its rounded ends was occupied by a spotter and Dumaresq operator; the middle section was used by signallers.[16] This fire-control position was not as well protected as Jellicoe wished; in addition, the view was obstructed ahead by the conning tower and astern by the mast legs and superstructure. It was not repeated in the *Australia* and *New Zealand* but, since they were not completed until almost two years after *Indefatigable*, their arrangements will be described in a later section. However, all three ships resembled the *Neptune* in having only a lightly protected after torpedo director position of 1in plating, although in their case it was built into the after superstructure.

Colossus *and* Hercules

Laid down in July 1909, these ships embodied both the changes anticipated in Jellicoe's minute. They were given a single mast which, once again, was stepped abaft the fore funnel. As in *Dreadnought*, the arrangement seems to have been adopted mainly to provide a support for the boat derrick. However, by 1909, the DNO was placing less importance in the position aloft; in November, he informed his successor that 'The end to which we have been working is to spot from the deck armoured position and abolish the aloft position'.[17] Bacon did not say how this would affect rangefinding and, in the new ships, the control top on the mast was actually more spacious than those fitted to the *St Vincent* class. As completed, it had a 9ft rangefinder on a traversing mounting.[18]

The capital ships that followed Dreadnought *were fitted with two full tripod masts, each carrying a fire-control top. The* Colossus, *seen here in 1913–14, reverted to the single main armament control top of the* Dreadnought *and, unfortunately, its position abaft the fore funnel. This fault proved more serious for her sister ship,* Hercules, *whose Yarrow boilers could generate funnel gases of a higher temperature.* (CMP)

Midships view of Conqueror *soon after completion with her original small bridge abaft the spotting tower.* (IWM, Q38540)

Colossus and *Hercules* were also the first ships provided with a new design of conning tower. This was almost circular (14ft 6in fore and aft by 15ft athwartships), constructed of 11in armour and contained both conning and signalling positions. On its roof was erected a smaller spotting tower of 6in armour, thereby creating the lower, protected fire-control position discussed previously. There being only limited space between the fore funnel and 'B' turret, the bridge was constructed above the conning and spotting towers so that, as completed, the top of the bridge was almost level with the top of the fore funnel.

Given the relative positions of bridge, fore funnel and control top, it is hardly surprising that these ships were bedevilled by smoke interference. 'The short fore funnel proved troublesome to bridge duties and was raised in 1912'[19] but this only brought it closer to the control top. Even so, when the traversing rangefinder mounting was replaced by the Argo gyroscopically-stabilised mounting, it was installed in the control top of *Colossus*,[20] while the tower containing the director sight for the main armament was subsequently erected on the roof of the control top, as far as possible from the top of the funnel. For reasons to be explained, the funnel smoke problem was even worse in *Hercules*. The Argo rangefinder was tried in the control top but 'on account of smoke trouble' it was moved to the compass platform above the conning and spotting towers.[21] The main armament director tower was also located on the same platform.

The Orions *and* Lions

As a result of the Navy Scare of 1909 and the agitation that 'we want eight and we won't wait', the 1909 Programme eventually consisted of six battleships and two battlecruis-

ers in 'the greatest accession to our armoured forces ever undertaken in a twelvemonth'.[22] After *Colossus* and *Hercules*, the remaining ships marked a radical development in that they carried 13.5in guns in centre-line turrets on a substantially increased displacement. However, *Colossus* and *Hercules* were not completed until (respectively) July and August 1911, so the remaining ships of the programme were designed without any operational experience of their predecessors' novel fire-control arrangements. The four *Orion*s and two *Lion*s merely repeated the flawed layout with a single tripod mast stepped abaft the forefunnel, the mast carrying a control top large enough to accommodate fire-control instruments and personnel. They were all completed with almost identical spotting towers (with 6in walls)[23] on the roofs of the conning towers. In the *Lion*s, as in *Colossus* and *Hercules*, the bridge was built out so that it completely overhung the spotting and conning towers; however, in the *Orion*s, the bridge structure was much more restricted and, because it was erected up against the funnel, could not obstruct the view or, if damaged by gunfire, collapse on top of the spotting tower.[24] All six battleships of the 1909 Programme had similar after torpedo director towers, of 3in armour, all the castings being ordered at the same time.[25] In the battlecruisers, only 1in protection was provided for this after position.

On 29 April 1910, the Admiralty agreed to purchase forty-five sets of Argo gyro-stabilised rangefinder mountings with their associated transmitters and indicators[26] with the intention of providing one to each battleship and battlecruiser.[27] On the 10 November following, a conference was held at the Admiralty to discuss the question of fire-control for future armoured ships including how best to utilise the new rangefinder mounting. At that time, *Colossus* and *Hercules*, *Orion* and *Lion* were fitting out, the remaining ships of the 1909 programme still being on the slips. However, it was already realised that 'as the Foremast is placed between two funnels ... it is quite likely that circumstances may occur when the fore control is useless owing to funnel smoke'.[28] Furthermore, 'owing to the advent of ships with one mast, the number of control positions has been reduced in our later ships and although provision has been made for an Armoured Spotting Tower forward and a combined director and control tower aft there was a consensus of opinion that these fell a long way short of requirements'. The conference therefore reached the following decisions.

1. Duplicate primary fire-control positions were required, one in the fore control top, the other in an aft armoured tower, but that 'the provision of a forward Tower [ie the spotting tower on the conning tower] is not necessary for controlling fire'.

2. The fore control top would accommodate the Argo mounting (carrying a 9ft rangefinder), a pair of Mark III Dumaresqs and the spotter.

3. The armoured tower aft would be fitted with an armoured 9ft rangefinder, a small (Mark II) Dumaresq and two torpedo directors; it, too would house a spotting officer.

4. 'B' and 'X' turrets should be equipped with the necessary transmitters so that they could act as secondary control positions.

5. All turrets should be equipped for local control with a 9ft rangefinder (in an armoured hood), a turret Dumaresq and a range-keeping instrument.

6. Ships should retain both the fore and after TS and be equipped with communication and switch gear so that fire could be controlled from either TS in conjunction with any of the four control positions.

The walls of the armoured tower aft were to be 6in thick[29] and its dimensions 7ft (fore and aft) by 5ft 6in and 'as the Director Towers of the 1910–11 Armoured Ships[30] have not yet been ordered propose [a] mock up [which] at first should not include a rangefinder so that a suitable tower may be settled for them and that after this the mock up may be altered to include a rangefinder for future ships'. The DNO also submitted that some degree of protection for personnel in the control top should be provided by making the floor (and, if possible, the sides) of 1in steel.

These new arrangements both replicated many of the fire-control functions and placed them behind armour, thereby considerably enhancing the fire-control's resilience to battle damage. However, the fore control top was still liable to interference from funnel smoke, which could therefore disable the aloft rangefinder on its gyro-stabilised mounting. This was the only rangefinder elevated well above interference from gunsmoke, sea spray and enemy hits and shorts.

After the conference, there was a further exchange of minutes but without any significant changes of policy, which was finally concurred with by the First Sea Lord (Sir Arthur Wilson) on 1 April 1911. This meant that a 'spotting tower [is] not to be fitted to Conning Tower in ships laid down since January 1911', *ie* the *King George V* class and *Queen Mary*, the latter having originally been designed in 1910 with the same layout as *Lion* and *Princess Royal*.[31] However, no action was planned to tackle the fundamental problem, the stepping of the mast abaft the fore funnel. It was also decided that 'no alteration to be made in the Conning Towers of ships fitted with Spotting Towers'.

This last intention was soon undermined as it became apparent that the problems with the single-masted ships were even worse than anticipated. On 30 November 1911, Lord Charles Beresford, no doubt with relish and some exaggeration, put down a parliamentary question, 'To ask the First Lord of the Admiralty whether he is aware that ... in the control positions of HMS *Orion* [and her sisters], *Lion*, *Princess Royal*, *Colossus* and *Hercules* ... the Spotter is liable to be suffocated [and that] the heat from the funnel often produces a temperature of 220 degrees'. Rather lamely, the Admiralty submitted to reply that 'The control positions which are on the foremast in the ships mentioned were based on experience with *Dreadnought*' and that 'some modifications are under consideration'.[32] In fact, matters were worse than Lord Charles knew, particularly with the battlecruisers. When *Lion* ran her trials at the beginning of 1912, it was found that the bridge supports limited the view from the spotting tower and her captain, A A M Duff, reported on 'the impossibility of finding any place from which the main armament can be controlled ... With the wind aft, it would be impossible to stay [in the control top while] steaming at any speed ... The next place one would look to would be the spotting tower ... but with a roll

of 5deg, and we have so far never had less at sea, the bridge completely obscures the view from this'. These serious defects required attention at the highest level and were considered at a conference held on 29 March 1912 attended by the First, Second and Third Sea Lords, the DNO[33] and Captains Bartolomé and Craig, the latter commanding HMS *Orion*. The conference was concerned with 'the mast and funnel question' and by the time it was held it had become clear that, in *Lion*, the top was untenable whenever the forward boilers were alight and that, in addition, the 'heat and fumes from the funnel render upper bridge uninhabitable and make it difficult to use manoeuvring compass'. In fact, the problems were so numerous and urgent that, at an earlier conference at the Admiralty held on 9 February, it had already been decided that radical modifications were necessary to *Lion* and *Princess Royal*. These were based on decisions previously made concerning the ships of the 1911 Programme (the *Iron Duke*s and *Tiger*), namely 'to abolish the control top, to alter the relative position of the mast and funnel, and to make the conning tower the main steering position in war and peace'.[34] Although the first of these ships was not laid down until January 1912, on 25 November 1911 the uncertainty created by the problems with the newly commissioned ships caused the DNC to propose a note on the drawings for the 1911 battleships to read 'The position, sizes, etc of the mast and funnels may be modified'.[35] It therefore seems probable that the details of the new layout had not been worked out until the growing crisis demanded immediate solutions not only for the ships already completed and about to start building, but also for the *King George V* class which had much the same layout. Consequently, on 11 December 1911, the Controller sent telegrams to Portsmouth and Devonport commanding that 'All work on masts, bridges, boiler hatches and uptakes of *King George V* Portsmouth and *Centurion* Devonport to be suspended until further orders'.[36] The new fire-control arrangements were then worked out, firstly for the *King George V* class, and then adapted for the *Lion*s and the *Iron Duke*s. They were influenced by the facts that 'whenever the control top is above the funnel there must be a liability to interference under certain conditions of wind and speed [and] that there is a distinct change in the general opinion of the Service afloat ... it [being] that interference from gases and smoke from funnels is greater than from the smoke of the guns and that it is preferable to find a control position below the top of the funnel'. The solution adopted was to move nearly all the fire control instruments and personnel from the control top to an armoured position on top of the conning tower. This consisted of a rotating hood, 3in thick, which protected the rangefinder, a small MkV Dumaresq and the spotting officer; the Argo mounting was placed in the lower, non-rotating section of this position, inside the conning tower. A light top was retained for an additional spotter but, since it did not house any fire-control instruments other than spotting glasses, it did not require a rigid tripod mast, which was removed from both the *Lion*s and *King George V* class. In the battlecruisers, the fore funnel was shifted aft and all funnels were increased in height to 81ft above the load water-line; the original pole mainmast was fitted ahead of the fore funnel as the new foremast and given a small spotting top. The bridge was reduced in size so that there was no overhang above the new conning tower, from which the ships were now worked. The spotting tower was removed from the conning tower and the latter was 'enlarged by cutting the two side plates in halves and interposing two additional side plates' in order to create space for the rangefinder mounting in the lower section of the armoured hood.

In his statement to Parliament on the Navy Estimates for 1912–13 (given on 4 March 1912), Winston Churchill, the First Lord, disingenuously reported that, respecting *Lion*, 'opportunity has been taken for carrying out certain alterations which experience has shown to be desirable'; she was finally completed in May, while the same alterations were made to *Princess Royal* and *Queen Mary* after they were launched. The radical surgery seems to have solved the immediate problems effectively but it failed to take into account an important new fire-control device which, although still being developed, was soon to be ready for deployment, production orders being placed in 1913.[37] This was the director, which also required a vibration-free, elevated position. The *Lions*' unstayed pole masts were not at all suitable for this purpose, which may explain why these ships, despite the expectation that they would be among the first to make long-range contact with the enemy in a fleet engagement, were not fitted until relatively late in the programme of director installations.[38] It was then necessary to stiffen the mast with small struts so that, in Parkes' words, 'the big tripod found its substitute in a piecemeal-assembled makeshift'. Even so, the platform for the director tower could not be raised very high and was positioned almost level with the top of the fore funnel. It appears that, to the end of their operational life, these ships suffered from smoke interfering with their fire-control since, by 1918, *Lion*'s forefunnel was fitted with a clinker screen.

To return now to the conference of 29 March 1912: their Lordships noted the alterations already approved for the *Lion* and *King George V* classes and went on to consider the question of 'whether any alterations are required in the 6 battleships of the *Colossus* and *Orion* classes'. In considering the 'effect of heat and fumes from forward funnel in rendering control top untenable', they noticed that 'the more boilers served and consequently greater area of funnel, the more heat is produced. It appears probable that this factor was not sufficiently taken into account when the principle of mast behind funnel which had been approved for *Dreadnought* was applied to some of the later ships developing much greater horse power'. It was also remarked that 'Yarrow boilers can be forced more than Babcock and Wilcox and produce greater heat'. Table 1 (summarised from the notes of the conference) indicated 'that heat interference might have been expected to be greater in *Lion* and *Princess Royal* than in the battleships; and that of the latter, *Monarch* and *Hercules* are most likely to be defective'.

Captain Craig of the *Orion* advised against any immediate changes to the *Orion* class, stating that 'he personally preferred to put a forward rangefinder in B turret and was conducting experiments ... to gain more experience'. The conference decided that 'No further immediate extensive alterations are required beyond what is already approved' though the notes do not explain why *Hercules*, in particu-

lar, was expected to be any better than the *Lion*s. As a result, she remained unaltered and, as we have seen, continued to be plagued with smoke interference. The *Orion*s also were not modified so the rangefinders on the Argo mountings in their control tops[39] must have experienced some smoke interference; *Monarch* would have been particularly prone to this problem, though to a lesser extent than *Hercules*.

Thus the aloft fire-control positions of the first class of 13.5in gun battleships were significantly inferior to those of the two-masted ships with 12in guns. In these earlier classes, Argo mountings were installed in the foretops which, where necessary, were increased in size.[40] When they came to be fitted with directors, the foremast also provided a rigid support and a position for the director tower platform well forward of the fore funnel; usually, this platform was located just beneath the control top. The directors were similarly located in the *Orion*s, which does suggest that, in service, their control tops did not suffer excessively from smoke interference. However, a better position for the director would have been on the roof of the control top, where it was placed in *Dreadnought* and *Colossus* (as well as in the later 13.5in gun ships and the *Queen Elizabeth*s). The explanation for the choice of the lower position in the *Orion*s may lie in the selection of *Thunderer* as the second ship to be fitted with the director. If the installation was based on that in *Neptune* and it proved reasonably free from smoke interference, it may have been decided merely to repeat the same arrangement in the other ships of the class.

Australia *and* New Zealand

The second and third ships of the *Indefatigable* class were paid for by the two dominions and were laid down in June 1910, only one month after the final ship of the 1909 programme. They retained the *Indefatigable*'s mast arrangement but, instead of the separate spotting-and-signal tower, were given the same conning tower with armoured spotting tower that was originally intended for all the 1909 ships. The bridge partly overhung the spotting tower but not to the same extent as in the *Lion*s. The masts were equipped with the enlarged pattern of top which could accommodate the Argo rangefinder mounting.[41]

Despite their other inadequacies as fighting ships, the fire-control positions of *Australia* and *New Zealand* retained the older and more satisfactory mast position, while greatly improving on the armoured spotting position fitted to their sister ship. When they and *Indefatigable* came to be fitted for director firing, the fore tripod mast provided a rigid support for the director tower which was placed just beneath the top.

King George V *class and* Queen Mary

The reader will recall that, after the Fire-Control Conference in November 1910, it was intended that the ships of the 1910–11 programme were to be similar in layout to the *Orion*s and *Lion*s, except that the spotting tower atop the

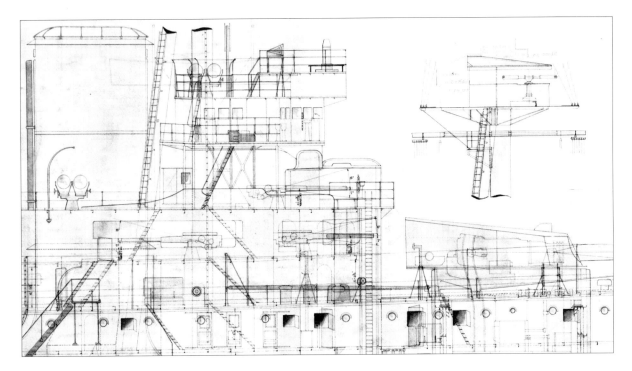

conning tower would not be repeated: and that an after control-tower, protected with 6in armour, would be fitted. However, as soon as the problems with the earlier single-masted ships became apparent, it was realised that 'similar

The Queen Mary *showing pole mast (before installation of the director) and small spotting top. Note both the proximity of the bridge to the fore funnel and the armoured rangefinder hood with additional ports for the control officer, Dumaresq operator and rangefinder trainer. This photograph was taken soon after completion (September 1913), before the control officer's hood was fitted atop the armoured hood.* (IWM, Q21661A)

Part of the official as-fitted profile of the New Zealand *showing the conning tower with the spotting tower on the roof. This type of spotting tower was first introduced in* Colossus *and* Hercules *(in which the bridge overhang was much greater than in* Australia *and* New Zealand*). The same type was retained in the* Orion *class but the bridge was kept well clear.* (NMM, NPB7804)

changes in position of funnels, masts, etc, to those proposed for 1911–12 Battleships could be made in ships of *King George V* class [and *Queen Mary* though] if it is desired to make these alterations, action should be taken as soon as possible ... at an extra cost of £20,000 per vessel'. On 20 December 1911, the new First Lord, Winston Churchill, minuted 'It is very satisfactory that these marked improvements [sic] can be introduced in the 1910–11 vessels. I approve the changes proposed and the expenditure'.[42] The new and larger conning tower design was first worked out in detail for the *King George V* class, the DNC proposing, on 16 January 1912, that Portsmouth dockyard should construct a mock-up of the conning tower complete with the revolving hood for the Argo rangefinder.[43] The conning towers of both the *King George V* class and *Queen Mary* were circular with an internal diameter of 18ft;[44] following the usual practice, the armour thickness was 11in in the battleships, 10in in the battlecruiser.

When the five ships were modified, a makeshift foremast was constructed in the *King George V* class from one of the struts of the earlier tripod;[45] as with the *Lions*, this supported only a small control-top. Consequently, when director gear was fitted, alignment problems were recorded in both *Ajax* and *Centurion* which were attributed 'to insufficient stiffness of the director platform and mast'.[46] Both these ships and *Audacious* were given half-height tripods but the mast of *King George V* was first stiffened with flanges until, in 1918, she was given a full height tripod. In

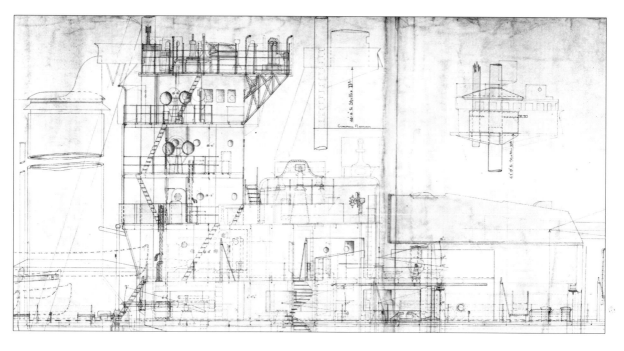

Part of the official as-fitted profile of the Lion *showing the conning tower as modified to take the revolving armoured hood over the Argo rangefinder mounting, which was placed on top of a conical pedestal. The drawing was corrected at Rosyth Yard in 1920 and this section shows a number of modifications. The Argo tower, the rangefinder and its support have been struck through and replaced by a fixed lookout position and a 15ft rangefinder tower has been added to the fore end of the conning tower roof; these towers are visible in postwar photographs of* Lion. *The profile of the foretop at top right has been overdrawn by the enlarged version fitted during 1917–18 and, above the conning tower, a sub view shows a profile of the director and its platform which was fitted on the foremast in 1915. Note the funnel cap, or clinker screen, fitted to the fore funnel – an addition made in 1918:* Lion *was the only battlecruiser so fitted.* (NMM, 196260)

his memoirs, Percy Scott fulminates against the decision to replace the rigid tripod with an unstayed mast unsuitable for carrying a director tower. However, it should be remembered that, when the decisions on modifications were taken at the very start of 1912, only one ship, *Neptune*, was fitted with a fully engineered director. This was still a unique, experimental design which had given promising results during test firings in early 1911: so much so that, in March 1911, the DNO (Captain Moore) had recommended 'that ships building should be wired for director gear on the same lines as *Neptune* commencing with *Orion* and *Lion* and that director firing should be provided for in the specifications of the 1911–12 armoured ships.' However, subsequent trials were 'rather disappointing' and the *Neptune* director was not considered reliable enough for use in battle practice.[17] A new design of director (in many ways the prototype for the production version) was ordered for *Thunderer* in late 1911 but the ship was not completed until June 1912 and the conclusive trial with *Orion*, which demonstrated the superiority of director control, did not take place until November 1912. Thus the decision to fit unstayed masts to the three *Lion*s and four ships of the *King George V* class was taken when the director had shown significant promise but was still not proven as an operational system. Even so, Scott does seem justified in his criticism of what looks like a short-term expedient to overcome an immediate, not to say embarrassing, problem.

By the middle of 1912, another decision of the 1910 fire-control conference was also being dropped. Although the 6in aft control-tower was being fitted, it had been abandoned as a control position for the main armament, 'B' turret (with its turret rangefinder) acting as the alternative control for the heavy guns. It was therefore decided that the after tower should be used principally for torpedo control. Since there was now spare space available, a hole was cut in the roof and a rangefinder mounting sunk into the tower; a 'light hood attached to the revolving part of the mounting would ... cover the observer's head and protect him from splinters'. This hood is shown on the 'As Fitted' drawings for the battleships and for *Queen Mary*.[48]

Once the ships which had been equipped with the armoured rangefinder hood on the conning tower entered service, the control officer evidently found it difficult to perform his duties. His view was limited by the ports in the front of the hood; also space was more restricted than originally planned since it had been found necessary to work the Argo rangefinder mounting with two operators. So, 'in order to afford an all round view to the Control Officer, it has been decided to fit a look out hood in the top of the existing hood in HMS *Queen Mary* for trial ... with a view to fitting such hoods in HM Ships of the *King George V* class, HMS *Lion* and HMS *Princess Royal*'. The hood for *Queen Mary*, of 3in armour, was ordered on 16 August 1913; the trials were evidently a success since hoods for the other ships were ordered in turn on 10 October 1914.[49]

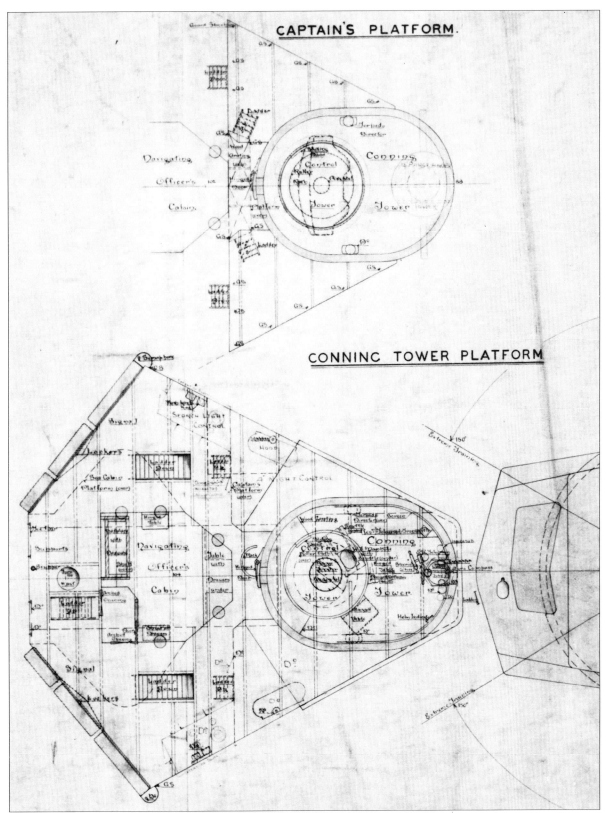

Part of the Lion's *as-fitted plan views showing the conning tower with the rangefinder pedestal and, in outline, the armoured hood. The* Queen Mary *and the* King George V *class were similar except that their conning towers were circular. Again the drawing has been corrected, resulting in the somewhat confused annotation in the lower view.* (NMM, NPN5451)

The Iron Duke *class and* Tiger

The ships of the 1911–12 programme were able to benefit from earlier mistakes, though not without significant changes in design along the way. As noted above, the decision had been taken in principle before the end of 1911 to locate the mast ahead of the fore funnel. During the first quarter of 1912, attempts were also made to revert to the *Orion* arrangement with the fore funnel serving only six boilers but, while it was in the end necessary for each funnel to take the exhausts from nine boilers, it was possible to increase the distance between the fore funnel and the conning tower by 6.5ft.[50] At that time, it was still not intended that the foremast should be a tripod but in a note dated 18 March 1914 on 'Alterations and Additions to Designs since the Retirement of Sir P Watts', a list of 'principal alterations made since August 1912' includes 'struts added to foremast and mast moved further forward of forward-funnel for director firing'. Exactly the same modifications were noted for *Tiger*.[51] Thus, albeit by degrees, the 1911 ships regained a rigid tripod mast both high enough and sufficiently far forward to elevate the control top and director sight well clear of smoke interference.

These ships also introduced improvements in the fire-control positions atop the conning tower. In previous ships, the armoured rangefinder hood rotated directly on top of

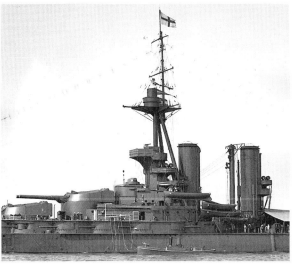

The Iron Duke *with the director tower above the control top. The fixed spotting tower can be seen on the roof of the conning tower, beneath the revolving hood. The slits for the 6in control are visible in the side walls of the conning tower.* (IWM, Q39292)

Part of the official as-fitted profile of Iron Duke *showing her as built and with corrections made to the drawings in 1921 and 1923. This shows the original conning tower with fixed spotting tower and revolving armoured rangefinder hood for the 9ft rangefinder and the light hood for the 15ft rangefinder, added during the war, attached to the back of the armoured hood. Note also, at top left, the original circular spotting top, with the director on its roof, and the extensions added to it during the war; the semaphore on the roof of the conning tower and the 25ft rangefinder added to the rear of 'A' turret.* (NMM, NPB4692)

the conning tower; in the new design, the armoured hood was elevated on a squat spotting tower 3ft 9in high and 9ft internal diameter.[52] The control officer and the Dumaresq operator were placed in this fixed part of the fire-control tower, thus leaving the hood free for the two Argo rangefinder operators. The commanding officers of *Lion* and *King George V* had also reported problems with the arrangements for training the armoured hood; this was driven by an electric motor under the control of a 'hunting' switch (supplied by the Argo company) which was supposed to ensure that the hood always followed the movements of the rangefinder. However, this switch was prone to sticking, thereby causing the training motor to come to a standstill. Furthermore, 'the speed of rotation of the hood

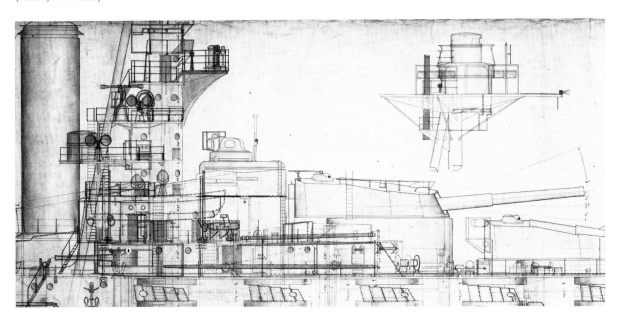

is unnecessarily great [being] 90deg in 15$\frac{1}{2}$secs on the first speed of the hunting switch and is less than 11sec with the second speed contact making' whereas, even in the most unusual tactical circumstances, no more than 110deg/min was required. Despite these problems, it was decided on 21 October 1913 'to adhere to electrical training in HM Ships of the *King George V* [and *Lion* classes] but to adopt hydraulic training in HM Ships of the *Iron Duke* class and HMS *Tiger*. A new type of [electrical] control switch is now being made to replace [that] which has shown to be imperfect'[53] in the earlier ships. The hydraulic swashplate training engine and hunting valve were supplied by Vickers

against an order placed on 6 November 1914.[54]

As in the ships of the previous year's programme, the *Iron Dukes* and *Tiger* retained a 6in armoured control tower for the torpedo directors and 'as a control position for the after groups of the secondary armament'. The tower was equipped with a '9ft rangefinder, the observer and mounting being under protection as in the *King George V* class'.[55]

During the war, it soon became apparent that 9ft rangefinders were insufficiently accurate for actual battle ranges. In the *Iron Dukes*, the deficiency was remedied by attaching a 15ft rangefinder, in a lightly protected housing,

Part of the Iron Duke's *as-fitted plan views showing the conning tower, armoured revolving hood and the attached hood for the 15ft rangefinder. The extensions on each side of the conning tower for the 6in control positions can also be seen.* (NMM, NPB4700)

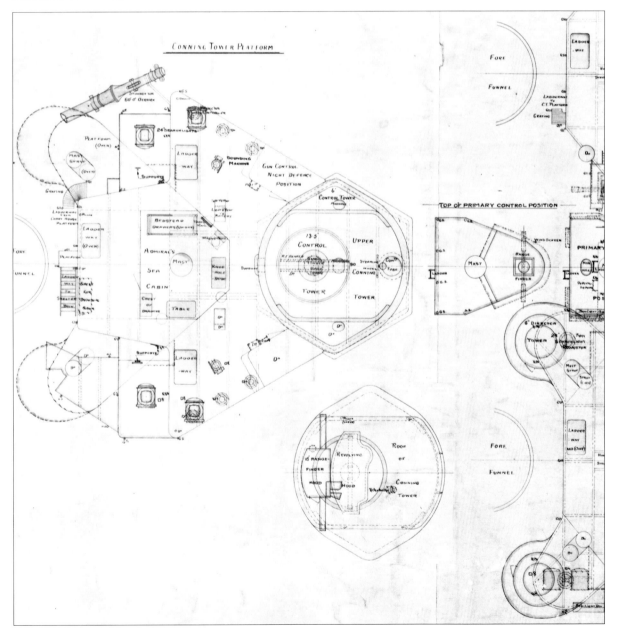

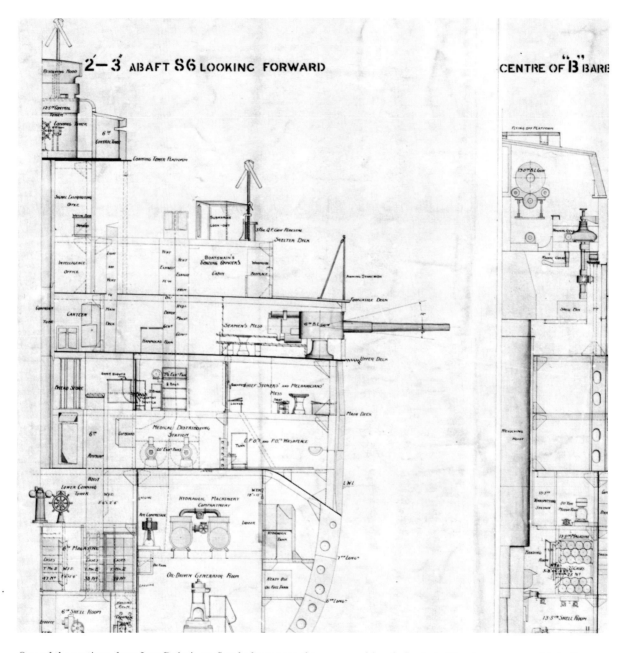

One of the sections from Iron Duke's *as-fitted plans; note the armoured hood, fixed spotting tower recessed into the main conning tower and the 6in control positions on each side.* (NMM, NPB4717)

to the outside of the armoured hood on the conning tower; initially, the original 9ft instrument was retained inside but later it may have been moved to the fire-control top.[56] On the after control tower, the 9ft instrument was replaced by a 15ft rangefinder under a new hood.

Iron Duke and *Marlborough* were launched in October 1912, while *Benbow* and *Emperor of India* followed in November 1913 and *Tiger* in December 1913. Thus the spotting towers had to be installed when the first two ships were nearing completion (in March and June 1914 respectively). These two are listed among the ships fitted with main armament directors by August 1914 while their sisters were similarly equipped by May 1915. In this class, the main armament director tower was installed on the roof of the control top, taking full advantage of the height of the big tripod mast; the same high position was used for *Tiger*'s director.

In the *Iron Duke*s and *Tiger*, the Royal Navy reintroduced a secondary armament of 6in guns. To provide protected control positions for these guns, the sides of the conning tower were extended to create two compartments which, being separated from the main conning tower by a flat armoured partition, in plan resembled flattened triangles, the apices being outboard.[57] Secondary armament directors were fitted to the battleships in 1917;[58] they were installed on either side of the bridge platform but Parkes states that, since they were level with the top of the fore funnel, they 'used to get badly smoked out at times'.

The Queen Elizabeth *Class*

Queen Elizabeth and *Warspite* were laid down in October 1913, just before the rough weather trials in November during which *Thunderer*, controlling her fire with the new design of director sight, demonstrated its superiority in such conditions over individual laying as used by *Orion*. It is an indication of the lack of support for director firing prior to this crucial shoot off Berehaven[59] that the foremast of the *Queen Elizabeth*s was originally designed without struts. However, by January 1914, the height of the mast was being increased, struts added to create a full tripod and provision made for a director tower (which was on the roof of the control top).[60] The first two members of the class had received their directors by May 1915, while *Barham*, *Val-*

iant and *Malaya* were fitted before May 1916.[61]

As with the masts, the initial design for the conning tower and rangefinder hood had followed the original arrangements for the *Iron Duke*s; it was even decided in November 1912 to place a joint order of eight armoured hoods for both classes.[62] As described in the previous section, by September 1913 the *Iron Duke*s were being altered by the addition of a fixed spotting tower under the hood. However, by the following January, much more radical changes were being considered for the armoured hoods of the new 15in gun battleships. First, the 9ft rangefinder on its Argo mounting was replaced by a 15ft instrument (the Argo mounting being moved to the control top[63]). Second, the hood was enlarged so that the tower could also contain a second director sight, protected by its 3in armour. Third, as in the *Iron Duke*s, a fixed spotting tower was located between the hood and the conning tower; the last-named was itself enlarged when the other alterations were made but its plan was very similar to the towers in the *Iron Duke*s, with the 6in control positions in the sides.[64]

On 24 March 1914, Vickers were requested to tender for the supply of the hoods 'complete with support for Range Finder Mounting and Director and with ports in it as may be required for range-finder and director sights ... and all necessary gear for training ... either by hand or hydraulic power through the medium of a "Hunting" valve gear between the sight and hood'.[65] The rangefinder was mounted in rear of the hood but, as in a turret rangefinder, could be

The Queen Elizabeth *at Mudros (detail). The conning tower (with 6in control position), fixed spotting tower and revolving hood are shown, together with the director tower on the roof of the control top. (IWM, Q13838)*

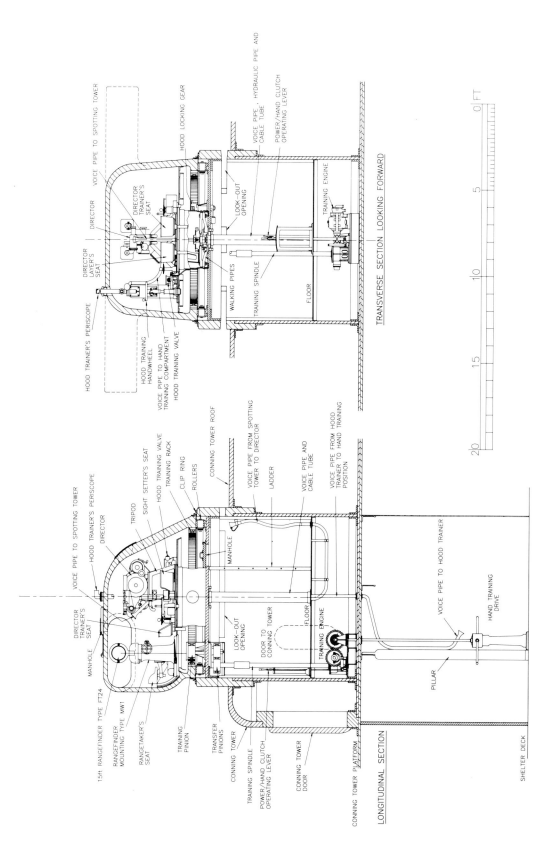

General arrangement of the armoured revolving hood and spotting tower fitted in the Queen Elizabeth class, Royal Sovereign class and the Canada. This drawing, and that of the later model for the Renown, etc, is based on the Vickers design drawings for the revolving armoured hoods held by the Cumbria Record Office. However, the drawing has been expanded to include more details of the director, rangefinder and the ship's structure taken from the Admiralty Director Firing Handbook, the Admiralty Handbook for Rangefinders and reference to the 'as fitted' drawings of Barham, Resolution, Repulse and Courageous. (Drawn by John Roberts)

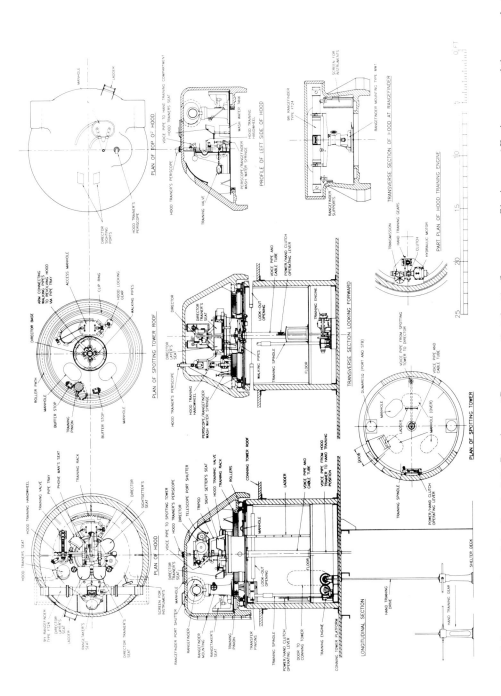

General arrangement of the armoured revolving hood of the Repulse and Renown – that for the Courageous, Glorious and Furious was of the same design. This was essentially of the same type as that fitted in Queen Elizabeth except that the hood was a different shape – overhanging the spotting tower on the outside – and carried a 9ft rangefinder in place of the 15ft. Later, these ships were also fitted with 15ft rangefinders which involved the fitting of extensions to the armoured hood to accommodate their increased length. The director was fitted to the roof of the spotting tower and not the hood, which revolved separately. The hood trainer could train the hood onto the target using the periscope or keep the hood in line with the director as it was trained by keeping a mark on the hood in line with a pointer on the director. The hood and director were interlocked so that they could not be misaligned in training by more than 10 degrees – when the hood was power-trained the power was cut off at 7 degrees, when hand-trained it would pick-up the director at about 10 degrees and carry it round to the stops, if the director was trained independently of the hood it was brought to a stop at 10 degrees by a mechanical interlock. (Drawn by John Roberts)

The forward turrets and bridge of the Queen Elizabeth*: the armoured hood (with ports for the 15ft rangefinder and the director sight) and the top of the spotting tower can be seen above the conning tower roof.* (IWM, Q13238)

trained a few degrees left or right before fouling the inside of the hood. As completed, the hood was trained by a dedicated operator with a wheel-operated control-valve; he could either follow the director or align on the target with his periscopic sight.[66] Since the director sights only had narrow fields of view through the hood ports, it is probable that the latter method was used when first 'acquiring' the target. By 1915, the spotting tower was referred to as the Gun Control Tower, though later this term was used for both the fixed tower and the revolving armoured hood.[67] As in the *Iron Duke*s, the after tower (again of 6in armour) was utilised for the torpedo directors and a control position for the after groups of the secondary armament. For these purposes, it was provided with a 9ft rangefinder under a light armoured hood.[68]

The *Queen Elizabeth*s also introduced one further novelty in the shape of a bow spotting position. The idea was discussed in a number of minutes written in the latter half of 1913 and at a conference held on 11 November that year.[69] It was agreed that in the first two classes of 15in gun ships, small scuttles would be cut each side of the stem and that, additionally in the *Royal Sovereign*s, a small 2in thick hood or hatchway would be fitted overhead. The position would be provided with a fall-of-shot transmitter connected to receivers in the fore TS, the gun control tower and the spotting position aloft. However, in *Excellent*'s report of *Valiant*'s gun trials (dated February 1916), it was suggested 'that the fall of shot instrument in the Bow Compartment should be shifted to "A" turret'[70] which indicates (perhaps not surprisingly) that the bow spotting position was of little use. It is not mentioned at all in the Ships' Cover for the *Royal Sovereign* class. However, the bow position excepted, the *Queen Elizabeth* arrangement – spotting top and director tower aloft on a tripod mast together with a gun control tower on the conning tower – became the norm for the subsequent classes completed up to the end of the Great War.[71]

Conclusions

Dreadnought herself was built with a single lofty fire-control top supported by a heavy, rigid tripod mast. The top itself was unprotected but sufficiently capacious to accommodate the control officer and the 9ft rangefinder, the Dumaresqs and the fire-control personnel. A weakness of

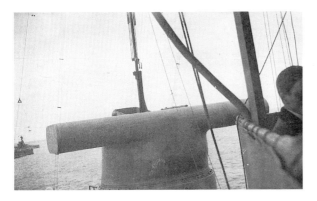

An unusual view of the rear of Resolution's *armoured hood showing the extensions which protected its 15ft rangefinder. Note the semaphore on the roof of the hood.* (CMP)

the arrangement was that the tripod was stepped abaft the fore funnel as a support for the main boat derrick; however, the distance from the top of the funnel to the control top ($39\frac{1}{2}$ft) ensured that, in most circumstances, the top was not affected by smoke and hot gases. Even so, the layout was not repeated in the following classes, which were given two tripods of equal height, the foremast being stepped forward of the funnels. The control tops on the masts were very similar to that in *Dreadnought* and contained the same instruments and personnel. In service, the main mast top was of little use but the foremast proved satisfactory so that, when these ships were fitted with director towers, the mast could easily carry an additional smoke-free platform below the control top.

The heavy tripods did, however, present a conspicuous target. Admiral Bridgeman's suggestion of October 1908 that they should be abolished altogether was not accepted, the DNO then insisting that an elevated position was essential for rangefinding prior to opening fire and for spotting afterwards. However, it was agreed that the mainmast was unnecessary and that a lower, protected, spotting and control position was desirable. Thus, *Colossus* and *Hercules* reverted to a single mast and they were given an armoured spotting tower atop the conning tower. However, the need to provide a support for the boat derrick seems to have outweighed any concerns arising from problems of smoke interference experienced with *Dreadnought*'s fire-control top; once again the single mast was stepped abaft the fore funnel, even though rangefinding still depended on the aloft position. This proved to be a serious mistake, not only for the two ships concerned, since the other six ships of the 1909 programme (the first battleships and battlecruisers with 13.5in guns) were given the same fire-control positions. In all the 1909 ships, the fire-control tops were closer to the top of the fore funnel than in *Dreadnought*; while (the *Orion*s excepted) this funnel also served more boilers, some of which, being of the Yarrow type, could also be forced to produce yet more furnace products.

Even before any of these ships were completed, concern was mounting about smoke interfering with their fire-control. By the end of 1910, ideas had changed again about a lower, protected, control position and it was proposed that, in the *King George V* class, the spotting tower should

be omitted and replaced by a second fully equipped after armoured control position, complete with armoured range-finder hood; on the other hand, the new Argo gyro-stabilised rangefinder mounting was to be located aloft in the masthead fire-control top. These intentions required drastic alterations once the problem of smoke interference in the 1909 ships became apparent at the end of 1911. At that time, a final choice between the Pollen and Dreyer fire control systems had not yet been taken,[72] but it was already clear that both depended equally on the Argo rangefinder mounting's ability to obtain gyroscopically stabilised and corrected bearings.[73] Thus, the design alterations provided an opportunity to create for this vital instrument a new position which combined the earlier concepts both of an armoured position atop the conning tower and of a revolving hood to protect the rangefinder. The new armoured rangefinder hood, first worked out for the *King George V* class and then adapted for the *Lion*s, accommodated not only the rangefinder and Argo mounting but also the principal fire-control officer and a Dumaresq. Since the main observational instruments were now removed from the top, only a small and lightly supported top was required for a second spotter; consequently, although it was necessary to move the mast forward of the funnels, only a light pole was fitted.

The new arrangements anticipated well the needs of the still developing fire-control systems, at once protecting the only rangefinder which could obtain both ranges and stabilised bearings, while elevating the instrument above the guns but well below the funnel smoke. No such foresight was displayed respecting director firing, even though it

Close-up of the bridge structure of the battleship Resolution *taken at Aberdeen in about 1929. Note that the revolving armoured hood is of the same design as that in the* Queen Elizabeth *class. The extensions on the face of the hood are probably wind baffles, a feature that seems to be unique to this member of the* Royal Sovereign *class.* (CMP)

This view of Renown *(nearest camera),* Hood *and* Valiant
*during gunnery exercises in June 1935, illustrates well
the problems of visibility that were created by cordite
smoke and the fact that the control tops provided a
position that was reasonably clear of this problem.* (CMP)

had already shown considerable promise during the *Neptune* trials in the spring of 1911. The pole mast therefore proved quite inadequate when required to carry a director sight and various more or less satisfactory expedients were necessary when the *Lion* and *King George V* classes were fitted for director firing. The early designs for the ships of the 1911 and 1912 programmes repeated this unsatisfactory type of mast but, fortunately, it was possible to work-in proper tripods before the ships were completed.

The armoured control position with revolving hood atop the conning tower, although introduced in haste as a solution to the problems with the 1909 ships, proved to be a satisfactory concept. It was further developed in the *Iron Dukes* and *Tiger* by the addition of a fixed spotting tower beneath the hood. Finally, in the *Queen Elizabeth* and later classes, it became the 'Gun Control Tower', on which an enlarged armoured hood protected not only the principal

rangefinder but also one of the director sights. However, by the time these ships were completed, it was apparent that battle ranges would often exceed 15,000yds, so unprotected but fully elevated positions were also provided at the head of the tripod mast for a rangefinder, spotting personnel and a second director sight. With the exception of the last-named, the arrangements aloft were therefore little different from those first adopted in the *Bellerophon*s and *Invincible*s: although, unlike the older vessels, the 15in gun ships also duplicated the fire-control functions below the funnel tops, at a height where they could be well protected under an armoured hood.

The progressive development of the fire-control positions in British dreadnoughts suffered a severe setback when the decision was taken to revert to a single mast and to step if abaft the fore funnel, a mistake which was compounded by repeating it in the unprecedented number of ships started as part of the 1909 programme. The resulting crisis was tackled vigorously though, perhaps inevitably, by adopting some short-term solutions which had to be remedied later. Eventually (as in so many other respects) the designers of the *Queen Elizabeth* class found a well-balanced layout for the ships' fire-control which reconciled the conflicting demands of a high viewpoint, immunity from

Table 1: *RELATIVE FUNNEL AND CONTROL TOP POSITIONS IN BRITISH DREADNOUGHTS*

Ship	*Type of boiler*	*Distance of top of screen of control top above top of funnel: vertically (ft–in)*	*Distance of fore edge of control top from after edge of funnel: horizontally (ft–in)*	*Area of foremost funnel (sq ft)*	*Number of boilers served*
Dreadnought	Babcock & Wilcox	39–6	7–0	75	6
Colossus	Babcock & Wilcox	35–6	7–0	157	12
Hercules	Yarrow				
Orion class except: *Monarch*	Babcock & Wilcox Yarrow	34–6	2–0	81.5	6
Lion class	Yarrow	32–0 as designed	8–6	134.7	10

smoke and protection from enemy fire. Even so, the Royal Navy entered the Great War with a number of dreadnought classes in which fire-control suffered from the errors made when the mast and funnel question had still not been answered satisfactorily.

Acknowledgements

The author would like to thank Professor Jon Sumida for his most helpful advice and also for the copies of many vital documents, including those specifically acknowledged in the notes. He is also most grateful for David Hughes' guidance through the Vickers Archive at the Cumbria Record Office; and from the staff of the National Maritime Museum for the help received with the Ships' Covers and plans.

Notes

1 D K Brown, *Some Thoughts on Fire Control and Warship Design*, 1994.
2 Oscar Parkes, *British Battleships*, Seeley Service (London 1957, reprinted 1990) p562.
3 The Dreyer Table MkII, incorporating an Argo Clock MkIV.
4 John Roberts, *The Battleship Dreadnought*, Conway Maritime Press (London, 1992), p238 (H4). A second 9ft rangefinder, also on a traversing mounting, was placed on top of the signal tower which was amidships, between the funnels.
5 Admiralty, *Manual of Gunnery, 1907*, p59 and Plate XXXVI.
6 It must be emphasised that experimental procedures to correct range rate by spotting were not promulgated until 1909: letter to the author from Professor J T Sumida, 17 August 1994. For rate spotting in 1910 and 1913, see Jon Tetsuro Sumida, *In Defence of Naval Supremacy* (London, 1989), p204, and *Home Fleet General Orders No14, Fire Control Organisation*, 5 November 1913, pp3–4.
7 Admiralty, *Report of the Committee on Designs*, 1905, pp8, 14, 68–9.
8 Parkes, *British Battleships*, p483. Unless indicated otherwise, basic facts on funnels, masts, mast positions and dates for ships are taken from this source.
9 Drawing NPB 4640 (This and all subsequently quoted drawings are held by the National Maritime Museum unless otherwise indicated).
10 Admiralty, *Handbook of Fire Control Instruments, 1909*, p6.
11 Ships' Cover 247/9 (Ships' Covers are held by the National Maritime Museum).
12 He indicated that, if the rangefinders then being tried in turrets were successful, they would be sufficient.
13 Ships' Cover 243/15.
14 *Paper prepared by the Director of Naval Ordnance for the Information of his Successor, 24 November, 1909*, p18; henceforth abbreviated to *DNO to Successor*. Copies courtesy of Professor Jon Sumida.
15 Percy Scott, *Fifty Years in the Royal Navy*, John Murray (London, 1919), p247. This source is also used for other dates relating to the director.
16 Ships' Cover 224/52 and /114 and drawings NPN 4663 and NPB 4359.
17 *DNO to Successor*, 1909, p16.
18 Principal sources for this section are Ships' Cover 247/15, 52 and 105 and drawing NPA 8935.
19 Parkes, *British Battleships*, p522.
20 Drawing NPA 8935.
21 Ships' Cover 248A/4.
22 Parkes, *British Battleships*, p519: Arthur Marder, *From Dreadnought to Scapa Flow, Vol 1*, Oxford UP (London, 1961), pp151–185.
23 For the *Lions'* fire-control, see mainly Ships' Cover 25/124 and 159.
24 Parkes, *British Battleships*, p526. In service, the bridge proved too cramped and was extended both forward and around the fore funnel.
25 Ships' Cover 248/73.
26 Sumida, *In defence of Naval Supremacy*, p198.
27 *DNO to Successor*, 1912, p15.
28 *Fire Control in Future Armoured Ships* G 0635/10 in Ships' Cover 260/68: copy courtesy of Prof Jon Sumida. The conference was attended inter alia by the DNO, ITP, the Captain of *Excellent* and representatives of the DNC's department.
29 In the preceding March the DNO had requested better protec-

[30] The *King George V* battleships and *Queen Mary*.

[31] Drawing NPB 9567.

[32] Ships' Cover 248/122.

[33] Respectively Bridgeman, Battenburg, Briggs and Moore. The notes of the Sea Lords' conference are in Ships' Cover 251/159, which is the source for unattributed quotes in this section.

[34] Ships' Cover 260/134, memorandum dated 14 December 1911.

[35] Ships' Cover 268/58.

[36] The two ships had already been launched in October and November respectively: Parkes, *British Battleships*, p538.

[37] Admiralty, *Technical History and Index: Fire Control in HM Ships, 1919*, p9; henceforth abbreviated to *Technical History and Index*.

[38] *Lion, Queen Mary* and *Princess Royal* were fitted respectively by May and December 1915 and May 1916: ibid. pp10–11.

[39] Drawing NPN 2358 for *Conqueror* shows the characteristic 'footprint' of the Argo mounting and its gyro controlled training gear: see also NPA 8935 for *Colossus*.

[40] Roberts, *The Battleship Dreadnought*, pp34–5, 89 and 238 for *Dreadnought*, drawings NPA 8841 and 8844 for *Collingwood*.

[41] Drawing NPB 7804.

[42] Ships' Cover 260/134: memoranda dated 6, 14 and 15 December 1911. Churchill succeeded McKenna on 25 October 1911: Marder, *From the Dreadnought to Scapa Flow* Vol 1, p251.

[43] Stephen Roskill, *Admiral of the Fleet Earl Beatty*, Collins (New York, 1981), p167 refers to the hood and rangefinder as the 'Argo Tower'; this term does not appear in the Ships' Covers but is found in documents from the immediate post-war period.

[44] Ships' Cover 267/68 and drawings NPA 4913 and NPB 9595.

[45] Ships' Cover 260/134.

[46] Ships' Cover 260A/96.

[47] Ships' Cover 251/143: *DNO to Successor*, 1912, p13: William James, *The Sky was always Blue*, Methuen (London, 1951), p74.

[48] Ships' Cover 260A/28 (DNO's submission of 26 June 1912): drawings NPA 4917 and NPB 9588.

[49] Ships' Cover 268A/3, 267/101 and 251A/16. The hood can be seen in the photograph of *Centurion* on page 54 of R A Burt's *British Battleships 1919–1939*, Arms and Armour (London, 1993).

[50] For the *Iron Duke* class, see Ships' Covers 268/97, 130, 131 and 148, and 268A/8, 14 and 83.

[51] Ships' Cover 279/69.

[52] The order for the spotting tower casting (6in thick) was dated 2 September 1913.

[53] Ships' Cover 268A/8

[54] Drawing 19048 of 20 October 1914 in the Vickers Archive at the Cumbria Records Office.

[55] Ships' Cover 294/34. Vickers drawing 19027 for *Empress of India* dated 6 October 1914.

[56] Photographs (Q38423 and Q13955–7) in the Imperial War Museum show similar rangefinders fitted to *King George V* and *Centurion*.

[57] Drawings NPB 4692, 4700 and 4717.

[58] *Technical History and Index*, p16; temporary installations were put into *Emperor of India* and *Benbow* (also *Queen Elizabeth*) in November and December 1916.

[59] Peter Padfield, *Guns at Sea*, Evelyn (London, 1974), p248.

[60] Ships' Cover 294/120.

[61] *Technical History and Index*, pp10–11.

[62] Ships' Cover 294/54. *Malaya* was laid down later, in October 1913.

[63] Sumida, *In Defence of Naval Supremacy*, p323, note 82, based on the recollections of Admiral Roger Dick, is the only known evidence for this location of the Argo mounting.

[64] Ross Watton, *The Battleship Warspite*, Conway Maritime Press, (London, 1986), p76 (E3/2). Likewise, in 1917, 6in directors were installed on either side of the bridge.

[65] Ships' Cover 294/126. 'The training gear is to be similar to that supplied...for the "Iron Duke" class'. Vickers responded on 11 June 1914.

[66] Vickers drawings 18800 and 18834 (Cumbria Records Office).

[67] Ships' Cover 294A/58aand *Technical History and Index*, p33.

[68] Watton, *The Battleship Warspite*, p74.

[69] Ships' Cover 294/103. The idea was also under consideration for the *Iron Duke*s (Ships' Cover 268A/17) though not, it seems, implemented.

[70] Ships' Cover 294A/124.

[71] Drawings 19940 and 20454 in the Vickers Archive show that the *Repulse* and *Renown*, and also the 'large light cruisers', initially carried 9ft rangefinders in their gun control towers.

[72] Sumida, *In Defence of Naval Supremacy*, pp220–35.

[73] Gyro stabilisation also made it easier for the operator to take ranges.

ON THE BRINK OF ARMAGEDDON

Capital ship development on the eve of the First World War

In August 1914, to all outward appearances, the Naval Race was running as intensively as ever. All the nine battleship-building countries were hard at it and several others, who could not build their own, were having them constructed abroad. The size of battleships had roughly doubled since 1905 and seemed likely to go on increasing. The prestige of the type seemed to be re-established; the menace of the torpedo, whether launched from on, under or even above water, appeared to have been cut down to size by the development of internal protection, the destroyer and light cruiser, and the use of powerful and accurate secondary batteries. Though no-one could have realised it at the time, the long-expected outbreak of war was to bring a great reduction in this mighty effort, and in some countries ended it altogether. In this article Keith McBride examines where the naval powers had got to technically in 1914 and what lines of capital ship development they were following.

The rivalry between Britain and Germany had been slightly limited by a 1912 agreement by which, over the years 1912–17, Britain would build 4–5–4–5–4–5 capital ships and Germany 2–3–2–3–2–3. This was later reduced by both countries dropping the 'odd' ships in 1915 and 1917. Ships bought by subscription were excluded, which gave Britain the battleship *Malaya*. The 1913–14 Programme saw the introduction of the *Royal Sovereign* class, the first battleships designed under the control of the new Director of Naval Construction (DNC), Eustace Tennyson d'Eyncourt. These were 21kt 'ordinary' battleships, natural successors to the *Iron Duke* class of the 1911–12 Programme, the intervening oil-fired *Queen Elizabeth* class being a special fast type intended to act as a semi-independent flanking force. The changes in the *Royal Sovereigns*, from the *Queen Elizabeth*s, included a reversion to coal-firing and a reduction in size from 27,500 tons to 25,750 tons 'legend' or 'Navy List' displacement. However, the armament remained unchanged – eight 15in (the finest and most powerful gun in the world at the time) and sixteen 6in. Armour was actually increased; the *Royal Sovereigns* had much more 13in armour than their predecessors, but

the price of the 6.3 per cent reduction in size was a reduction in sea-keeping qualities; it was foreseen in the design stage that they would be wet. They were to design 'T1'; designs 'T2' to 'T4' were larger, with nine or ten 15in, and cost about £100,000 to £200,000 more than 'T1'. The 'T1' design originally had two thin funnels close together, like the *Reshadieh* (later to become HMS *Erin*), but the *Royal Sovereigns* actually completed with a single funnel following the 1914 change to oil firing only.

The British 1914–15 Naval Estimates included three modified *Royal Sovereign* class battleships and one improved *Queen Elizabeth*. The latter was provisionally named *Agincourt* and it was planned to build her at Portsmouth Dockyard. It is thought that she would probably have been to design 'X2', one of two studies prepared in the spring of 1914, or some modification of it. The tapered armour of previous designs, which was very difficult to roll, was replaced by parallel armour with the thickness reduced to 12in and the armoured deck was increased from 2in to 2.5in. This increase may sound trifling but armoured decks, because of their great area, were very heavy. The barbette armour was thickened by 1in and the

The British battleship Resolution *in 1924. She and her sister ships of the* Royal Sovereign *class were the last battleships to be completed from prewar programmes. Britain did not lay down another battleship until 1922, although several battlecruisers, most of doubtful utility, were built during the war.* (CMP)

ammunition supply for the forward 15in turrets was increased from 80 to 100 rounds per gun (rpg). The secondary armament was rearranged, twelve guns out of sixteen being placed in a two-storied battery amidships; a reversion to the practice of the 1890s, trading length against topweight.

A very big and significant change was in beam, which was increased to 94ft – comparable with German designs. The price was that very few existing docks could be used. The parallel design 'X1' had 13in untapered armour and the same 75,000shp as the *Queen Elizabeth*; 'X2' was longer and just about attained the desired 25kts on only 60,000shp. However, her fuel consumption was only 80 per cent of that of 'X1'. The other three ships would have been one dockyard-built ship and two contract-built ones to designs derived from the *Royal Sovereign*.

The DNC's staff was working on several projects at the time; 'U1' and 'U3' were relatives of the *Queen Elizabeth*, designed for Canada, who had serious ideas of acquiring capital ships at one time. These were stopped by a vote of the Canadian Senate in 1913, after suggestions of corruption had been made. Bearing in mind the *Entente Cordiale* and the traditional connection between France and Canada,

The original outline design for the Royal Sovereign *class showing the two closely spaced funnels that were later replaced by a single uptake.* (Drawn by John Roberts)

one wonders what would have happened if a French shipbuilder had put in a bid.

If there was a project 'V', no record of it survives, but 'W1' of early 1914 was for a dockyard built *Royal Sovereign* with double decked secondary battery, slightly thinner armour and increased displacement. She appears to have been submitted to the Third Sea Lord twice, in February and May 1914; one ship, the *Resistance*, was planned for Devonport Dockyard. A separate design for contract-built ships was prepared, and may have been the missing 'V'; why a separate design was required is not clear. It differed little from the 'T1' design. Two ships were ordered, the *Renown* and *Repulse*, but these were later cancelled, materials gathered for their construction later being employed in the battlecruisers with the same names.

The 'U' series continued to be developed but it is not clear whether the later designs were for Canada. These differed greatly from previous ideas – the 'U2', 'U4' and 'U5' had the same armament but with the main turrets all on the same level. The 'U2' and 'U4' had their turrets on the centreline but the two foremost in 'U5' were *en echelon*. A conning tower was between the two foremost turrets in each design (presumably for use in action only) with a tripod mast, bridge and funnel aft of the second turret. Twelve of the sixteen 6in were in a double decked battery amidships, the other four in main-deck casemates abreast the first and fourth turrets. The 'U4' and 'U5' seem to have been some 25ft longer than 'U2', though this is not mentioned in the data given. As with 'U1' and 'U3', speed was to be 25kts.

One wonders as to the purpose of these designs; the Russians and Italians had gone in for centreline turrets on the same level and the British 'J' design series of 1906 had followed the same philosophy. Turrets on the same level reappeared in 1920 in preliminary sketch designs 'LII' and

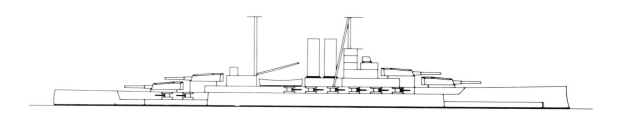

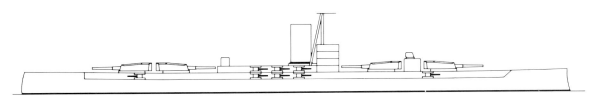

Sketch design U4 of 1914. U5 was the same except that the two forward turrets were en échelon, *'A' to port, 'B' to starboard and both faced forward.* (Drawn by John Roberts)

'LIII' for the never-built 1921 battleships. That layout almost precluded end-on fire; as of 1914 it was impossible for British ships anyway, owing to blast effects. Placing the turrets on the same level meant spreading them over a greater length, with all the docking problems involved, as well as the need for more armour, more power and more men for the longer hull. Pitching might have been worse, rolling better; gunnery might have been improved. It is possible that they were 'Aunt Sallies', put forward to show how much better was the design which the DNC (and/or the Controller?) preferred, which may have been 'U1' or 'U3'.

One more design was to appear before the outbreak of war; this was 'Y', a further development of the various 25kt projects, speed being raised to 30kts, while armament remained at eight 15in, disposed in orthodox fashion, with the usual 6in, torpedo tubes, and four of the new 3in AA guns – of which the *Iron Duke*s carried two. Armour was 1in less than the earlier battleship projects; 11in sides and 10in turret faces, and the power plant appears to have been the same as the *Tiger*'s. Displacement was 31,350 tons 'Legend' and cost £2,450,000 without guns. It seems a reasonable guess that the Admiralty had got wind of the new German 1914 battlecruiser, the (fortunately for Britain) uncompleted *Mackensen*. To judge from Oscar Parkes' *British Battleships*, intelligence reaching the British showed an armament of six 15in; in fact, after much argument, the Germans scaled down their 15in gun to a 13.8in and gave the *Mackensen*, basically a much enlarged *Lützow*, eight of them. Despite the British ship's much heavier armament, I suspect that the *Mackensen* would have had the edge. At the time, 'Y' was rejected for lack of

The German Mackensen *class battlecruiser design of 1913.*

torpedo protection.

Several of these late projects, including 'U3', 'U4', 'U5' and 'Y' incorporated a protected spotting position in the extreme bow; this apparently resulted from gunnery tests against the old *Empress of India* on 4 November 1913. During these, it was noticed that smoke from fires blanketed fire-control positions amidships but left the top and the extreme bow clear. The top became the main control position and it was suggested that an emergency position in the bow might be useful. However, with the latter there might well have been trouble with spray – or green water – over the bow, and communications might have been difficult, while any fire-control equipment in the bow might have been shaken up. Nevertheless, at least some USN ships had spotting positions in the bow and stern, as well as on the masts and in superfiring turrets.

In the event, Armageddon intervened, and there were more immediate needs than battleships. Of the four 1914–15 ships, two were replaced very rapidly, with very fast battlecruisers, and the other two were never laid down. However, the 'X2' and 'Y' concepts reappeared during 1915, in the series of battleship studies which led up to the *Hood*. At a deeper level, it looks as though the 'Line of Battle' concept was beginning to be very slowly replaced by the idea of faster ships which could fulfil both the battleship and battlecruiser roles.

Germany

Across the North Sea, the 15in gun had been very reluctantly adopted for the 1913 *Baden*s, which were very similar in general concept to the *Royal Sovereign*s.

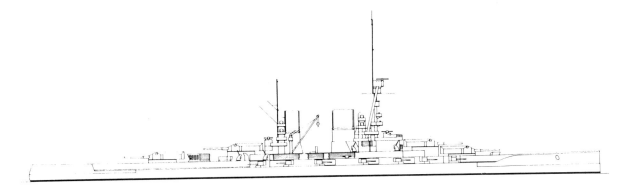

The German 15in gun battleship Bayern *as completed in
1916. She and her sister* Baden *were contemporary to the
British* Royal Sovereign *class and, like them, were the
last battleships of the prewar programmes to be
completed. Other capital ships were begun during the war
but none were completed.* (CMP)

Development of the battlecruiser type had been continued
and, as mentioned above, the *Mackensen*s were an extrapo-
lation of the *Lützow* concept. Parallel with her, two further
*Baden*s were authorised for 1914, with the addition of
diesel power on the centre shaft in the *Württemburg*, which
necessitated higher funnels. This idea was a favourite of
German marine engineers and had been planned for the
Prinzregent Luitpold, though the diesel engine was never
installed. Generally the Germans were more willing to try
new engineering developments than the British, though
their ships seem to have suffered more breakdowns. It was
proposed to fit Fottinger hydraulic transmissions in the
*Mackensen*s. This might have led to trouble; the medium-
sized liner *Tirpitz* (later *Empress of Australia*) had to be
converted to geared turbines after several years' service
with Fottinger transmission.

The Germans had met the challenge of the *Dreadnought*
by deepening the Kiel Canal, which had only been completed in the 1890s, and building new, larger ships while
the canal work was being done. Unfortunately, the increase

The German Sachsen *class battleship design*

in battleship size had again outpaced them; their later
battleships and battlecruisers had to unload a lot of coal to
pass through, which meant that any transit of the canal put
the ships out of action for two or three days. Such limitations hampered everyone except, at this stage, America.
The planned width of the locks of the Panama Canal had
been 100ft, increased at the last moment to 110ft, just in
case. By 1914, ships with such a gigantic beam were only
just coming into the picture.

France

Another country much affected by docking limitations was
France; the *Bretagne* class of her 1912 programme was
similar to the British 'Super Dreadnoughts' but very
cramped and the *Normandie*s, four of which were authorised in 1912 and one in 1913, were limited to 170m–172m
(557ft to 564ft). The Government was aiming at a fleet of
twenty-eight battleships by 1920 but, apart from the size of
her docks, France was also hampered by her weak industrial base; she could only build six big ships at any one time
and she tended to be a bit behind the other powers in
armament. However, her ordnance engineers were as good
as anyone's, and in 1911 they came up with a notable new
development – the quadruple heavy turret.

The triple had appeared in 1906, at first in Britain, then
spread to Austria, Italy, Russia and America. It appears
that France considered this idea but preferred the quadruple, possibly because French designers preferred to put as

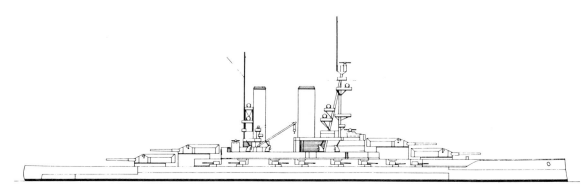

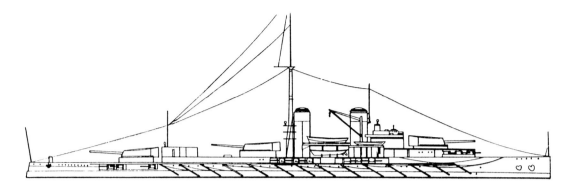

much turret weight as possible on the centre axes of their turrets. Design work on the never-completed *Normandie* class battleships began in the autumn of 1911 and the designers, led by M Lyasse the French Director of Naval Construction, were much influenced by the concern of the *Conseil Superieure de la Marine* – the French Navy's 'think tank' – about the blast effects of the amidships turret in the *Bretagne*s. The *Conseil* remembered the troubles experienced by the *Redoubtable*s of the 1880s.

The quadruple turret had been first proposed for the *Bretagne*s and the St Chamond company had made enough progress to justify its adoption for the 1913 ships. The initial proposals were for sixteen 12in in four quadruples, superfiring fore and aft, or for twelve 13.4in (340mm) in two quadruples fore and aft, with twins superfiring over them. As in most French battleships, the secondary armament was to be 5.5in (138.6mm). To save weight, and possibly to improve the arcs of fire, a twin 5.5in had been developed, with two guns in a common sleeve, the left gun being slightly lower and further forward than the right one. Ten such pairs were to be fitted, compared with twenty-two single casemated guns in previous ships. The hulls had to be short to fit into existing docks and it appears that the weight left for protection was insufficient as a radically different design had to be adopted.

This had three turrets, fore, amidships and aft, the *Con-*

The French Normandie *class design of 1912.*

seil's worries on blast having evidently been satisfied or brushed aside. The change from two twins and two quadruples to three quadruples saved 240 tons in armament weight and 500 tons on total displacement. Though the quadruple turret was now completely adopted, the twin 5.5in was rejected by *L'Artillerie Navale*, who pointed out that it weighed much the same as the single 7.6in (194.7mm), which had proved rather too large for convenient hand training. A design with five twin turrets was developed in parallel for some time but then abandoned. One minister favoured a mixed secondary armament of 5.5in and 3.9in but the uniform 5.5in prevailed; it proved possible to fit twenty-four with their own fire-control system. The quadruple turrets were electrically operated and allowed 16deg elevation, giving 16,000m range, which was regarded as the limit of normal visibility. The four guns were in two pairs, divided by a longitudinal armoured

The French battleship Bretagne *in the late 1930s. She and her sister ships were modernised during 1932–35, a process which included fitting replacement 13.4in guns originally built for the cancelled* Normandie *class battleships.* (CMP)

bulkhead, and the basic design could have been used for two guns of much larger calibre.

The 5.5in were in casemates disposed in three groups of six, one of four and one of two. One of the groups was in the forward end of the shelter deck, under the barrels of the forward 13.4in but inboard of them, so that they should have been fairly safe from blast. They had good arcs ahead, whence destroyer attack would come and, at least in theory, the two foremost guns could cross fire.

Machinery was unusual; the French Navy had been unfavourably impressed when its first turbine-powered battleships, the *Danton* class pre-dreadnoughts, completed in 1911, proved to be coal eaters. The *Jean Bart*s and *Bretagne*s were too far advanced to be altered, but the first four *Normandie*s were given a mixed plant, with reciprocating engines on the outer shafts and turbines on the inners. The former were to be used for speeds up to 16kts, the turbines being brought in for higher speeds. Steam was fed to all four power plants simultaneously above 16kts; this was not the 'Harland and Wolff' idea of driving the turbines by exhaust steam from the reciprocators. No cruising or astern turbines were provided, all manoeuvring being done on the outer shafts. The screws were of different sizes for the two types of machinery. In 1913, only one battleship, the *Béarn*, was provided but by then there was sufficient confidence to give her an all-turbine power plant, which may have led to her being chosen for conversion to a carrier when her sisters were scrapped incomplete. Displacement was 24,830 tonnes (25,387 tons 'Navy List'). The *Bretagne* armour arrangement was finally adopted. To assist radio transmission, a rig was adopted with the principal mast aft of the second funnel; a short fore mast was provided for visual signalling. The designers felt that the class would have been good seaboats and good steamers; though the designed speed was 21kts, 22.5kts was hoped for in good conditions.

The Lyons

Design of the next class, the four *Lyon*s, planned for the 1915 programme, began in September 1913. Two major changes affected them; new docks would be available, permitting greater dimensions, and M Lyasse had retired, after his short stint as Director. During that time, he had carried out a drastic reorganisation , of necessity stepping hard on many toes. He was replaced by M Doyere, who in fact had been much more prominent in the world of naval architecture.

L'Artillerie Navale put forward three possible natures of armament:

1. A 38cm (15in) gun. This existed on paper only and two years would be needed to build a prototype and bring it to proof trials.
2. A 50cal 34cm gun, firing a 630kg (1386lb) shell.
3. A 45cal 34cm gun but firing a 590kg shell as against the 540kg shell intended for the *Normandie*s.

A ship with eight 38cm or fourteen 34cm was estimated at 27,500 tons, one with sixteen 34cm at 28,500/29,000 tons. M Doyere noted that twenty 305mm were feasible but he did not recommend them! Some experience had now been gained with geared turbines and it was proposed to fit these and not to repeat the mixed power plant of the *Normandie*s.

It is clear that the designers favoured the third armament arrangement but, to their horror, the then minister chose the second, which involved much more weight and bigger turret rings. Before long, they had to report that they were up to 32,000 tons – at 3000 gold francs (£125) per ton. However, M Doyere, being an old hand, told them to design on. After a few months, as often happened under the Third Republic, the government fell and it proved possible to twist the new minister's arm and get the third armament arrangement adopted. Even with the 45cal guns, displacement reached 29,600 tons before work was stopped.

Profiles and sketches were prepared for the new design; the turrets were to be placed one forward, one amidships and two aft, to improve seakeeping. However, design work was far from complete when the outbreak of war brought French battleship building to a temporary end. None of the four ships were ever laid down.

As part of its 1913 examinations, the French Naval Staff College asked its students for sketch designs of a class of battleship to succeed the *Normandie*s. Bearing in mind the problems of the supply of gun mountings, and of impressing the examiners, most proposed variations on the *Normandie*. Lieutenant Durand-Viel, however, went on a different tack, proposing battlecruisers with quadruple

The French Lyon *class design*

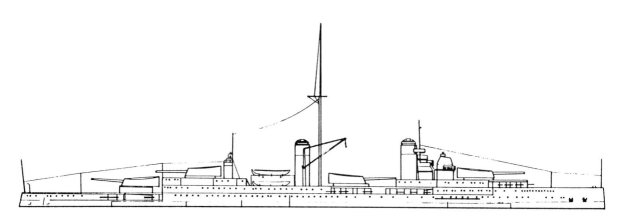

turrets fore and aft and bigger machinery amidships. One version had eight 34cm and another, by using thinner turret armour, eight 37cm. At about the same time, a constructor, M Gille, visited the Admiralty and on his return proposed a 26,500 ton ship with one quadruple 34cm forward, two aft, and a speed of 26.5kts. Nothing came of these at the time but, in the late twenties, Durand-Viel, now a Vice Admiral, was able to get the *Dunkerque* and *Strasbourg* authorised. Experience gained with the turrets for the *Normandie*s was drawn upon for them, while some of the *Normandie*s' actual guns were fitted into the *Bretagne*s.

Both the 1913 and 1914 designs were essentially slow 'ships of the line' comparable functionally to the British *Royal Sovereign*s. Their secondary batteries were divided in traditional French style, which might have made the main magazines vulnerable, and it seems that they would still have been that little bit smaller and less well protected than foreign ships. The idea of faster ships, presumably with similar armament, had not quite 'gelled' as of 1 August 1914 but was to reappear in the inter-war period. Everything would have depended on how well the quadruple turrets worked and it is almost certain that changes would have been necessary to adapt them for combat at longer gun ranges than 16,000m. The French tradition of originality was well alive in 1914.

Italy and Austria-Hungary

At the outbreak of war, Italy had one dreadnought completed and five under construction, all with 12in guns mostly in triple turrets. Her 'Potential Enemy No 1' was Austria-Hungary, who likewise had one 12in triple-turreted dreadnought complete and others building or completing. As a member of the Triple Alliance with a long and vulnerable coastline, she also had to bear France in mind. Italian designers had to contend with a very limited industrial base and a lack of funds – much dependence was placed on Britain for ordnance designs and for some heavy gun mountings. There was a tradition of very fast battleships – in effect Italy was building battlecruisers in the 1870s.

After the design of the two *Diulio*s, consideration was given to ships with heavier guns for the next batch and it was rumoured at the time that attempts had been made to obtain 13.5 or 14in guns for the *Cavour*s and *Diulio*s, while, naturally, a close watch was maintained on what was going on across the Adriatic. The rivals had rather similar ideas, both emphasising high speed, heavy armament and, in the latter case, remarkably small displacements for the armament carried. There was a strong body of opinion in Austria-Hungary which was against a large navy, and more especially against big ships for such a small arena. Once the construction of the *Viribus Unitis* class was in hand (1909–10), thought and planning for their successors became intense but the opposition, and the needs of the Army, delayed the authorisation of any further ships until after the outbreak of war.

The old *Monarch* class coast defence ships of the early '90s were due for replacement and the projected ships became known as the 'Ersatz Monarchs'; officially they were the Improved *Tegetthoff*s. Both 14in and 15in guns were considered for these ships, with eight of the latter to be carried on 24,500 tons, as compared with 27,500 for the fast *Queen Elizabeth*s and 25,750 for the slow *Royal Sovereign*s. The weapon finally selected was 35cm (13.78in) and the chosen design carried ten, in two twins and two triples on a displacement of 24,500 tons.

Side armour was 12.2in (310mm), speed 21kts – about average for dreadnoughts – and a heavy secondary and tertiary armament of 5.9in and 3.4in guns was carried. Two layouts were proposed, one with the triple turrets superfiring and one with the twins uppermost. Initially, a very heavy secondary armament was proposed – eighteen 5.9in guns, fourteen in a main-deck battery and four in the fore shelter deck. The latter were omitted in the final design, which had the effect of making all the 5.9in vulnerable to spray and heavy seas – and it can get very rough in the Adriatic! The 'twin turrets uppermost' alternative was adopted for the main armament, no doubt from considerations of stability.

Because of the delay in authorising these ships, the naval authorities became worried that they would be outclassed by the time they were completed – in about 1917. Accordingly, larger designs were prepared during the winter of 1913–14. The 35cm gun was retained but twelve in four triples, or thirteen in three triples and two twins – the *Cavour* arrangement – were to be carried, the displacements being 29,600 and 32,000 tons respectively. Side armour was thickened to 320mm and speed increased to 24kts, with 45,000shp, for the twelve gun ship and 23kts, with 50,000shp, for the thirteen gun ship – against 21kts, with 31,000shp, for the much smaller 'Ersatz Monarch'. The twelve gun ship's nominal displacement exactly equalled that for the 21kt *Lyon*, which, however, would have carried four extra guns thanks to her quadruple turrets. The two 'January 1914' designs bore the same relationship to the 'Ersatz Monarch' as the *Pennsylvania* did to the *Nevada*.

Across the Adriatic, the Ministry of Marine had decided earlier on fast battleships and by 1913 they had come up with a 28,000 ton 25kt design, carrying ten 14in guns in two twin and two triple turrets. There was to be a powerful secondary battery of twenty 6in guns. Oil fuel only was to be used (Italy had been a pioneer of this) and 48,000shp was to be provided, which seems inadequate – possibly this was sustained power only. I do not know whether this design preceded the British *Queen Elizabeth*, (which was to develop 56,000shp, 'sustained' and 75,000 'full power') but clearly similar tactical, engineering and constructional ideas were in Italian and British minds simultaneously. The Italian pair, given the historic names *Dandolo* and *Morosini* at an early stage, were to be of 28,000 tons, compared with 27,500 tons – on different bases – for the *Queen Elizabeth* and *Nevada*. It seems probable that the 14in guns would have been of Armstrong design, similar to those of the Chilean dreadnoughts.

The *Nevada*, the 'Ersatz Monarch' and the Italian *Dandolo* project form an interesting comparison, all being of about the same date, the same dimensions, and carrying similar main armaments, similarly disposed. The great differences were the much heavier armour of the American

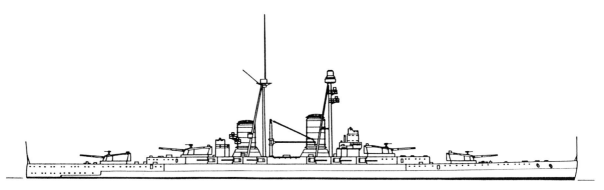

The final version of the Caracciolo *class battleship design.*

ship and the higher speed provided in the Italian one. The Austrian ships were planned for 21kts – given the Austrian predilection for high speed, this would probably have been higher but for a shortage of funds, and probably of large enough docks.

Strategically, the Italians' 25kts would have been useful in hit and run operations against a more powerful but slower French fleet in the Tyrrhenian Sea. In the Adriatic, one can imagine attempts to cut off the Austrians before they could get back among the Dalmatian islands, though the Austrians would probably have been quite ready to fight, given reasonable odds. In fact, as many had predicted, the rival big ships hardly dared to emerge from port for fear of the new submarines, torpedo boats, mines and aircraft. Furthermore, the Italians invented, and used, many ingenious ways of getting at the dinosaurs in harbour.

Naturally, the Italians soon got word of the Austrian 'January 1914' designs: their information, received during 1913, told of twelve 14in guns – near enough to the truth for practical purposes. Desiring, like that noted artillerist Baron Munchausen, to outgun the enemy, they put in hand a huge design of 35,000 tons, with twelve 15in guns. This was almost certainly the biggest ship yet projected anywhere but, on consideration, it was rejected as beyond Italy's resources. The number of guns was therefore reduced to eight or nine, although the larger calibre was

The July 1914 design for the Austria-Hungary battleships of the Improved Tegetthoff *class.*

retained – quite likely technical information was obtained from Britain for the guns and their mountings. The resultant class was the *Caracciolo*s, named after a distinguished Neapolitan naval officer, executed with the active assistance of Nelson. They carried eight 15in on 28,000 tons and were designed by Edgardo Ferrati, a design by Cuniberti with nine 15in being rejected. The change from 14in to 15in guns probably arose from a realisation that the original *Dandolo* design would have been outclassed before the ships were completed.

In concept, the *Caracciolo*s came about midway between the *Queen Elizabeth*s and the later *Hood*, with a normal speed of 25kts and a maximum of 28kts. Armour was to be extensive – 11.8in on the waterline, 8 to 9in above it, 6in at the ends, and there were to be anti-torpedo bulkheads and close subdivision. Visually, the outstanding feature was the wide gap between the pairs of turrets fore and aft; they were placed like the after ones in the *Derfflinger* and *Tiger*, the objects being:

1. To reduce blast interference when firing end-on (sighting hoods were still in use).
2. To reduce the concentration of weight and recoil effect on the ship girder.

In this connection, in 1920 Tennyson d'Eyncourt, in describing the *Hood* to the Institution of Naval Architects, mentioned the problems involved in getting sufficient longitudinal strength to support the pairs of turrets; each pair was closely spaced but the two pairs were a long way apart because of the great length of the machinery spaces. It has been suggested that this problem may not have been fully solved in the *Hood* and that the resulting weakness, plus,

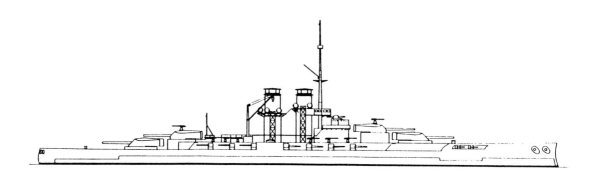

Unlike the European powers the United States maintained a substantial battleship construction programme during the First World War, laying down six such ships against the Japanese Navy's four. This is the New Mexico, *laid down in 1915 and completed in 1918, in about 1919.* (CMP)

possibly, over-strain at launch, may have assisted her rapid destruction. The *Caracciolo* layout might have produced bad pitching – there is always a price to be paid!

The secondary armament of twenty 6in, as in the 35,000 ton project, was reduced first to eighteen and then to twelve. Considerable attention was paid to anti-aircraft guns; at one time the *Caracciolo* project had twenty-four, remarkable for that era, while anti-bomb grilles were placed on the funnels.

The class was actually laid down, and the *Caracciolo* herself was duly launched but there were no funds to complete her. Ideas were floated of converting her, like some of her contemporaries, into an aircraft carrier or a giant freighter, but nothing came of them. Her 15in guns were fitted into monitors and used against the Austrians; many years later this experience was to help in the design of the *Littorio*'s guns.

Experience in the Adriatic suggested that the big gun-carrier was almost useless in that theatre; she was constantly exposed to the torpedo or mine at sea, while in harbour air attack was a growing threat, quite apart from that of the intrepid characters who swam under, climbed over or cut away harbour defences to get at the vulnerable giants within. It is clear that the Italians retained their traditional predilection for speed and this was to continue into the future.

The United States

Unlike the European countries, the United States was able to continue building capital ships. The *Pennsylvania* and *New Mexico* classes of 1912 to 1914 continued the development started by the *Nevada* – moderate speed, heavy armament, very heavy and comprehensive protection on the 'All or Nothing' system, which permitted a great increase of the main armour, without too great an increase in dimensions. This must be understood relatively; the 1912–14 ships were

the first in the world to exceed 30,000 tons and the USN wanted ships of over 40,000 tons but they were prevented by President Woodrow Wilson's administration from going beyond the size of *Pennsylvania*. The US battleships also had the great advantage of complete oil firing.

The USN was worried by its lack of modern scouting craft and devised a 'Battle Scout', intended to have a 6kt margin of speed over battleships, permitting it to scout ahead of them in any weather. They were to be capable of fighting battlecruisers on fairly even terms, destroying light cruisers and torpedo craft, and breaking through the enemy's cruiser screen. Designs for this type were of many varieties, with different main armaments and scales of protection. During development they tended to become more like the (fairly) conventional battlecruiser and two of them were completed as carriers after the Washington Treaty.

Apart from heavy armour, the USN put a lot of effort – comparable with that of the Germans – into developing underwater protection. Near perfection against the weapons of that day was reached with the multi-bulkhead system introduced in the *California* class of 1915. Great effort was also put into the development of propelling machinery – turbo-electric machinery was used in battleships from 1914 and turbine development rapidly caught up with the British.

Aircraft offered another way of locating the enemy's battleships and the USN was early interested in scouting seaplanes for cruisers. However, it is also clear that, in their eyes, the battleship still reigned supreme.

Japan

By 1914, Japan had reached maturity in ship design and construction, and was designing and building her own battleships. Her first dreadnought type, the *Settsu*, was restricted by the small number and obsolescence of available guns and mountings but she had just acquired the very up-to-date *Kongo* and the details of her armament. Financially and economically, she was still suffering the aftermath of the Russo-Japanese War but rivalry with the United States was becoming clearer and stronger and first the 'Four-Eight' and then the 'Eight-Eight' construction programmes were put forward to strengthen the Imperial Navy. Three more *Kongo*s were to be built at home, giving the IJN a heavy bias towards battlecruisers, but a pair of new dreadnoughts were laid down early in 1915, to be quickly followed by two more.

The new ships were very much bigger and more powerful than the *Settsu*, carrying essentially the same twin 14in turrets as the *Kongo*, but there were six turrets per ship. Armour was about on the same scale as in contemporary British battleships, with a maximum of 12in on the sides and it was arranged in a similar manner. The American 'All or Nothing' philosophy had no influence as yet. Secondary armament was 6in in casemates, and there were the usual submerged torpedo tubes, six 21in compared with four in contemporary British ships. Fuel was mixed – 5022 tons coal and 1026 tons of oil, giving a theoretical endurance of 8000 miles at 14kts, which was good for 1911/12. Designed speed was 22kts, one knot faster than British or American contemporaries.

The design was something like the British 'Super Dreadnoughts', though larger and faster, and quite unlike the American ships of 1911 and later. There was a slight drift towards the battlecruiser concept, though of course armament and armour were increased at the price of engine power and speed. The writer wonders whether the Elswick design 'No645' prepared for Brazil in 1910 and actually

The Japanese battleship Hyuga *in 1926. She, and her sister* Ise, *were laid down in 1915 to a modified version of the prewar* Fuso *design.* (CMP)

accepted at one time, formed the basis for the *Fuso*. Having been rejected by Brazil, it could be offered to another customer and would have saved the latter a great deal of time, costly drawing board work and calculation, while being readily adaptable to their requirements. The obvious difference was that 'No645's' amidships turrets were slightly *en echelon*, while the *Fuso*'s were on the centre line, but 'No 645' was so arranged solely to provide clearance for the gun muzzles. Does anyone know the answer?

The *Ise* and *Hyuga* of 1912 were slightly larger and appreciably faster – 23.6kts on 45,000hp, a most creditable increase. Main armament was the same as *Fuso*'s, but was better disposed, in the same arrangement as USS *Arkansas* and *Wyoming* of 1909. This meant that the available space could be much better utilised. The secondary armament was of 5.5in calibre, which was more suited to small Japanese gunners – though Togo's men had handled 6in more than adequately! Future Japanese development was very much on 'Fast Battleship/Battlecruiser' lines; though the only ships to be completed as battleships were the *Nagato* and *Mutsu*, which had thinner 'all or nothing' armour, the newly introduced 16in gun and the very high speed of 26.5kts, which remained a closely guarded secret for many years.

The ships of the 1916 'Eight-Eight' programme were almost all sacrificed to the 1921 Washington Treaty, but showed the same characteristics. In a sense these reappeared in the Japanese 8in gun cruisers of the 1920s and 1930s, while their American 'oppos' continued *their* country's characteristic heavy armament and protection. Tactically, the Japanese favoured lightning cut and thrust, while the Americans prepared for long, hard slugging matches.

Russia

Russia in 1914 was in a strange state, a huge country of great resources, misgoverned, unstable but at the same time engaged in a mighty effort at reform and modernisation. A large naval building programme (despite its title of 'The Little Programme') was in progress, though as yet few large ships had been completed. The programme provided for four capital ships to be laid down every other year. Russia had yet to complete a dreadnought and she had only

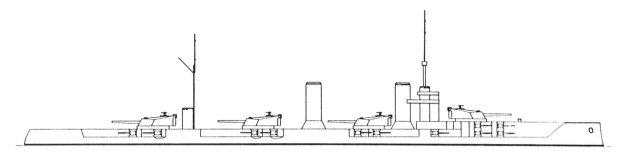

The Russian Borodino *class design of 1913.*

four battleships in commission outside the Black Sea, where the elite of her navy was locked up.

Twelve dreadnoughts were building, four *Gangut*s and four much larger *Borodino*s in and around St Petersburg and four *Imperatriza Maria*s, closely related to the *Gangut*s, in the Black Sea. All followed the same basic layout, derived from the Masdea/Cuniberti designs of the Italian Navy. After considering a vast number of designs, the Imperial Russian Navy had gone whole-heartedly for the triple turret, originally a British idea but rejected at the time in the land of its birth.

From the bitter experience of 1904/05, the Russians had drawn the conclusion that shells must be kept outside the ship if at all possible and had therefore adopted medium thickness armour spread over the widest possible area – the very opposite of the Americans' 'All or Nothing' system. For secondary armament they used their existing 4.7in and then a new 5.1in, the first of which were British designed. Their big guns were firstly a very powerful 52cal 12in and then a 14in, some of British and some of Russian manufacture. They were already thinking further ahead and had 16in guns under development both at home and by Vickers in Britain. These were for use in some even more gigantic ships, which they proposed to lay down in the Black Sea ports in 1916–17.

The ships already under construction were big enough

The Russian battleship Poltava *shortly after completion. The layout is typical of the Russian dreadnoughts of the time, flush decked with all the main armament turrets at the same level on the centre line - the sole exception was the uncompleted* Borodino *class which adopted a forecastle and consequently had the fore turret at a higher level.* (IWM, Q64259)

in all conscience – the 12in ships of some 23,000 tons and the *Borodino*s of 32,000 tons. Their 'balance of qualities' was between that of a fast battleship and a battlecruiser, with moderate armour. The turrets in each case were all on the centre line, none being superimposed.

Strategically, they proposed to fight the much more numerous Germans from behind the cover of minefields in the Gulf of Finland; hence the emphasis on long-range gunnery, and the comparatively thin armour. Presumably the fairly high speed of the *Gangut*s and the very high speed of the *Borodino*s could have been used to sally forth if the opportunity arose, and if they were certain that the rest of the German fleet was not lying in wait.

The *Borodino*s were authorised in June 1912, and were intended to outdo the German *Mackensen*s. The first design selected carried nine 14in in three triple turrets, forward, amidships and aft. The secondary armament comprised twenty-four of the new 5.1in, arranged in a series of small main-deck batteries, clustered around the main turrets as in the *Gangut*s. Because of the very high designed speed of 28kts – faster than the British battlecruiser *Lion* – a short, high forecastle was fitted, and here the 5.1s were on two levels. Information on armour is contradictory but it seems likely that most of the side plating was only 9.4in, not very different from the *Gangut*s.

At that period, the Russian planners were trying to give their ships a common silhouette as far as possible, and at an early stage a fourth triple 14in turret was added, bringing the ships up to 32,000 tons from the original 29,400 and of course requiring a vast amount of re-calculation. This change required a reduction in speed to 26.5kts -albeit still

very fast. It seems doubtful if the 'common silhouette' was the sole reason for the change as the same result could have been achieved with four twin 14in turrets, without a big increase in size. The heavier armament and higher speed suggest that a rather more aggressive policy was to be adopted when the *Borodino* class were ready. Final dimensions were 750ft × 100ft × 33.5ft, the draught being rather deep for the Baltic.

The four ships were laid down on 19 December 1912, and were intended to be completed in 1917. They represented a gigantic effort, and the engines for two of them had to be ordered abroad. The coming of the war slowed and then halted construction and after the Revolution they were sold for scrapping abroad. One wonders what they could or would have done if completed – in the Baltic such huge ships would have been like whales in a bathtub, constantly vulnerable to mines, torpedoes and grounding. A battle between them and German battlecruisers would have been spectacular but the combatants would have had to alter course frequently, like the sailing ships at Styrsudden, to avoid climbing up someone's coastline. The reader may like to consider Dogger Bank transferred to the Baltic.

In its few First World War combats, the Imperial Russian Navy showed a very impressive standard of gunnery and the *Borodino*s would probably have had the advantage, provided that they could keep at long range but would this have been possible in the Baltic? Bearing in

mind the 45,000 tonners planned for the Black Sea, it must be assumed that the next Russian ships would have been very big and that funds would have been forthcoming. It seems doubtful whether any of the Russian ships would have been completed on schedule and their effectiveness is questionable. They would have made more sense in the Far East, though one suspects that their arrival, or even the possibility of it, would have been taken by Japan as a *casus belli* – a possibility mentioned by Admiral Rodzhestvensky at the time.

Spain

Spain, the last of the nine countries to build their own battleships, had previously limited her efforts to one ship, the pre-dreadnought *Pelayo*, very similar to the French *Jaureguiberry*. Spain's industrial base was weak, and her finances shaky; in 1898 a lot of ships were incomplete or lacked their armament, after many years on the stocks, and the *Pelayo*, fortunately for all concerned, had not been ready in time to join in Cervera's gallant but futile expedition. However, by 1913, Spain had three 15,460-ton *Espana* mini-dreadnoughts of about 1906 vintage in hand. American experience with the *South Carolina* suggests that, in the words of Mark Twain, there was 'no sich animal' as a small dreadnought and that 16,000 tons was the minimum practical size. Their eight 12in were of a very powerful model but armour and speed were poor. Much material had to be imported from Vickers in Britain, and delivery of this was delayed during the First World War, so that one ship was not completed until 1920, and the ships were of prestige value only.

The Spanish Jamie I – together with her two sisters were the smallest dreadnoughts ever built. She was the last of the class to be completed (in 1921) – the first, España, *being laid down in 1909 and completed in 1913.* (CMP)

In spite of this, some Spaniards, including King Alfonso XIII, still had naval ambitions, and there was some discussion of a proposal to build three more battleships or battle-cruisers. First thoughts were of 21,000-ton ships, but a later proposal was for 24,500-ton ships with eight 15in guns. I do not know whether these would have been very much cut-down *Queen Elizabeths* (not entirely a suitable ancestor for Spanish ships) or a derivative of the Austrian projects. In any case the displacement seems inadequate for the armament given that the *Queen Elizabeth* has been criticised as too small for her armament and engine power.

If Spain had put such ships in hand, she would inevitably have been drawn into the contemporary European naval rivalries – her fleet being strong enough to cause suspicion and alarm, while its numbers, its technical and logistic support, and the qualities of the ships would have been inadequate for Spain to hold her own at sea. Bearing in mind that the financial problems arising from the earlier 12in ships were not resolved until 1953, it seems just as well that the later ones remained on paper.

Conclusion

Looking back on all this effort, there is a sense that the days of the long line-of-battle were numbered and that something like the Second World War situation was bound to arrive sooner or later, with smaller numbers of larger 'fast battleships' or battlecruisers operating in close co-operation with numerous carriers and small craft of every kind. The push to higher speed and larger gun calibres was clearly 'on', and inevitably pushed displacements up – which eventually led to the *Yamato*. The air threat was clear, though obviously only feeble as yet, and many navies converted incomplete but already obsolete capital ships into carriers. The great floating gun-carrier was on its way to suffering the same fate as the knight in armour: the cost of protecting it against contemporary threats made it no longer worth building.

THE DAY THE ADMIRALS WEPT

Ostfriesland and the anatomy of a myth

How great a threat the aeroplane presented to the battleship, or if it presented a threat at all, was debated endlessly during the years between the World Wars. R D Layman examines the creation of a continuing legend that both fuelled and obfuscated the controversy.

The sinking of the former German battleship *Ostfriesland*[1] on 21 July 1921 by aircraft led by Brigadier General William Mitchell has become a mythic event in air power history.[2] Popular legend has it that the moment that aerial bombs put her under the waves, was also the instant that the reign of the battleship ended; at one stroke 'Billy' Mitchell had rendered obsolete and useless, then and forever, every dreadnought in the world.

An Unsinkable Ship

Controversy still surrounds some aspects of the bombing tests off the Virginia Capes – did Mitchell turn a carefully planned experiment into a propaganda stunt? Did the US Navy deliberately try to obstruct him? This article does not address these matters but focuses on the myth depicting *Ostfriesland* as a nautical Goliath – the ultimate battleship, the strongest dreadnought ever built, an 'unsinkable' marvel of naval architecture.

That is how the vessel has been portrayed for decades by air power historians and Mitchell biographers in hyperbole, grossly exaggerating her technical features and giv-

Profile of the Ostfriesland *in 1918.*

ing her an imaginary history.

Mitchell himself was in large part responsible for creating the myth. Writing of *Ostfriesland* in 1925, he declared 'She was called the "unsinkable ship". She had participated in the battle of Jutland, had been hit by many projectiles, among them some of large caliber, and in addition two mines had hit her below the water line. In spite of this she had made harbor under her own steam'.[3] Mitchell indicated he could see 'the vicious scars of the battle of Jutland still on her'.[4]

Years later, his sister, Ruth Mitchell, magnified this description, calling *Ostfriesland* 'the most heavily armored "unsinkable" vessel ever built, recently the fine flower, the highest engineering accomplishment, the pride of the German Navy',[5] and continuing 'The great battleship was in fact the strongest vessel then in existence. Admiral Jellicoe in his book *The Grand Fleet* marvelled at her. In the Battle of Jutland... the *Ostfriesland* received so many direct hits from the heaviest guns and by mines that she was believed to be sinking and was reported by the British as a total loss'.[6]

Mitchell biographer Roger Burlingame has described *Ostfriesland*'s supposed damage more specifically: 'She had survived eighteen hits from 12- and 14-inch guns...; in her final retreat from the encounter she had struck a mine... yet had limped home under her own steam. [Her protection]

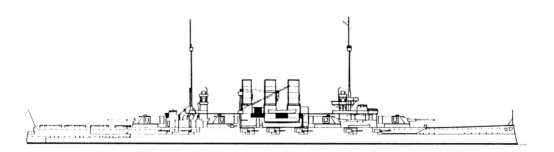

The Ostfriesland *shortly before the commencement of the bombing trials.* (US National Archives)

made her ..., in the opinion of naval experts, unsinkable'.[7]

Echoing this, another Mitchell biographer, Burke Davis, called *Ostfriesland* 'as formidable as any ship afloat, designed...to be practically unsinkable. [At Jutland] she took eighteen hits from big shells and struck a mine, yet made her way to port'.[8]

Similar descriptions could be cited but those quoted are sufficient to establish the theme of the *Ostfriesland* myth; namely that she was unique, the most heavily armoured battleship ever built and was thus considered unsinkable – as proved by her having survived severe damage at Jutland. The corollary was that if such a wonder ship could be sunk by aircraft so too, of course, could every other dreadnought in the world.

The Ostfriesland *Design*

The truth is far more prosaic. The *Ostfriesland* was not unique but one of four sister vessels, a fact of which the quoted writers were either ignorant or chose to ignore. These ships were the second generation of German dreadnoughts and although heavily armoured and well-compartmented (as were all German dreadnoughts) were in some respects antiquated even as they were completed during 1911–12. They displaced somewhat more than 24,000 tons at full load (nearly 10,000 tons less than some American battleships afloat in 1921), had a principal armament of twelve 30.5cm (12in) and fourteen 15cm (5.9in) guns and

could steam at about 20kts. They were powered by reciprocating engines, not the more efficient and more powerful turbines of later German capital ships (so much for Germany's 'highest engineering achievement'). Their main battery layout was inefficient; eight of their big guns were in wing turrets, two on each beam, reducing the potential broadside firepower by a third.[9] In the decade since their completion great advances in battleship design and construction had made them hopelessly obsolescent.

Far from being the 'pride of the German Navy', *Ostfriesland* was a rather operationally obscure vessel with a lacklustre career typical of most German battleships of the First World War. Her guns had seldom been fired in anger – notably only at Jutland, where she had helped damage the battleship *Warspite* and sink the armoured cruiser *Black Prince*.

The *Ostfriesland* was not struck by a single shell at Jutland; out of what hat the number of eighteen hits was plucked is a mystery. She did strike a mine after the battle – one mine, sustaining damage that kept her under repair for about six weeks. Contrary to Ruth Mitchell, there is not a single mention of *Ostfriesland* in Admiral Jellicoe's book.[10] Nor was she ever 'reported by the British as a total loss'. The original British communique on Jutland did erroneously claim two German dreadnoughts sunk (both sides

Smoke rises from the Ostfriesland *as a result of a direct hit by a large bomb. The wash in the foreground is from another large bomb, one of several dropped close alongside the ship to test the 'mining effect' of such weapons.* (USAF)

exaggerated the other's losses before matters were sorted out) but neither was identified by name, then or later.

The origin of the legend of *Ostfriesland*'s supposed unsinkability also remains a mystery. The 'naval experts' to whom the claim has been attributed have never been identified. If the claim indeed was made, it was as hyperbolic as some of the assertions of Mitchell's partisans. No rational sailor or naval architect has ever failed to realise that any ship will sink if a sufficient volume of water enters its hull. Certainly the US Navy did not consider *Ostfriesland* unsinkable – it was prepared to send her to the bottom by internal demolition or shelling by the battleship *Pennsylvania* if she survived the aerial bombs.

The Weeping Admirals

An enduring element of the *Ostfriesland* myth is what may be called the Legend of the Weeping Admirals. 'It is recorded on unimpeachable authority' wrote Ruth Mitchell, that upon the ship's sinking 'old seadogs wept aloud, admirals sobbed, tears streamed from the eyes of younger navy men, and bigwigs of all sorts unashamedly used their handkerchiefs'.[11]

Although she does not name her 'unimpeachable' source,

others have identified him as former US Assistant Secretary of War Benedict Crowell, who was among the three-hundred or so persons who watched the tests from aboard the transport *Henderson*. Crowell's credentials as an objective observer may be open to doubt. A strong proponent of an independent air force, and thus not exactly a friend of the navy, he had only recently resigned from his War Department position in protest at cuts in Army Air Service appropriations and personnel.[12]

Regardless of the origin of the story of the weeping admirals, it has been repeated by virtually everyone who has written about the *Ostfriesland* sinking – and not only by such popular writers as this article has quoted. Recent credence was given to it by Robert L O'Connell.[13] Interestingly, however, not one of the alleged weepers has ever been identified by name. They are anonymous 'admirals and captains', 'numerous captains and admirals', 'gray-headed, gold-braided admirals'.

It is puzzling why *Ostfriesland*'s demise should have provoked such a lachrymose display (if indeed it did). It was certainly not because an obsolescent vessel, destined in any case to be destroyed, represented anything of value to the US Navy. As all USN officers were aware, their service possessed a number of dreadnoughts immensely superior to *Ostfriesland* and twelve even more powerful ones were under construction.[14] Instead, it is argued that the tears were induced because the sunken vessel was a 'battleship', the prime symbol of sea power, the tragedy being that such a venerated icon could be sunk by a new (and therefore automatically to be detested) weapon. As O'Connell puts it, 'To those men the battleship was the single most important artefact of their professional exist-ence'[15] and consequently 'The destruction of this ship must have cut very deep into the naval soul.'[16] Perhaps so, but until more definite proof is supplied and some names at-tached to the alleged weepers, their tears must remain another part of the *Ostfriesland* myth.

Conclusion

It has long been realised and accepted, save by air power zealots, Mitchell hagiographers and battleship-bashers, that *Ostfriesland*'s sinking was far less significant than it has so often been made out to be. It proved only that an obsolescent and somewhat decrepit vessel, designed when aircraft were not yet a menace, unable to manoeuvre, un-able to put up defensive fire, undefended by friendly air-craft, lacking a crew to repair damage, could be sunk by dropping unlimited amounts of explosives on and near it from altitudes low enough to guarantee accuracy.[17] Time would prove that even Mitchell's preferred form of attack, level-flight bombing, was a chimera – it would be the dive bomber, the torpedo plane and ultimately the guided mis-sile that would put paid to the battleship.

In view of the recognised artificiality of the test, one must wonder why the *Ostfriesland* myth was created and has continued to flourish. Mitchell may perhaps be some-what forgiven for his role in its creation. Writing before the full facts of Jutland were widely known, he may have been honestly ignorant – although the 'vicious scars' he suppos-edly saw on the ship were obviously products of his imagi-nation.

For later writers there can be no excuse. Well before the writers quoted were published, Jutland had been exten-sively described and analysed, *Ostfriesland*'s part in it well known and her technical particulars long in print.[18] The unwillingness of Mitchell biographers to accept estab-lished fact or their failure to investigate anything that would challenge their preconceived ideology must be at-tributed to what can only be called idolatry. To depict *Ostfriesland* as anything but a super-ship whose destruc-tion would cause admirals to weep would be to diminish Mitchell's accomplishment, tarnish his image as an aerial prophet and cast doubt on the invincibility of air power.

The *Ostfriesland*'s sinking was influential but, paradoxi-cally, not in the direction Mitchell and his partisans had expected. They believed that aerial destruction of a battle-ship would be a prima-facie demonstration of the supe-

The Ostfriesland *sinking by the stern and slowly capsizing to port on 21 July 1921*. (USAF)

riority of air power over sea power and thus a commanding argument for the creation of an independent air force. The immediate result, however, was to reinforce the US Navy's realisation of the growing power of aviation and strengthen the resolve of its progressive officers (of whom there were many) to strive for a strong air arm as an integral element of the fleet. The *Ostfriesland* myth lives on and will probably never be laid to rest, but for the reality of what her sinking presaged one must look to the aerial might of the US Navy two decades later.

Notes

[1]   *Ostfriesland* was allocated to the United States under the terms of the peace treaty which divided the remaining eight German dreadnoughts (others having been scuttled at Scapa Flow) among the Allied and Associated Powers, with the stipu-lations that none could become an active warship and all had to be disposed of within five years. Designated 'Battleship H', *Ostfriesland* was commissioned into the US Navy at Rosyth, Scotland, on 7 April 1920. Crossing the Atlantic with an Ameri-can crew, she was decommissioned at New York on 20 Septem-ber and thereafter neglected until selected as a target ship for the bombing tests. She was originally to have been sunk by naval gunfire.

[2]   For instance, *Ostfriesland*'s sinking received the fifth listing in an editorial, 'Significant Aviation Events', in *Air Power His-tory*, Vol 36, No 3, 1989.

The Ostfriesland *on her beam-ends during the role to port that ended with her sinking stern first and upside down*. (USAF)

3   William Mitchell, *Winged Defense: The Development and Possibilities of Modern Air Power – Economic and Military*, reprint by Kennikat Press (Port Washington, New York 1971), p42–3.

4   Ibid, p72.

5   Ruth Mitchell, *My Brother Bill: The Life of General 'Billy' Mitchell* Harcourt, Brace, (New York, 1953), p253.

6   Ibid, p257–8.

7   Roger Burlingame, *General Billy Mitchell: Champion of Air Defense*, reprint by Signet Books (New York, 1955), p9. Why this author should have mentioned 14in guns is odd; the only British battleship at Jutland armed with 14in guns was HMS *Canada*, which fired only a few salvoes that hit nothing.

8   Burke Davis, *The Billy Mitchell Affair* Random House (New York, 1967), p100–1.

9   For details of *Ostfriesland*, see three related articles, under the general title 'SMS Ostfriesland,' in *Warship International*, Vol 12, No 1, 1975. These are 'A Technical Look at SMS Ostfriesland' by Robert S Egan and Richard M Anderson; 'Chronological Career of SMS Ostfriesland' by Fregattenkäpitan a D Paul M Schmalenbach, and 'More Fact than Fiction – The Sinking of the Ostfriesland' by Gene T Zimmerman. The third of these is a detailed description and analysis of bomb damage inflicted before the sinking, based on official reports of naval observers who inspected the ship at intervals during the tests.

10 Admiral Viscount Jellicoe of Scapa, *The Grand Fleet 1914–1916: Its Creation, Development and Work* George H Doran (New York, 1919).

11 Ruth Mitchell, op cit, p266.

12 See Davis, op cit, p57–61.

13 Robert L O'Connell, *Sacred Vessels: The Cult of the Battleship and the Rise of the US Navy* Oxford Paperbacks (New York and Oxford, 1991). O'Connell misidentifies Crowell as a former Secretary of War; he was in fact assistant secretary, under Secretary Newton Baker.

14 These vessels, six battleships and six battlecruisers, would have displaced nearly twice as much as *Ostfriesland* and would have dwarfed her in terms of protection both above and below water. Their construction, save for two battlecruisers that became the aircraft carriers *Lexington* and *Saratoga*, was cancelled under terms of the Washington Treaty.

15 O'Connell, op cit, p3.

16 Ibid, p2.

17 Zimmerman, op cit, speculates that even minimal damage control measures after the first bombs hit could have delayed or perhaps even averted the sinking.

18 Two well-researched, full-length English language books on Jutland had been published in the United States before the Second World War – Langhorne Gibson and J E T Harper, *The Riddle of Jutland: An Authentic History*, Coward McCann (New York, 1934) and Holloway H Frost, *The Battle of Jutland* United States Naval Institute (Annapolis, 1936). *Ostfriesland*'s main particulars were published as early as 1913 in *The Naval Annual* (later *Brassey*'s) and given in even more detail in the 1919 edition of *Jane's Fighting Ships*.

BRITISH HEAVY COAST-DEFENCE GUNS IN WORLD WAR II

As a result of Britain's limited need for very heavy coast-defence guns between the wars, few such weapons were in service during the Second World War. Those that were employed, at Singapore and Dover, were naval guns on special coast-defence mountings. In this article John Campbell describes the background history and technical details of these weapons, the difficulties of long-range cross-channel firing at Dover and examines why the arrangements for the Singapore guns were flawed.

The 15in MkI was the most powerful gun ever mounted in British coast-defences, although guns of larger calibre had been mounted in the days of the MLR (muzzle loading rifle); namely two 17.72in(450mm) at Malta and two more at Gibraltar, and two 16in(406.4mm) in a turret at Dover. Apart from these, heavy coast defence MLRs were normally of 12.5in(317.5mm) or lesser calibre. With the reintroduction of BLs (breech-loaders), the calibres were reduced to 10in or 9.2in(254mm or 233.7mm) apart from eighteen 12in(304.8mm) at Portsmouth (ten in Horse Sand Fort and eight in No Man's Land Fort) and one 13.5in(342.9mm) in a disappearing mounting at Penlee Point, Plymouth. These BLs were only up to 32cal in bore length.

The next stage was to standardise on 9.2in of about 47cal. The first such guns, introduced in 1897, were thirteen MkIX, followed by the improved MkX which remained the standard gun until the abolition of coast artillery in 1956. A further improvement of more modern construction, MkXV, was introduced in limited numbers in the Second World War. It should be noted that the accuracy of the MkX was much improved in later years by the use of a smaller grain propellant which did not burn as far down the barrel as the earlier MD37. Initially these guns were liable to 'steel-choke', but this was eliminated by improvements in the location of the inner 'A' tubes.

Defending the East Coast

During the First World War it was soon realised that the 9.2in was inadequate against the heavily armoured German battlecruisers which shelled the poorly defended English east coast in 1914 and 1916, where nothing heavier than 6in(152.4mm) engaged them. However, the British army had no guns of 12in or larger calibre and such elderly reserve guns of this size that the navy could spare went to provide railway guns for the field army or, in the case of three 12in/45cal MkX and four spares, as counter-battery guns on the Belgian coast. For a time some of the older pre-dreadnoughts were stationed at vulnerable places on the east coast to provide some heavy gun defences and later in the war monitors were similarly employed. The only modern guns were four Bethlehem 14in (355.6 mm)/45cal, known in Britain as MkII, mounted in the monitors *Havelock* and *Roberts*, stationed at Lowestoft and Gorleston for most of the time from May 1916 (after the last battlecruiser raid) until the end of the war.

In one instance a new 12in shore battery was begun. The old battleship *Illustrious* (four 12in/35cal Mk VIII), stationed at the Tyne, was paid-off in 1916 and her two twin turrets removed for modification to 30deg elevation, and installation at Hartley and Marsden to the north and south

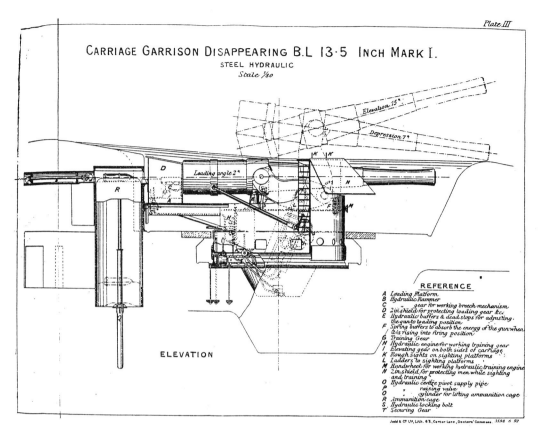

Plate III

CARRIAGE GARRISON DISAPPEARING B.L 13·5 INCH MARK I.
STEEL HYDRAULIC
Scale 1/80

Elevation 15°

Depression 7°

Loading angle 2°

ELEVATION

REFERENCE

A Loading Platform.
B Hydraulic Rammer
C   "   gear for working breech mechanism
D 2in.shield for protecting loading gear &c.
E Hydraulic buffers & dead stops for adjusting.
   the gun to loading position
F Spring buffers to absorb the energy of the gun when
   it is rising into firing position
G Training Gear
H Hydraulic engine for working training gear
I Elevating gear on both sides of carriage
K Rough sights on sighting platforms
L Ladders to sighting platforms
M Handwheel for working hydraulic training engine
N 2in.shield for protecting men while sighting
   and training
O Hydraulic centre pivot supply pipe
P   "   raising valve
Q   "   cylinder for lifting ammunition cage
R Ammunition cage
S Hydraulic locking bolt
T Securing Gear

Jedd & Cᵒ Lᵗᵈ, Lith. 63, Carter Lane, Doctors' Commons. 3598 6 92

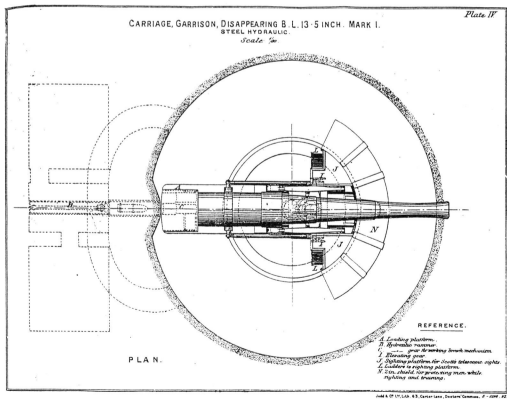

Plate IV

CARRIAGE, GARRISON, DISAPPEARING B.L. 13·5 INCH. MARK I.
STEEL HYDRAULIC.
Scale 1/80.

PLAN.

REFERENCE.

A Loading platform
B Hydraulic rammer
C   "   gear for working breech mechanism
I Elevating gear
J Sighting platform for Scott's telescopic sights.
L Ladders to sighting platform
N 2in.shield for protecting men while
   sighting and training.

Jedd & Cᵒ Lᵗᵈ, Lith. 63, Carter Lane, Doctors' Commons. 5 - 3598 . 92.

Profile and plan of the disappearing mounting for the 13.5in MkI gun mounted at Penlee Point, Plymouth.

of Tynemouth. There was no kind of urgency shown and the turrets were not proved until September 1921 when the guns were nearly obsolete; they were scrapped in April 1926.

After the First World War matters were much changed. It was only in the Far East that attacks by capital ships could be expected and there was no longer a shortage of surplus heavy naval guns. A list of January 1920 has the following on offer to the army:

Six 15in 42cal MkI
Six 14in 45cal MkII
Eighty-five 12in 45cal MkX
Sixty 12in 40cal MkIX
Thirty-nine 12in 35cal MkVIII

Against the capital ships of 1914–18 the 12in MkX would have been valuable but (pre Washington Treaty) postwar ships were likely to be of a different order of power with at least 16in (406.4mm) guns, and of the above largesse only the 15in were suitable for coast defences likely to engage postwar capital ships.

In most countries the heaviest coast defence guns were the same as those mounted in actual or projected ships, the main exception being the USA where coast defences were taken more seriously than in Britain and more resources were available. Even here only seven of the very powerful 16in/50cal M1919 were ever mounted and later 16in/50cal guns were the somewhat less powerful naval Mk2, intended for the ships cancelled under the 1922 Washington Treaty.

The Singapore Guns

The first installation of 15in MkI guns in coast defences was at Singapore where five were mounted during 1937–39. Their purpose was to engage Japanese capital ships, though the opportunity never arose. The disgraceful disaster of the fall of Singapore on 15 February 1942 will not be described here, but some of the factors responsible included the persistent underestimation of Japanese warlike abilities; Churchill's obsession with the Mediterranean and Middle East; the failure to construct adequate defences against landings on the north shore of Singapore island, combined with the ultimately futile attempt to defend the whole of Malaya; the lack of a balanced naval force; the high proportion of low grade troops and the lack of any first class aircraft. The dithering and delays from the first inception of the naval base project in June 1921 were also unhelpful.

The provision of five 15in was somewhat miserly. The Admiralty had originally wanted eight, and in 1929–35 a country as impecunious as Spain strengthened coast defences by eighteen 15in/45cal Vickers Mk 'B'.

The monitor *Terror* (two 15in on 30deg mountings) was stationed at Singapore from January 1934 until January 1940, though under refit for the last months. In April 1937 she took part in a joint shoot with the first two of the shore guns against a high speed towed target. Her planned war station was between sandbanks to the south east of the naval base and she would have been connected to the fortress fire-control system. It is a tragedy she was not still there in 1942 to help defend the north shore of Singapore island.

The 15in was an elderly gun with design origins dating to 1911, which first saw service in the battleship *Queen Elizabeth* completed early in 1915. It was of wire-wound construction with Welin screw breech-block and 'pure couple' breech mechanism. It was heavy at 100 tons (101,605kg) including breech mechanism, but the rear part had been made heavier than necessary for strength purposes in order to move the centre of gravity towards the breech and allow for a smaller turret (details are given in Table 1). By post-Washington standards the 15in was still a formidable gun.

The five Singapore guns were supplied from naval resources; the first, No78 (made by Vickers), on 4 November 1930 and the remainder, No54 (Woolwich), No88 (Beardmore), No146 (Elswick) and No174 (Vickers), on 15 January 1932. The first three, mounted at Johore, had been relined

Profile of the 15in MkI, or Singapore mounting. (Drawn by John Roberts)

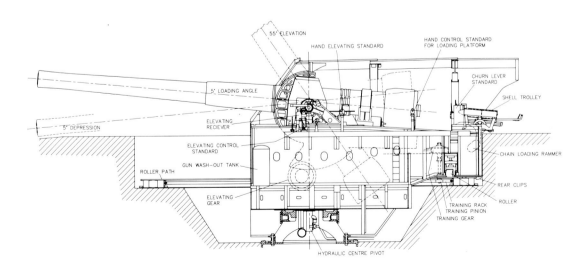

Table 1: *CUMULATIVE EFCS FIRED BY THE 15IN GUNS OF THE WANSTONE BATTERY*

	Gun No27	Gun No114
22 Aug 1942	54	59
18 Sep 1942	85	79
3 Nov 1942	104	93
14 Dec 1942	164	149
	Gun No17	Gun No18
31 Mar 1943	43	41
1 May 1943	79	77
1 Jun 1943	105	101
1 Aug 1943	–	120
1 Oct 1943	130	123
4 Oct 1943	169	162
1 Nov 1943	183	–
	Gun No32	Gun No34
1 Nov 1943	42	46
1 Dec 1943	64	67
1 Jan 1944	124	131
1 Feb 1944	236	245
	Gun No114	Gun No162
29 Feb 1944	45	45
1 Apr 1944	136	135
1 May 1944	142	135
1 Aug 1944	155	148
1 Sep 1944	155	148
1 Oct 1944	363	359

Notes: The guns were issued to the battery on the following dates: Nos27 and 114 – 7 Apr 1942; No17 – 26 Feb 1943; No18 – 18 Feb 1943; Nos32 and 34 – 12 Oct 1943; No 114 (for second time) – 2 Feb 1944; No162 – 7 Feb 1944. The last pair to be issued, Nos97 and 98 on 5 July 1945, have no efcs recorded.

in 1930–31. No78 had been completed as an experimental 14in, while No54 had been in the battleship *Valiant* and No88 in her sister *Barham*, both at Jutland. In May 1938 when the Johore battery was ready, No78 was in its second quarter of life, while the other two together with No146 and No174 for Buona Vista, were in the first quarter.

The 15in Mountings MkI and II

None of the twin naval turrets allowed more than 30deg elevation, which restricted the range of the guns, and high-angle single mountings were provided for Singapore. These comprised one MkI, also known as the 'Singapore mounting', with gun No78, in the right-hand position at Johore, and four MkII, also known as the 'Spanish mounting'. MkI was an Armstrong design, similar to the German 38cm BSG mounting as fitted at Batteries *Pommern* and *Deutschland* on the Belgian coast, adapted to a separate hydraulic pumping unit. The centre-pivot was supported on a roller path of 7ft(2.13m) mean diameter, and the rear of the mounting by spring loaded rollers running on a 360deg track, of 44ft 7in(13.59m) mean diameter, in a 50ft(15.24m) diameter concrete pit. The gun was carried on a saddle type cradle of the usual pattern but this was not a naval spare. The training rack adjoined the rear roller

Profile of the 15in MkII, or Spanish mounting, four of which, together with one MkI, formed the heavy coast defence battery of the Singapore Naval Base.

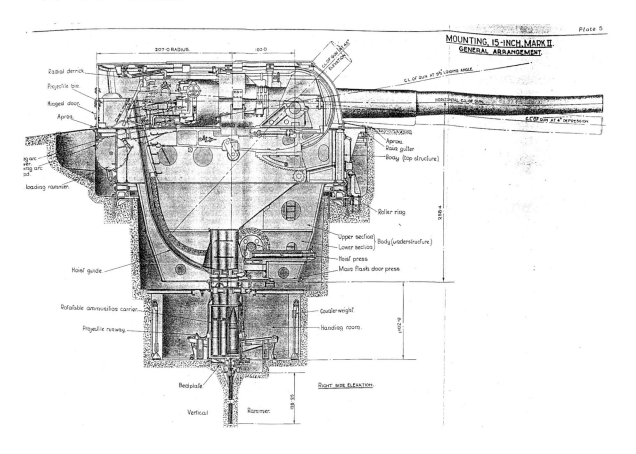

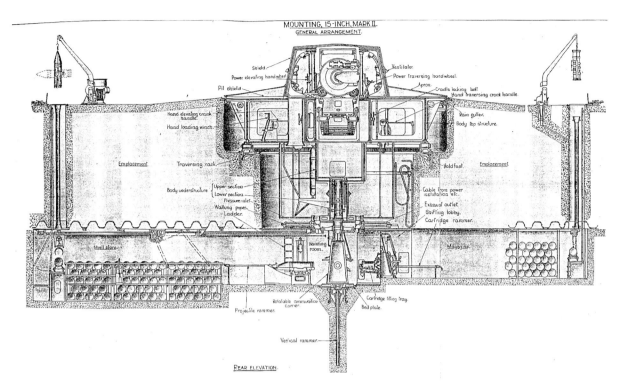

Cross section of the 15in MkII mounting.

track (Max training speed was 5deg/sec) and elevation was through a worm and spur pinion train working on a toothed arc giving 55deg elevation to 5deg depression; loading was at 5deg elevation. Hydraulic pressure was fed to the mounting via a central swivel, as in many Armstrong designs, and this should not have limited the arc of training. As the Singapore site was not ready, the mounting was erected in a concrete pit at Shoeburyness for trials from 1934 until 1936. The arc of training at Singapore was only 67^1/$_2$deg to 247^1/$_2$deg measured clockwise from true north (the reasons for this limitation are not clear). The shield was partly open-backed and was only 2in(50mm) thick, though original designs show twice this. It extended down to the level of the training rack. Recoil was 45in(114.3cm),(47in[119.4cm] max).

Shell and charge were loaded into a trolley, with extensible handles, at the base of the magazine and shell room hoist and pushed to the gun at the top. The distances involved are not known. The trolley was located on a moving platform and shell and charges were rammed home by a hydraulic chain rammer.

The MkII mounting was very different and in many ways resembled a turret but lacked heavy armour. It was a Vickers-Armstrong design and generally similar to the 15in mountings supplied to Spain. The roller path was 28ft(8.53m) mean diameter, there was no barbette, and the upper part of the concrete gun pit was 35ft(10.67m) internal diameter. Hydraulic power was fed to the rotating structure by walking pipes which allowed 290deg training, limited by buffers to 240deg, an excessive safety margin. The actual arcs of training for the two guns most likely to fire at the north shore, were 60–300deg for the Johore centre gun and 75^1/$_2$–315^1/$_2$deg for the left gun, both clockwise from true north. If extra care had been used in training, there seems no reason why the buffers could not have been

removed, which would have increased these figures to 325deg and 340^1/$_2$deg at the landward end. Gun saddles and elevating gear resembled those in MkI, except that elevation was +45deg – 2deg with loading at +9^1/$_2$deg, and there was a 22,932lb(10,402kg) counter-weight on the rear saddle.

Shell rooms and magazines were in the concrete understructure below the mounting. One shell and two half charges were loaded vertically in a rotatable carrier, which was raised one floor level by a vertical hydraulic ram. They were then transferred vertically to the hoist cage which ran on curved guide rails and was raised by a thrust chain operated by a hydraulic press, rack and pinion and sprocket wheel. As the cage was raised, it was turned to the loading angle by the guide rails, where shell and charges were loaded by a hydraulic chain rammer.

The shield was complete but only 2in thick. A pit shield fixed to the gun shield, covered the gap between mounting and gun pit, and was apparently a little under 2in, scarcely an adequate alternative for a heavy barbette. Recoil distances were as in MkI.

In the event there was some firing in February 1942 towards Johore Bahru and the Race Course area, but observation was lacking and only APC shells were available. These were intended to burst after piercing 12in or thicker armour plate and against unarmoured targets they would behave as shot not shell. No HE shell was obtainable in time.

At the surrender four of the five guns were destroyed but one, at Buona Vista, was undamaged and some of the hydraulic pumping equipment in both batteries was repairable. This one gun was recovered at the Japanese surrender and occurs in a 1946 list of British coast defences.

Table 2: *PARTICULARS OF HEAVY COAST DEFENCE GUNS*

Gun	Bore length (calibre)	Shell weight (lbs/kg)	Propellant (lbs/kg–type)	Muzzle velocity (fps/mps)	Range (yds–m) /elevation (deg)
15in MkI	42	1920/871	432/196–SC280	2467/752	34640–31675/45
		1938/879	432/196–SC280	2458/749	38500–35205/45
		1938/879	486/220.4–SC300	2638/804	44150–40370/45
14in MkVII	45	1590/721	486/220.4–SC500	2850/869	50800–46450/44
13.5in MkV	45	1400/635	423/192–SC450	2830/863	40670–37190/40
		1250/567	400/181.4–SC390	2950/899	48900–44710/40
16in M1919	50	2340/1061	832/377–NC	2700/823	49140–44930/53
16in Mk2	49.7	2240/1016	648/294–NC	2650/808	45100–41240/47
40.6cm SKL/34	48.6	2271/1030	648/294–RPC/40	2657/810	47100–43100/47
		1323/600	739/335–RPC/40	3445/1050	61240–56000/51$^{1}/_{2}$
38cm SKL/34	48.4	1764/800	569/258–RPC/40	2690/820	46040–42100/47
		1091/495	651/295–RPC40	3445/1050	60000–54900/51
30.5cm SKL/50	47.4	915/415	268/121.5–RPC/38	2789/850	45170–41300/48
		551/250	315/143–RPC/38	3675/1120	56200–51400/49
28cm SKL/50	47.4	626/284	262/119–RPC/38	2936/895	42400–38600/49$^{1}/_{2}$
28cm SKL/45	42.4	626/284	262/119–RPC/38	2871/875	40350–36900/49
28cm K5	72.5	563/255.5	383/173.9	3700/1128	68000–62200/c52
21cm K12	153	237/107.5	551/250	5330/1625	126000–115000/c55

Notes: The effect on range of the shape of the shell was considerable. This was indicated by the calibre radius head (crh) which was a measure of the radius of the head, from the point to the body, in multiples of the calibre of the shell. In British shells there was usually a curve inward at the start of the nose ogive and consequently a double figure was given for head form, the first figure being the crh appropriate to the length of the ogive and the second its actual radius. The 15in, 1920lbs shell was 3.05/4crh; the 15in, 1938lbs shell 5/10crh; the 14in was 6/12crh while the 13.5in, 1400lbs shell was a nominal 4crh and the above mentioned 13.5in, 1250lbs shell was 8/16crh. German shells were usually 10crh, or 8crh in the 28cm SKL/45 and 50, and US shells about 9crh.

The Wanstone Battery

The other 15in battery, Wanstone near Dover, had a more fortunate history. Its purpose was to prevent German traffic passing through the Straits of Dover near the French shore, beyond the effective range of smaller coast defence guns. The first directive seems to have been in September 1940, Vickers-Armstrong's completed the mounting drawings in January 1941 and the two guns were in place in April–May 1942. Although far-sighted individuals might have predicted the collapse of France in 1940, if they had realised the evil effects of the Popular Front government of 1936–7 and other malign influences of the 1930s, such views would have been received with even less credibility than the truth about Japanese efficiency, and nothing was done until the French collapse to provide very heavy long-range guns.

By early August 1940 the Germans had concentrated their 28cm railway guns, which included six of the very long range K5, as well as the extreme range 21cm K12, on what was now their side of the Channel. Four 28cm coast-defence guns from Pillau were also ready and, later in the month, were joined by three 30.5cm from Wangerooge and two 28cm from Fehmarn (respectively batteries *Grosser*

Kurfürst, Friedrich August and *Prinz Heinrich*). In mid September the first two 38cm guns of battery *Siegfried*, later named *Todt*, were ready and were subsequently joined by two more. All these and many lighter guns of 24cm and smaller, were an essential part of the German invasion plan though the 28cm railway guns would have been of little use against naval targets, and the 21cm K12 was really a propaganda gun only.

It was a difficult problem to provide a counter to these German guns in the very short time available. The 15in Wanstone battery was many months away, and without super-charges and/or special long-range shells, which did not exist, the required range was too great. Such shells had been available since the First World War to German guns of 30.5cm and over. There were only two mountings for very heavy guns which allowed elevation of over 40deg – No26 Proof Structure and the former 18in Monitor Mounting. It was possible to make two 14in Mk VII guns and one spare available. These were for the *King George V* class and, with normal full charges, they did not have an adequate performance. However, they could withstand a very heavy supercharge which gave sufficient range. The first gun, No96, generally known as 'Winnie', was first fired across the Channel on 22 August 1940. It was in No26 Proof Structure, and was changed for No119 in December 1940

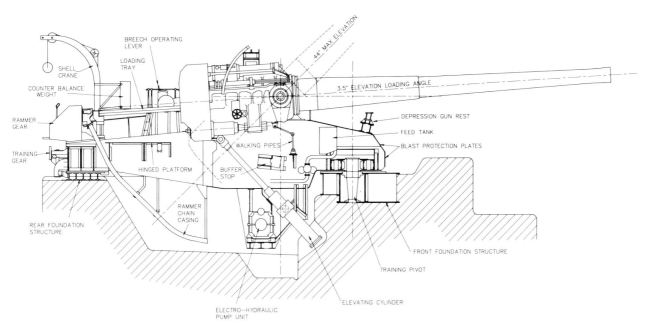

after 104efc (1 supercharge = 2 full charges). The second gun No83, 'Pooh', in the former 18in Mounting was not ready until 9 February 1941, apparently due to rammer problems.

By early 1941 serious risk of invasion had passed for the time being and there was little point in cross-channel duels with the German guns, the main result of which was extensive damage to Dover. There was even less point after the three 40.6cm guns of battery *Lindemann* (ex *Gross-deutschland*, ex *Schleswig Holstein*) had been moved from Hela by late 1941, which gave the Germans greater superiority. By 1943 the two 14in had been reduced to care and maintenance and both guns were sent for relining at Vickers Armstrong's Elswick works. They were reactivated in May 1944 to engage slow moving targets beyond 15in range and, in conjunction with the latter, to support the Canadian attack on the channel fortifications in September, during which both guns were worn-out, efc's (cumulative) in this period were:

No119 'Winnie'
7 July 1944 – 38
5 Sept 1944 – 107
21 Sept 1944 – 335

No83 'Pooh'
15 May 1944 – 26
5 Sept 1944 – 113
21 Sept 1944 – 341

The 14in Guns and Mountings

The 14in Mk VII guns were of built-up construction with inner 'A' tube, 'A' tube and jacket. The usual Welin breech block was used with hydraulic Asbury breech mechanism. Weight with breech mechanism, but without balance weight, was about 79 tons(80,270kg). No26 Proof Structure had a forward fixed pivot and only 9deg of training which

Profile of No26 Proof Structure, with 14in MkVII gun, which was erected at Dover in 1940 as part of the Wanstone battery. (Drawn by John Roberts)

took about 50secs to traverse so it was not a coast defence mounting. With power loading by chain rammer, it had 44deg elevation and 2deg depression and a fixed loading angle of $3^1/_2$deg. Elevation was by hydraulic cylinder, with the piston rod working on the cradle which was cylindrical, as in naval turrets. Hydraulic power was supplied by an electric motor and pump unit on the mounting, and ammunition was raised from a platform wagon by crane to the loading position. The rate of fire could reach one round per minute. Recoil was 45in(114.3cm),(47in [119.4cm] max). There was no protective shield.

The former 18in Monitor Mounting was of similar general type. It had 43deg elevation, 2deg depression and a loading angle of 10deg. The elevating cylinder was far forward in the mounting and there were differences in the rammer and location of the pump unit.

Railway Guns

There was little effective support for the two 14in guns. Attempts to obtain two 16in, 50cal Mk2 from the USA failed. The British army, with a tradition of opposition to very heavy mobile guns unless forced to change their views, had contrived to mislay their only four large railway mountings, and these were not rediscovered (at Chilwell) until late 1939. These were a First World War product intended to take the 14in/45cal MkI* or MkIII guns, which had a similar performance to the MkVII gun without supercharge, or else the 18in/35cal howitzer, a formidable weapon at up to about 25,000yds(22,860m) with improved shell, though not with the performance to be expected from a 35cal gun. Of the four 18in howitzers extant (four more to a modified design were cancelled), only one was mounted,

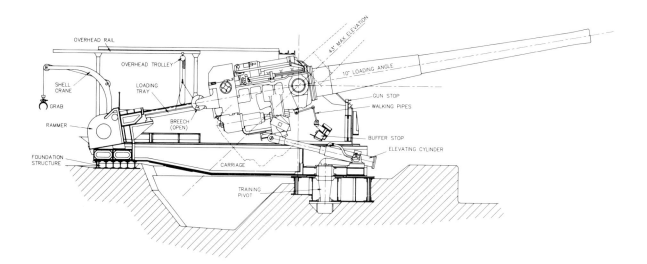

Profile of the 18in BCD mounting as converted for the 14in MkVII gun. (Drawn by John Roberts)

the other three railway mountings being fitted with 13.5in/45cal Mk V guns of which the navy had retained fifty-four, twelve having fired less than 20efc.

In 1921 the Ordnance authorities had decreed that there was no need to perpetuate the 14in as the 13.5in would do. There was apparently no protest at the 10 per cent loss of power. The 14in MkI* and III were declared obsolete in June 1926. One of the unsatisfactory 14in/50cal MkVI was extant but it needed a special adapter to fit the railway mounting and its performance was lower than that of the 14in/45cal, so it was declared obsolete in May 1942.

The railway mounting only allowed 40deg elevation – 39deg with the 13.5in gun – and had to be aimed by the curve of the rail track apart from a small traverse on the mounting of ±2deg. There was no arrangement for mounting on a permanent base giving all-round fire as in the US 14in/50cal rail guns in the Panama Canal Zone and at San Pedro, California. The Dover rail guns were thus in no way coast defence weapons. To summarise, the standard 1400lb(635kg) shell was of inferior shape and, with a heavy supercharge, had barely sufficient range, but a lighter long nosed 1250lb(567kg) shell improved this. The strength of the mounting was dubious with these supercharges.

Serial numbers for 13.5in Mk V ran from No501. The first gun, No601, arrived at Dover in September 1940 and from October fired a limited number of rounds. No587 arrived in late November 1940 but the mounting was damaged on 10 December by a near-miss and the gun was not fired until a calibration shoot at 12deg 15min elevation on 1 May 1941 when seven super-charges were fired. One further supercharge was fired six days later and a full charge on 23 February 1942, giving a total of 23efc including the original six at proof in 1915. The third gun No662 arrived in May 1941 but no information has been found on the rounds fired. Like the two 14in, the guns had been worked by the RMA but in 1943 the 13.5in were transferred to the army as War Office reserve, and their supercharges were not used again.

The ability to fire across the Channel was still considered important, as it was one of the requirements for the last British very heavy gun, the 16in/45cal Mk IV which was intended for the redesigned battleships *Lion* and *Temeraire* cancelled after the war.

The 15in MkIII Mounting

Returning to the Wanstone battery, the Mk III mountings were quite distinct from MksI and II. There was no deep gun-pit except to allow elevation and recoil, and there was a forward fixed pivot with front and rear roller paths. The training rack was immediately behind the rear roller path and had a pitch circle radius of 38ft 9in(11.81m). The training arc was a symmetrical 160deg. The front roller path was for steadying and preventing overhang of the main hydraulic pump unit, which was on the movable structure and driven by an electric motor. The mean path radius was 5ft 3in(1.60m). The guns were in reserve naval saddles and slides, serial Nos36 and 45. There were no balance weights. Elevation was by hydraulic cylinder with the piston rod working on the slide. The limits were 50deg to 2½deg elevation with loading at the latter figure. Loading was by chain rammer and shells and cartridges were brought by powered trolleys to cranes respectively to right and left of the gun, from where they were raised to the loading position. An endless chain cordite hoist to replace the crane was designed in 1943 but it is not clear when or if it was fitted. Maximum rate of fire was about one round per minute. The mounting was fitted with a 2in thick shield of distinctive shape.

Unlike other batteries noted the Wanstone guns, which were changed four times, were much in use. They were manned by the Royal Artillery and not by the RMA. Table 1 gives the efcs fired (fractions are omitted).

The firing in the latter part of 1944 was very largely in conjunction with the 14in and super-charges were used, though these were relatively smaller than in 13.5in and 14in. They had first been introduced in September 1942 by the navy to improve the range of 15in guns still in 20deg mountings.

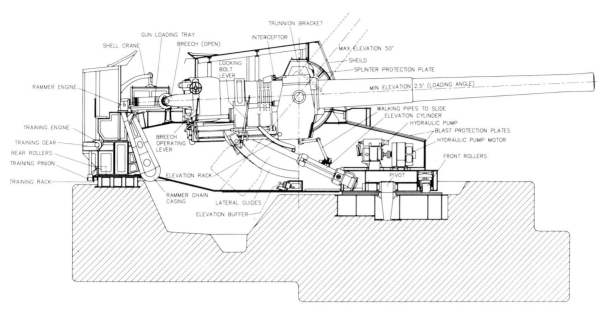

The 15in coast defence mounting MkIII of the Wanstone Battery. (Drawn by John Roberts)

THE 7600-TONNE CRUISERS

The French cruisers of the *La Galissonnière* class were among the most successful of prewar types. John Jordan looks at the key aspects of the design and traces the ships' employment between 1937 and 1942.

The first cruisers built for the Marine Nationale after the First World War were the three ships of the *Duguay Trouin* class. These were essentially updated and upgraded versions of the scout cruisers of the *Lamotte-Piquet* class, ordered in 1914 but subsequently cancelled. The new ships were intended to perform a similar rôle in direct support of the battle fleet. They were armed with eight 155mm (6.1in) guns in twin mountings and carried an exceptionally heavy battery of 550mm (21.7in) torpedoes – twelve ready-use, in four triple mountings, and a similar number of reloads. They were, therefore, well equipped both to support flotilla craft in making torpedo attacks against an enemy battle line and to repel hostile flotilla craft with their powerful battery of 155mm guns. Their high speed enabled them to manoeuvre rapidly ahead or on the flanks of the battle line and provided a degree of protection from the guns of heavier ships; armour protection was minimal, being intended to provide only splinter protection for the ship's vitals.

This line of development was effectively abandoned in

La Galissonnière, the lead-ship of the class, sorties with the Mediterranean Fleet for the first time on 17 November 1936, two weeks after commissioning. It was to be another year before her sister Jean de Vienne *would enter service.* (Marius Bar)

the wake of the Washington Treaty of 1922. France felt compelled to respond to the 'Treaty' cruiser construction programmes embarked upon by the other major naval powers; the 10,000 ton/8in gun maximum quickly became the standard, as none of the participants was prepared to be outgunned by its rivals. Between 1924 and 1930 the Marine Nationale duly ordered seven such cruisers, each successive ship or sub-group conforming to developments elsewhere, with armour protection being steadily increased at the expense of high speed.

Ironically, of the five major naval powers only the USA initially had a clear rationale for the deployment of these ships. The US Navy required large cruisers with sufficient endurance to scout well ahead of the battle fleet in the vast expanses of the Pacific. The Japanese quickly concurred with the US solution, while the British, who saw Japanese expansionism as a major threat to their empire in the Far East, regarded their own Treaty cruisers as protectors of the trade routes against predatory Japanese ships.

The French and Italian Treaty cruisers were more difficult to justify conceptually. Long range was simply not a requirement for either navy, given their likely opponents (each other, and in the case of France, a resurrected German Navy). The Treaty cruisers therefore came to have a mission not unlike that of the British and German battlecruiser fleets of the First World War. Organised into two squad-

rons of three/four ships they operated semi-independently from the battle fleet, performing a 'strategic scouting' rôle. They might engage their counterparts but would not be expected to stand up to the big guns of the enemy's battle line; their high speed meant that they could outfight any ships they could not outrun. In a further parallel with the battlecruiser, both navies provided their heavy cruiser squadrons with supporting ships: the Italians with light cruisers and destroyers, the French with divisions of *contre-torpilleurs*.

The London Treaty

When construction of the Treaty cruiser was terminated by the London Treaty of 22 April 1930, following intense pressure by the British who found they simply could not afford to build ships of this size in the required numbers, the proposal was readily accepted by France and Italy. The latter country had already embarked on a construction programme of small 6in gun cruisers of the *Condottieri* type in response to the French *contre-torpilleurs*. The Marine Nationale was about to begin a replacement programme for its older, prewar-built dreadnoughts, and the new fast battleships would need a new class of fleet cruiser for scouting, together with a new generation of destroyers for close escort.

The result was the six-ship *La Galissonnière* class, for which studies began in June 1930, just two months after the conclusion of the London Treaty. Fortunately, the Marine Nationale already had a modern 6in gun cruiser on the drawing board. Authorised under the 1930 Programme, the 6000-ton *Emile Bertin* was a fast minelaying cruiser with a powerful main armament of nine 152mm/50 guns and six 550mm torpedo tubes. The design would serve as the basis for the new fleet cruisers, there being considerable commonality with regard to hull-form, superstructure layout and armament.

However, the *Emile Bertin* was a lightly-constructed ship designed for high speed (39.66kts were to be recorded on trials), whereas the new fleet cruisers were required to be relatively invulnerable to destroyer fire and able to withstand hits from Italian cruisers armed with 152mm (6in) guns. A reduced speed of 31kts was therefore accepted as the price for armour protection which was almost on a par with that of the latest (and last) of the French 10,000-ton cruisers, the *Algérie*.

All postwar French cruisers, except the *Bertin* and the training cruiser *Jeanne d'Arc* (both built by Chantiers et Ateliers de St Nazaire (Penhoët)), had been constructed by one or other of the two naval dockyards at Brest and Lorient. However, the naval dockyards did not have the capacity for a cruiser programme on this scale (six ships authorised within two years) and it was decided that *La Galissonnière* would be allocated to Brest and *Jean de Vienne* to Lorient, while the four ships of the 1932 programme would be put out to private tender. The result was that each of the six ships was built in a different shipyard. In order to ensure uniformity of construction Brest was designated as the lead yard and was responsible for supplying detailed plans to the other shipyards. The first ship, *La Galissonnière*, was launched some 18 months before the second, the construction of all subsequent units being delayed to accommodate any modifications found to be necessary; this was to result in a number of detail differences between the name ship of the class and her sisters.

The French were particularly anxious to get the first two ships on the slipway prior to the next naval conference, which was scheduled for February 1932. However, because of the heavy workload on the two naval dockyards (Brest was involved in building the *Algérie* and the new fast battleship *Dunkerque*; Lorient was refitting the cruisers *Colbert*, *Suffren* and *Primauguet*), construction was not begun in earnest until much later, so that a period of 3 years 8 months elapsed between the laying down and launch of *Jean de Vienne*. The ships of the class therefore took some five years to construct, compared with 26–30 months for the contemporary British *Leanders*.

Armament

The armament proposed in the initial STCN studies for the project was virtually identical to that of the *Emile Bertin*: nine 152mm guns in triple turrets, four 90mm HA guns in twin mountings (the *Bertin* had one twin and two single mountings), eight 37mm Model 1933 in twin mountings, and eight of the new 13.2mm Hotchkiss MG in twin mountings, together with triple 550mm torpedo tubes amidships.

The General Staff was unhappy about the AA armament, its criticisms focusing on the excessive dispersion of

The first sortie of Montcalm *on sea trials, 7 January 1937.* (Marius Bar)

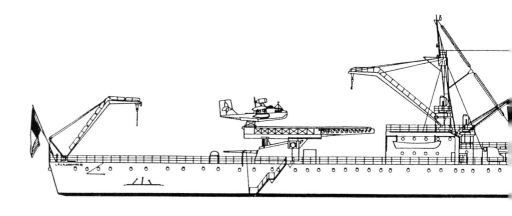

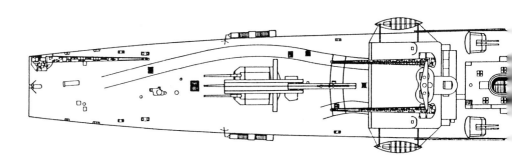

Profile and plan views of La Galissonnière, *based on official drawings produced by Brest Naval Dockyard and dated May 1937. Only the forward twin Hotchkiss AA mountings of the original design are shown, and these are as yet unshielded. Although the plan view clearly illustrates the quarterdeck rail transfer system for the Loire 130 seaplanes, it does not show the turntable atop the hangar, which was fitted in October of the same year. (Drawn by the author)*

fire resulting from its disposition. It demanded that the 37mm mountings be discarded in favour of a more powerful secondary battery of four twin 90mm HA, the additional weight being compensated by eliminating two of the six torpedo tubes. This would enable the twin 13.2mm mountings to be relocated at the after end of the forecastle deck,

in place of the 37mm.

The 152mm/50 Model 1930 mounting was an impressive piece of technology incorporating a high degree of automation. The guns were in individual cradles, and remote power control was fitted for drive and elevation, power being provided by an hydraulic unit driven by a 60hp Leonard electric motor. The breech mechanism was arranged to operate automatically, while a catapult rammer was used for shells and a chain rammer for cartridges. The shell rooms and magazines were separate, each turret hav-

Interior profile of La Galissonnière, *based on an official drawing dated Brest March 1937. Note the unit machinery arrangement, a departure from the traditional layout adopted for the first postwar light cruisers of the* Duguay Trouin *class. (Drawn by the author)*

Key:
1 main director control tower
2 admiral's bridge with 3m R/F
3 transmissions/operations centre
4 conning tower
5 navigation bridge
6 transmissions centre
7 fwd 152mm magazine
8 fwd 90mm magazine
9 aft 90mm magazine
10 aft 152mm magazine
11 steering compartment
12 aircraft mat handling room

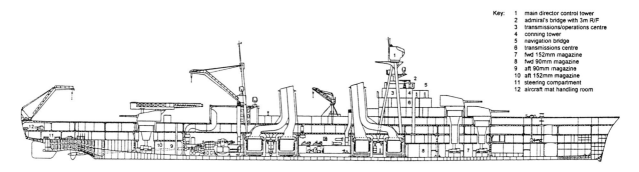

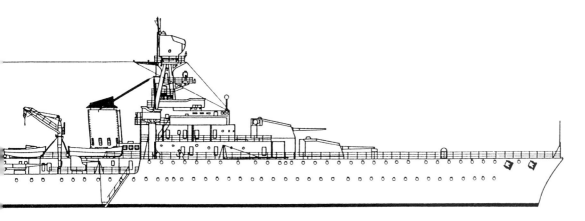

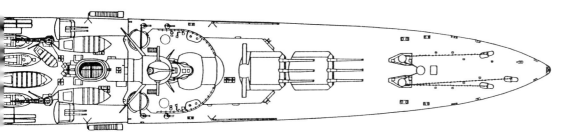

ing three shell and four cartridge hoists, all of the pusher type. Shells were tipped by hand into a slide which transferred them to the power-operated loading gear.

Unfortunately, the mounting was plagued by the customary problems associated with technological complexity and numerous modifications were necessary before the Marine Nationale was satisfied with its performance. During firing trials there were frequent breakdowns in the firing mechanism, the breech safety mechanism and the shell and cartridge hoists. Low standards of manufacture, incorrect settings and even poor maintenance were held to blame. As a result the rate of fire averaged only three rounds per minute per gun, half the figure anticipated. Simplification of the turret mechanisms aboard *Gloire* in 1938 eventually yielded a rate of fire of 9rpm at an elevation of 8deg. However, these modifications were not extended to all ships of the class and the maximum rate of fire sustained in service remained at around 5rpm.

Using the standard armour-piercing shell, the OPF, the 152mm/50 Model 1930 had a theoretical range of 25,000m at the maximum elevation of 45deg; in practice effective range was around 18,000m. The OPF, which weighed 54.5kg, could penetrate 100mm of steel at 11,000m and 120mm at 9000m. In its OPFK variant a coloured dye similar to that employed for the *contre-torpilleurs* was incorporated in the shell to enable each unit in a three-ship division to spot its own fall of shot. The OPF was complemented by the OEA HE shell.

Fire-control for the main armament was provided by three double OPL stereoscopic rangefinders with an 8m base, two integrated into the rear end of 'B' and 'X' turrets and the third into the main fire-control director. The latter, as in other contemporary French cruisers, was carried atop a heavy tripod foremast which straddled the forward superstructure.

The 90mm/50 Model 1926 HA gun was already in service aboard the heavy cruisers *Colbert* and *Foch*, and the twin mounting Model 1930 was currently being installed in the latest of the series, the *Dupleix*. The twin mountings in the *La Galissonnière* class weighed 13.7 tonnes and were fitted with remote power control; maximum elevation was 80deg and rate of fire 6rpm but loading proved difficult above 60deg. Each mounting was served by a ready-use ammunition park comprising sixty rounds. HA fire-control directors were fitted on circular platforms extending from the after end of the navigation bridge. Those of the first two ships incorporated 3m SOM Model 1932 rangefinders, while the later ships had the OPL 4m Model 1933.

The performance of the 90mm gun proved generally satisfactory but the fire-control system was unreliable, to the extent that under combat conditions the guns were often operated in local control, as was the case with *Montcalm* off Norway in April 1940.

Each of the four twin 13.2mm Hotchkiss mountings initially fitted was provided with a 1m rangefinder. From July 1937 the crews were given some protection against splinters and spray when shields were added to the mountings. Even before the ships entered service there was con-

The Marseillaise *makes her first major operational sortie from Toulon on 16 November 1937 as flagship of the* 3e Division de Croiseurs *(Contre-Amiral Decoux), in company with* Jean de Vienne, *the 1st and 2nd Cruiser Divisions (heavy cruisers) and the 9th DCT. Note the national markings on 'B' and 'X' turrets.* (Marius Bar)

cern about the inadequacy of the close-range AA provision. In January 1937 it was proposed to fit a quad 13.2mm Hotchkiss mounting, initially to starboard on the quarter-deck and later at the starboard after corner of the hangar. A shortage of quad mountings precluded this installation (the only ship so fitted was *La Galissonnière*, which trialled the mounting atop the hangar from January to April 1938) and the final solution, adopted in 1938, was to install two twin mountings at the after corners of the hangar, together with a 1m rangefinder on the after searchlight platform. The mountings installed in *Montcalm* and *Georges Leygues* were fitted with protective shields in 1940.

The torpedoes, launched from twin tubes amidships, were the standard 550mm Model 23D, which had a 4cyl radial engine giving it a range of 6000m at 43kts, 14,000m at 35kts and 20,000m at 29kts. The AG329 warhead contained 419kg of high explosive. There were two fire-control positions (Model 1935) in the bridge wings and two on the mountings themselves. The latter were fitted with shields from late 1937 to protect them from spray.

Protection

The hull of the 7600-tonne cruisers was of longitudinal construction with a double bottom from frame 13 to frame 158. The hull plates and frames were of steel with a resistance of 50kg/cm^2, while the armour plating had a resistance of 80kg/cm^2. The hull was divided into fifteen watertight compartments and there was a liquid ballast system fore and aft.

The armour protection scheme devised for these ships was necessarily a compromise, as it was for most foreign cruisers of the period. Armour thicknesses and coverage were almost on a par with the last of the Treaty cruisers, *Algérie*, but a degree of protection was assured only against the guns of light cruisers and destroyers. It was officially stated that the 105mm main armour belt, which was closed at either end by 60mm bulkheads, would resist 140mm shell beyond 9000m and 152mm shell beyond 14,000m. The horizontal armour, which comprised a 38mm main protective deck resting on the upper edges of the side

armour belt, was stated to be effective up to 19,000m against 140mm shell and up to 15,000m against 152mm shell. This gave a substantial immune zone against destroyer fire and a relatively small immune zone against the Italian *Condottieri* (although sources do not state the angle of fire on which these figures are based). There was no question of providing immunity against 8in (203mm) shell-fire, although this was also true for the 8in Treaty cruisers of the period.

In the conceptual stages of the design, studies were undertaken to determine whether effective protection could be provided against bombs and torpedoes, as well as against shellfire. It was found that protection against small bombs would have required an 80mm deck and that effective protection against a torpedo with a warhead of 300kg would require a torpedo bulkhead of 60mm (as against 20mm). The cost would have been an additional 1120 tonnes for the deck armour, and 300 tonnes for the torpedo bulkhead. These two measures would have raised standard displacement above 9000 tons, which was unacceptable given the desire on the part of the Marine Nationale to keep standard displacement within 8000 tons. The best possible compromise solution was therefore adopted, and the total armour weight of 1884 tonnes (24 per cent of displacement) compared favourably with any other light cruiser under construction at the time.

Propulsion

This level of armour protection was secured largely by reductions in the weight and space requirements of the propulsion system, which was significantly less powerful than that of the *Emile Bertin*. The number of boilers was reduced from six to four, thereby creating sufficient centre-line space between the second funnel and the after gun mounting for the elaborate aircraft arrangements demanded by the General Staff.

More controversial was the reduction from four to two shafts. Although shaft loading in the *contre-torpilleurs* had steadily increased to a point at which 40,000shp plus per shaft had become acceptable, there was considerable dis-

Table 1: *LIGHT CRUISERS ORDERED OR UNDER CONSTRUCTION AT THE TIME OF THE LONDON NAVAL CONFERENCE*

	Leander (UK)	*Montecuccoli(Italy)*	*Leipzig (Ger)*
Programme:	1929–31	1930–31	1927
Laid down:	1930–33	1935	1928
In service:	1933–35	1935	1931
Standard displacement (tons):	6,985	7,405	6,515
Dimensions(m):	169 × 17 × 6.2	182 × 16.6 × 6	177 × 16.2 × 5.7
Machinery:	6 boilers; 4-shaft geared steam turbines; 72,000shp = 32.5kts	6 boilers; 2-shaft geared steam turbines; 106,000shp = 37kts	6 boilers; 3-shaft combined steam/diesel; 72,400shp = 32kts
Oil fuel (tons):	1,680	1,300	1,235 + 380diesel
Armament:	4 × 2–6in (152mm), 4 × 1–4in (102mm) HA, 3 × 4–0.5in (12.7mm) AA. 2 × 4–533mm (21in) torpedo tubes, 1-2 aircraft.	4 × 2–152mm, 3 × 2–100mm HA, 4 × 2–37mm AA, 4 × 1–3.2mm AA. 2 × 2–533mm torpedo tubes, 2 aircraft.	3 × 3–150mm, 2 × 1–88mm HA, 4 × 2–37mm AA. 4 × 3–500mm torpedo tubes.
Protection (mm):			
belt:	75–90	60	20–50
deck:	30–50	20–30	20–25
turrets:	25	70	20–30
Protection weight (tons):	845	1,350	?
Complement:	570	588	615

Table 2: *CONSTRUCTION DATA*

Name	Builder	Laid down	Launched	In service
1931 Programme				
La Galissonnière	Arsenal de Brest	15 Dec 1931	18 Nov 1933	29 Oct 1936
Jean de Vienne	Arsenal de Lorient	20 Dec 1931	31 Jul 1935	9 Oct 1937
1932 Programme				
Marseillaise	A C de la Loire	23 Oct 1933	17 Jul 1935	26 Oct 1937
Georges Leygues (ex-*Châteaurenault*)	Penhoët	21 Sep 1933	24 Mar 1936	4 Dec 1937
Gloire	F C de la Gironde	13 Nov 1933	28 Sep 1935	4 Dec 1937
Montcalm	F C de la Méditerranée	15 Nov 1933	26 Oct 1935	4 Dec 1937

quiet in some quarters of the Marine Nationale regarding the wisdom of a reduction to two shafts in a major warship. The *Ingénieur Général du Génie Maritime* of the time proposed a third centre-line shaft powered by a 1000hp emergency electric motor, which in the event of action damage or breakdown could get the cruiser back home at a speed of 7kts. However, the economies in endurance (an additional 500nm at 18kts), weight (a saving of 80 tonnes) and men (a reduction in the complement by eighteen) inherent in the two-shaft solution swayed the balance and the decision to opt for two shafts was finally taken on 29 April 1931. Undoubtedly this decision was influenced by developments in the Italian Navy, which appeared content with two shafts even for its latest heavy cruisers. The British Royal Navy was a contrary influence, persisting with a conservative four-shaft solution for its own smaller 6in gun cruisers of the *Leander* class.

The propulsion plant finally adopted comprised four Indret vertical small-tube boilers with double superheaters, allied to two groups of Rateau-Bretagne or Parsons geared steam turbines. There were two boiler rooms, each housing two boilers in line, and two engine rooms in a unit arrangement. The forward machinery unit powered the starboard shaft, while the port shaft was powered by the after turbines. The superheaters were responsible for a number of problems on trials, notably in the *Jean de Vienne*, requiring a strengthening of the supports.

Each set of turbines was rated at a maximum of 55,000shp, and comprised HP, MP and LP turbines (the latter incorporating the astern drive), working in series with one (Parsons) or two (Rateau-Bretagne) cruise turbines. The cruise turbines had a maximum rating of 10,500–11,000shp and were capable of driving the ship at an economic speed of 18–19kts. The Parsons turbines proved to be more reliable than the Rateau-Bretagne turbines. The *Gloire*, which was fitted with the latter, suffered from numerous problems, sometimes at embarrassing moments, as when she suffered a complete engine breakdown while being shadowed by the heavy cruisers *Cumberland* and *Australia* off French Guinea in September 1940.

All ships of the class exceeded 35kts on the standard 9 hour speed trial, the fastest being *Gloire*, which attained 36.9kts with about 118,000shp. In service they comfortably maintained their designed speed of 31kts in formation. Endurance, although inferior to that of contemporary Royal Navy light cruisers, was adequate given their intended theatre of operations and was superior to that of their most likely opponents, the *Condottieri* of the Italian Navy.

Aviation Facilities

In the four years following the first installation of a catapult on a French cruiser (*Primauguet* in 1927), the Marine Nationale had become a firm convert to the shipborne reconnaissance aircraft. Each of the seven heavy cruisers completed from the late 1920s was fitted with either one or two catapults, for two or three floatplanes which were generally carried atop the catapults and atop the midships deckhouse, either between or abaft the twin funnels. By 1930 the interim FBA recce floatplane, which dated from the First World War, was being superseded by the purpose-built Gourdou Leseurre GL 810 HY, and plans for more advanced aircraft were on the drawing board.

Many British naval officers had strong reservations regarding aircraft on cruisers which they saw as superfluous and therefore serving only to detract from the fighting qualities of their ships, because the battle fleet would always be accompanied by aircraft carriers. The French, however, were not in the same fortunate position regarding aircraft carriers; their sole carrier, *Béarn* – adapted from a

the hull of a *Normandie* class battleship, was capable of only 21kts and could not operate with the most modern ships of the fleet. The Marine Nationale therefore adopted cruiser-borne aircraft more readily than the Royal Navy.

The aircraft arrangements on the light cruisers of the *La Galissonnière* class, which were intended to scout for the new generation of fast battleships, were the most elaborate yet. A capacious double hangar, for two seaplanes with folding wings, was fitted between the second funnel and 'X' mounting. The single catapult, powered by compressed air, was initially to have been located between the hangar and the gun mounting but was finally mounted atop the turret itself in order to clear the quarterdeck and improve launching arcs. Unusually, it was telescopic, having a length of 14.6m retracted and 22.15m fully extended; it was trainable between 55deg and 145deg to starboard, and between 215deg and 305deg to port. By 1935 it was envisaged that four aircraft would be carried: two in the hangar, one atop the catapult itself and a fourth atop the hangar. However, it was found that aircraft stowed atop the catapult were subject to vibration and blast damage, and the final aircraft complement was three.

The most interesting feature of the aircraft handling arrangements was undoubtedly the 'mat' deployed to en-

Schematic drawing of the novel aircraft handling arrangements adopted for the La Galissonnière *class ships. Two Loire 130 seaplanes could be stowed side-by-side in the hangar structure, with a third atop the hangar. The 12m by 8m canvas 'mat' was deployed through a narrow aperture in the stern to receive aircraft alighting from astern. The ship continued to steam at up to 15kts while the Loire 130 was hoisted aboard, an operation which took some 23–30min (including ramp stowage). The aircraft was then transferred to the hangar (or the hangar roof) via rails set into the quarterdeck. (Drawn by the author)*

1. Main director control tower
2. Admiral's bridge with 3m r/f
3. Transmissions/operations centre
4. Conning tower
5. Navigation Bridge
6. Transmission centre
7. Fwd 152mm magazine
8. Fwd 90mm magazine
9. Aft 90mm magazine
10. Aft 152mm magazine
11. Steering compartment
12. Aircraft mat handling room

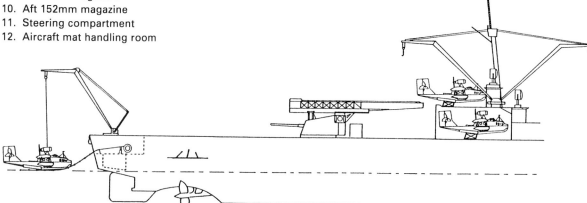

able the ships to recover aircraft while steaming at speeds of 10–15kts. This comprised a rectangular sheet of ribbed canvas measuring approximately 12m × 8m, which was deployed from a narrow aperture in the transom stern (the first application of this stern configuration to a French cruiser); the float-plane approached the mother-ship from the stern and, once safely aboard the mat was lifted by a stern crane on to the quarterdeck. The models installed were of German origin and comprised two different types, both of which were subject to modification as trials proceeded. Those fitted in the *Jean de Vienne* and the *Georges Leygues* were manufactured by Kiwull, those in the remaining four ships by Hein. The first was installed in February 1937 and extensive trials took place in the following year.

It took some 15min to deploy the mat and the recovery operation, which included hoisting the aircraft aboard and stowing the ramp, took a further 23–30min. The stern aperture was relatively close to the waterline and operations in heavy seas often resulted in the flooding of the mat hand-ling room. It also proved difficult to dry out the ramps after use, and after two years they had deteriorated to such an extent that it was decided to abandon them and to plate in the stern aperture. They were finally removed during 1941–42.

Three cranes, each with a 3300kg capacity, were provided to serve the aircraft (there were separate, smaller cranes between the funnels to handle the ships' boats). The cranes located atop the hangar, to port and starboard, served to transfer the aircraft between the quarterdeck, the catapult and the hangar roof. The stern crane was necessary to recover the floatplanes from the Kiwull/Hein mat. It took about 40min to transfer a floatplane from the hangar to the catapult. A set of quarterdeck rails linked the stern with the hangar (see drawings). Following a decision in July 1936 to install a stowage position for a fourth

The Marseillaise *leaves Toulon for Bizerta on 3 July 1939 following a minor refit. A prominent cowling has been added to the forefunnel to keep smoke clear of the main fire-control director. Note the Loire 130 seaplane parked on the hangar roof, and the double doors of the hangar. Shields have now been fitted to the 13.2mm twin Hotchkiss AA mountings abreast the bridge structure.* (Marius Bar)

aircraft atop the hangar, turntables were fitted from September 1937.

By 1935 it was envisaged that these ships would operate two of the Loire 130 recconnaissance floatplanes currently under development, together with two float fighters of an unspecified type. The first two ships completed, *La Galissonnière* and *Jean de Vienne*, embarked two GL 812 (the successor of the 810) and a single Potez 452 light spotter floatplane as an interim measure; the latter aircraft could not be catapulted. The Loire 130 began to reach service squadrons in late 1937. Its float fighter counterpart, the Loire 210, was duly ordered in March 1937 and deliveries began in late 1938. The Loire 130 proved successful but the Loire 210 experienced power/weight ratio problems throughout its chequered development, although twenty production aircraft were completed a number were lost during trials and the two squadrons were dissolved in

The Georges Leygues *leaves Toulon on 24 July 1940 for a training sortie off Porquerolles. One of her three Loire 130 seaplanes is atop the catapult, which is fully extended. On the forefunnel there is a single green band, marking her out as the first ship of the* 4e Division de Croiseurs; *the flag of Contre-Amiral Bourragué flies from the mainmast.* (Marius Bar)

November 1939. From that point onwards the cruisers operated three Loire 130, two being accommodated within and one atop the hangar. On occasions these were disembarked and operated from shore bases.

Service 1937–1942

With the exception of *La Galissonnnière*, all ships of the class entered service between October and December 1937. Both the Atlantic and the Mediterranean Squadrons were reorganised to accommodate them in November of that year. The *Marseillaise*, *Jean de Vienne* and *La Galissonnière* formed the *3e Division de Croiseurs* of the *Escadre de la Méditerranée*, while the seven heavy cruisers formed the 1st and 2nd Divisions. The *Georges Leygues*, *Montcalm* and *Gloire* formed the *4e Division de Croiseurs* of the *Escadre de l'Atlantique*, which was centred around the three elderly battleships of the *Bretagne* class and the carrier *Béarn*. The *Marseillaise* and the *Georges Leygues* were modified to accommodate an admiral's staff while fitting out and served as flagships for their respective divisions until November 1942.

With the entry into service of the new fast battleships *Dunkerque* and *Strasbourg* in 1938–39, the older battleships (redesignated the *2e Division de Ligne*) were transferred to the Mediterranean and the *4e Division de Croiseurs* were attached to their intended consorts. With the outbreak of war imminent, these ships, together with the latest *contre-torpilleurs* of the *Le Fantasque* and *Mogador* classes (formed into the 6th, 8th and 10th *Divisions de Contre-Torpilleurs*), would make up the élite *Force*

The Montcalm *leaves Toulon for exercises with the* 4e Division de Croiseurs *on 24 July 1940, shortly after the return from Algiers following Mers el-Kebir. Besides the national colours on 'B' and 'X' turrets, she retains traces of the British-style camouflage applied for the Norwegian Campaign three months earlier. The two green funnel bands mark her out as the second ship of the Division.* (Marius Bar)

de Raid based on Brest.

In the meantime their Mediterranean counterparts had become the focus of a second *Force de Raid* based on Bizerta, with the task of deterring Italian light cruisers based in Sicily from attacking French lines of communication between North Africa and Metropolitan France. Designated the *4e Escadre* in July 1939, this force comprised three divisions of *contre-torpilleurs* of the 2400 tonnes type (the 1st, 3rd and 11th DCT) led by the cruiser *Emile Bertin*, together with the *3e Division de Croiseurs* itself.

La Galissonnière *leaves Toulon in company with* Marseillaise, *the battleship* Strasbourg, *the 1st Cruiser Division and four* contre-torpilleurs *on 5 November 1940. Following exercises, this force would meet the old battleship* Provence, *escorted by five* torpilleurs *of the* Le Hardi *class, which was returning for dockyard repairs having been temporarily patched-up following the damage sustained at Mers-el-Kebir. Note the three yellow bands on the forefunnel, which mark out* La Galissonnière *as the third ship of the 3rd Cruiser Division.* (Marius Bar)

In the event none of these carefully-constituted forces was to operate in its intended rôle; at the outbreak of war the *Force de Raid* based on Brest was broken up into smaller groupings in a broad-area search for German commerce raiders, while the *3e Escadre* waited in vain for the Italians to enter the war, with the cruisers being utilised for the transport of French gold to Halifax and for the transport of French foreign legionaries from North Africa to Toulon and Marseilles.

For a brief period spanning the time of the Armistice of June 1940 the careers of the 3rd and 4th Cruiser Divisions merged when they operated together from Mediterranean North Africa, participating in the '*bataille de l'armoire à glace*', in which the major part of the French Fleet ended up pursuing its own shadow as a result of an erroneous report by a reconnaissance plane.

However, with the despatch of the 4th Division and the 10th DCT (*Le Fantasque*, *Le Malin* and *L'Audacieux*) to Dakar in September 1940 as 'Force Y' (to support the Vichy French authorities in French West Africa against the subversive efforts of the Free French), their histories again separated, with dramatic and unforeseen consequences. The 4th Cruiser Division would remain in West Africa until November 1942, when it would join forces with the victorious allies; the 3rd Division, repatriated to metropolitan France following the tragic assault by the Royal Navy on Mers-el-Kebir, would remain at Toulon until the 27th of that month, when all three ships were scuttled together with the remainder of the fleet.

Wartime Modifications

Following the outbreak of war the cruisers of the *La Galissonnière* class were fitted with a depth-charge rack conceived by a naval lieutenant called Krant. The rack held a total of twelve 35kg depth-charges, which were deployed over the stern in groups of three. There were three reloads. The depth-charges were used by the *La Galissonnière* against the Italian submarine *Dandolo* on 13 June 1940.

Further improvements in the ships' anti-submarine

The Marseillaise *on 28 July 1941. Twin 13.2mm Hotchkiss AA mountings are visible atop the hangar roof. The Loire 130 seaplane on the catapult has the distinctive red and yellow striped markings of Vichy aircraft applied to its tail surfaces. (Marius Bar)*

Table 3: *LA* GALISSONNIÈRE *CLASS: CHARACTERISTICS AS COMPLETED*

Displacement:	7600 tonnes standard, 8214 tonnes normal, 9100 tonnes full load
Dimensions:	172m pp (564ft), 179.5m oa (589ft) × 17.48m (57ft) × 5.35m (17ft 6in)
Machinery:	Four Indret boilers, 27kg/cm² (325°C); 2-shaft Parsons (Rateau in *La Galissonnière*, *Jean de Vienne*, *Gloire*) geared steam turbines, 84,000shp = 31kts (designed)
Oil fuel:	1569 tonnes; radius 7000nm at 12kts, 1600nm at 34kts
Armament:	Nine 152mm/55 Model 1930 in triple mountings Model 1930 (1850 rounds); eight 90mm/50 Model 1926 HA in twin mountings Model 1930 (2400 rounds + 200 starshell); eight 13.2mm/76 Model 1929 Hotchkiss MG in twin mountings Model 1931; four tubes for 550mm torpedoes Model 1923D in two Model 1928D twin mountings
Aircraft:	Three Loire 130 seaplanes
Protection:	belt: 105mm + 20mm torpedo bulkhead; deck: 38mm; CT: 95mm sides, 50mm roof; turrets: 100mm face, 50mm sides, 40mm rear, 45mm roof
Complement:	540 peace, 636 war

capabilities were planned in the form of G32 hydrophone detection systems, trialled by *La Galissonnière* and *Marseillaise* in January 1941. The results were poor; the equipment proved useless above 15kts and was subsequently removed from all ships.

In December 1940 it was decided to improve the AA capabilities of the ships by installing additional close-range guns. Given the proven inadequacy of the models then in service and a limited capacity for the manufacture of more advanced models, the modifications were necessarily of a piecemeal nature.

A twin 37mm/50 Model 1933 was installed atop the conning tower and two single 25mm/60 Hotchkiss Model 1939 atop the hangar in mid-1941. The three cruisers based in West Africa received further additions in the form of single Browning 13.2mm MG; *Georges Leygues* received four (two in the bridge wings, two atop the hangar), *Montcalm* three (two in the bridge wings, one in reserve)

and *Gloire* four (two on the bridge structure abaft 'B' turret, one on the after searchlight platform and a fourth in reserve).

These measures were of limited effectiveness given the inadequate number of guns, their lack of uniformity, and the primitive nature of the fire-control arrangements. The entire close-range AA armament would be removed and replaced by a powerful combination of quad 40mm Bofors and single 20mm Oerlikons when the cruisers of the 4th Division entered US Naval Dockyards for reconstruction in 1943.

Conclusion

The 7600-tonne cruisers constituted one of the Marine Nationale's most successful prewar designs and the three survivors of the Second World War went on to serve with distinction into the 1950s. Well-balanced, graceful ships combining a powerful main armament with protection sufficient to withstand 6in shellfire and a useful turn of speed, they impressed many foreign observers. They were also largely influencial in compelling the Italian Navy to aban-

The Georges Leygues *in 1949, little changed from her appearance at the end of the Second World War. She is still equipped with the quad 40mm Bofors and single Oerlikons fitted in the US during 1943 and carries aerials typical of British radar systems.* (CMP)

don the lightweight 6in gun cruisers of the early *Condottieri* types in favour of stronger, better-built ships with an adequate level of protection, culminating in the two fleet cruisers of the *Abruzzi* class, which constituted the true counterparts to the French cruisers.

Sources
Jean Moulin, *Les croiseurs de 7600 tonnes*, Marines (Bourg-en-Bresse 1993)
Official plans of *La Galissonnière*, Centre d'Archives de l'Armement
John Campbell, *Naval Weapons of World War Two*, Conway Maritime Press (London 1988)

The Montcalm *in October 1953. Note the postwar addition of a new mainmast.* (CMP)

THE LAST OF THE CHINA GUNBOATS

In 1967 the river gunboat HMS *Locust* was towed away to the shipbreakers. This vessel was not only the last of the China gunboats but had been refitted after the war to act as the third and last flagship of the Yangtse Flotilla. Records of the *Locust* and her sisters are somewhat sparse but in this account Richard N J Wright goes some way toward fleshing out the bare bones of those details to be found in works of reference.

China gunboats, or shallow-draught HM ships for service on the rivers of China, came into being at the end of the nineteenth century when six river gunboats, actually prefabricated for the Nile campaign but not ready in time, were imaginatively redirected to China. After the pioneering attempts by Mr Archibald Little to force the Yangtse gorges and open up Szechuen to trade, the two largest gunboats, *Woodcock* and *Woodlark*, became the first warships to reach Chungking. The China gunboat, for use in protecting British interests on the Yangtse and Canton's West River, had come to stay. Further small ships came out in crates over the next decade, to be reassembled at Shanghai to form the Yangtse Flotilla, their SNO's ship being the *Kinsha* (ex *Pioneer*), the one merchant-ship conversion. All were less than 200 tons, armed with 6pdr guns and drew only about 2ft of water and, apart from *Kinsha*, were named after birds. Other nations, notably France and Germany, followed suit, as trade followed the flag, and there was much trade to be found around the inland waterways of China.

In 1915 Messrs Yarrow designed and engined twelve gunboats to engage the enemy flotillas on the river Danube. These were the *Aphis* or 'Insect' class, of 645 tons, armed with 6in guns and capable of a speed of 14kts plus, they drew 4ft of water, had in-turning screws and reciprocating engines, and triple rudders which provided a high degree of manoeuvrability. In the event they were actually usefully employed elsewhere in support of the army but, from 1918, as they became available from war service, they were, with one exception, sent out to China, their 6in guns travelling separately. The *Bee* took over the role of first flagship from *Kinsha* when a Rear-Admiral Yangtse was appointed in 1920. The remainder were split between the Yangtse and the West River. The introduction of larger

ships with wireless led to an additional role for the China gunboats, that of W/T link for consulates in time of crisis.

In due course the older, smaller gunboats began to wear out and a replacement programme was instituted between the mid 1920s and mid 1930s consisting of seven gunboats in the 185–370 ton range, the earlier boats having a main armament of two 3in AA, the later ones a 3.7in howitzer which was first introduced in 1931. The smallest, *Sandpiper*, with a draught of 2ft, was custom-built to act as the Changsha guardship during the dry months.

Meanwhile, conditions in China had been slowly and relentlessly deteriorating. The weak and inefficient Manchu empire was overthrown in the revolution of 1911 but the succeeding Peking-based republican government, burdened by debt and jealousies, never succeeded in uniting the country. Competing warlords and pirates made the Yangtse a particularly hazardous place during the 1920s. The Kuomintang take-over of 1927–28 produced a Nanking-based Nationalist government. However, this was not only burdened by debt and jealousies but threatened by a growing Communist movement as well as ever-increasing Japanese aspirations, of which the Japanese take-over of Manchuria in 1931 and the Shanghai Incident of 1932 were only the start. During the 1920s and 1930s westerners, as well as the Chinese, viewed Japanese economic incursions into China with apprehension and distaste. In consequence five of the *Aphis* class were equipped for minesweeping in 1935, with an eye to the future defence of Hong Kong.

Replacements

After twenty years of almost continuous service some of the *Aphis* class began to show their age. The flagship *Bee*

The Scorpion *on trials in June–July 1938. The flat-fronted bridge distinguishes her from the* Dragonfly *class. From this angle no anti-aircraft armament is evident but note the hinged bullet-proof flaps to the upper bridge.* (IWM, HU69)

had lost her 6in guns to additional deckhouse accommodation which was required for her job; she was the first on the list for replacement. The Staff Requirements, worked out in 1935, no longer appear to exist, but *Scorpion*, of the 'second Insect Class' as presented in the 1936 Naval Estimates, was of approximately the same tonnage as her flagship predecessor. She had the same flat bottom, in-turning twin screws in tunnels, tunnel flaps for use in light draught, triple rudders and bullet-proof plating to the bridge and gun batteries. What differed, apart from the built-in staff accommodation, was the shorter hull, deeper draught, greater freeboard and higher speed, giving vastly improved seakeeping qualities. Obviously, the staff requirements, were for a more general-purpose craft than a specialised river gunboat. The generally quoted armament of two 4in LA, one 3.7in howitzer, two 3pdr saluting guns and ten machine guns was suitably all-purpose for a Yangtse flagship; except that on the face of it little attention appears to have been paid to AA defence. In fact, two quadruple 0.5in mountings were fitted specifically for that purpose. In addition, she was fitted for minesweeping.

The Naval Estimates for 1937, 1938 and 1939 contained five more replacements for the 'first Insect Class', *Dragonfly*, *Grasshopper*, *Mosquito*, *Locust* and *Bee*, all slightly smaller versions of *Scorpion* without the staff accommodation. With hindsight it is possible to venture one small criticism about the continuing use of insect names for the class: they became inextricably entangled with the First World War ships and as a result in post-war literature these modern craft are frequently referred to as 'aged', 'old', 'antiquated' or 'ancient'.

The Sino-Japanese War on the Yangtse

The *Scorpion* was ordered in November 1936 from Samuel White at Cowes. Less than a year later, in July 1937, the Japanese precipitated the Sino-Japanese war in North China, and in the following month invaded the Shanghai area. The Chinese immediately blocked the Yangtse near Kiangyin (in the lower reaches of the river), sinking as blockships twelve obsolete warships and about thirty merchant ships, interspersed with nearly two-hundred stone-ladened junks. Two more defensive booms, the Mud Fort, just downriver from Nanking, and the Matang, just downriver from Kiukiang, plus minefields and forts, completed the static defences; and paralysed traffic. China lost its few major warships in the defence of the Kiangyin barrier. In December, the Japanese broke through and in ten days had taken Nanking. The USS *Panay* was bombed and sunk at this point while escorting a convoy of American merchant ships with nowhere to go: and *Ladybird* was shot-up at Wuhu, the approximate limit of Japan's gains in 1937.

The Japanese advance restarted in June 1938, with the Matang boom defences and Kiukiang falling the following month. The events at Munich in September produced a new tension on the Yangtse; the British gunboats being cheek-by-jowl with Japanese warships and not knowing, should war result with Germany, whether the Japanese would come in on the other side. In the event the Japanese read appeasement into the Munich Agreement, and accordingly went ahead with the, previously diplomatically postponed, invasion of Canton, close to Hong Kong. Hankow, taken the same month, virtually completed Japan's conquest of the lower Yangtse. Now the Japanese, in addition to their territorial gains, had three vital strangleholds on the river in the form of the Chinese-built booms and barriers at Matang, Mud Fort and Kiangyin and, from mid-1938, started restricting passage on the Yangtse. This virtually cut-out western trade in favour of Japanese and the western gunboats could only move from port to port in convoy escorted by a Japanese warship. However, at least the majority of them could move, unlike *Sandpiper* which was marooned at her post at Changsha by a river full of Chinese-laid mines.

The Scorpion

The *Scorpion* was launched in December 1937. Her sea trials took place in June 1938, when a speed of just under 17kts was achieved. One of the main points arising from the trials was a requirement to be able to hinge the 4in and battery deck bullet-proof plating inboard. Finally, resplendent in the colour scheme of white with a buff funnel for service in hot climates, she was ready to join her station. The contract had stipulated delivery at Hong Kong. In due course *The Times* of 28 December 1938 reported:

> In making the passage from Cowes to Hong-kong [sic] under her own steam, the river gunboat *Scorpion*, which has just become flagship of the Rear-Admiral and Senior Naval Officer in the Yangtse, has given further testimony to the soundness of the construction of these sturdy little vessels.
>
> The *Scorpion*, of 670 tons displacement, was built by J Samuel White and Co of Cowes, and the contract called for her delivery at Hong-kong, where she was taken over by the Navy on November 10. Earlier vessels of the river gunboat class have been shipped in sections and reconstructed in China, or in very rare cases have been towed out after being strengthened for the passage by the fitting of extra bulkheads. The *Scorpion* made the voyage of 10,000 nautical miles under her own power.
>
> The vessel was taken over at Cowes by FP Barney and Co Ltd, ship and insurance brokers, who specialise in the delivery of vessels abroad, and left on September 2. She was under the command of Captain W G T Tingey, a master mariner who had been with the firm for several years, and had a crew of 17 all told. Calls were made at Gibraltar, Malta, Port Said, Aden, Bombay, Colombo, Singapore and Miri. The ship would have proceeded in the ordinary way from Singapore to Hong-kong, but because of an impending north-east monsoon the Captain elected to sail via Miri and the Palawan Passage. She

> reached Hong-kong on November 6. When it is remembered that the ship's draught of water is only 3ft in light condition and 6ft when loaded with bunker oil, with a mean draft of 5ft 2in at standard displacement, her arrival without the slightest damage at her destination reflects great credit on all concerned in the undertaking.

In fact, it will be seen that some at least of *Scorpion*'s bullet-proof plating had been shipped separately.

The *Scorpion*'s deck logs from November 1938 provide further information (the written content of deck logs tends to vary from ship to ship, as will become obvious). She was commissioned on 8 November 1938 (curiously enough at variance with the date of 10 November given by the *Times* and the *Navy List*) by the ship's company of HMS *Bee*, under a temporary commanding officer. Her particulars are given as 780 tons full load displacement, 4500hp and with an armament of two 4in and one 3.7in. Data for fuel consumption ranges from 2.2 tons per hour at a full speed of 16.9kts, to 0.53 tons per hour at an economical speed of 9kts. The ship was under dockyard control in refit until 14 December when she carried out sea trials, fuelled, and was formally accepted after the Commodore's inspection. Draught marks after fuelling were given as 5ft 8in forward and 6ft 3in aft. She sailed the following day for Shanghai, arriving 22 December. On 25 December the flag of Rear Admiral Yangtse was hoisted and his Chief of Staff, a Captain RN, assumed command.

The *Scorpion* was at Shanghai for a month, mostly in dockyard hands, during which time something, presumably the armour plating, was added forward as, when she sailed for trials in the Yangtse estuary, she was trimmed

The sting in Scorpion's *tail. A quad 0.5in machine gun mounting is fitted on the quarterdeck, in an octagonal guntub with hinged flaps. The black canvas-covered top of the other 0.5in mounting is just visible on the upper bridge, forward of the rangefinder and searchlight. The saluting guns are abreast the funnel and the 3.7in howitzer is just abaft the carley floats on the shelter deck. The object forward of the mizzenmast is the triple wheel for emergency hand steering. (Cowes Maritime Museum)*

The Dragonfly *on trials March 1939. The 0.5in mountings are uncovered, the forward one just visible aft of the two officers on the upper bridge.* (NMM, N11920)

on even keel. Her programme included engine and turning trials, 4in sub-calibre and full calibre firings, 0.5in MG and Lewis gun firings and minesweeping trials. At the end of the month, now fully operational, she visited Nanking and Wuhu. As flagship she was usually based at Shanghai but she visited Nanking and Wuhu again in March, and Wuhu, Kuikiang and Hankow in April. The Japanese escorts were ever present; for instance, in April *Scorpion*, *Cricket* and *Aphis* sailed together from Hankow for the Matang boom, led by IJN *Hayabusa*. In May *Scorpion* did a spell as 'Below [Kiangyin] Barrier Guardship' and in June visited Nanking for His Majesty the King's birthday. Maximum recorded draught marks while in the Yangtse were 6ft 6in forward and 6ft 8in aft.

Grasshopper *at speed on the Yangtse in July 1939. The bullet-proof flaps on the forecastle are hinged inboard. Note the rounded bridge front.* (NMM, G7079)

The Dragonfly *Class*

Meanwhile *Dragonfly* and *Grasshopper*, under construction by Thornycroft, were coming forward. The specification had stipulated inward turning propellers, but this had been amended to the more normal outward-turning propellers following the discovery that the original specification had been copied from an earlier reciprocating-engined ship (possibly *Sandpiper*) and the requirements of its machinery. Both ships were delivered by the contractors to Hong Kong, *Dragonfly* arriving on 18 May 1939 and *Grasshopper* (who with the P&O liner *Canton* had assisted with a shipwreck off Ceylon while on passage) a week later. *Dragonfly* was commissioned on 6 June 1939, with a Commander in command to relieve *Mantis*; *Grasshopper* commissioned a week later, with a Lieutenant Commander in command, to relieve *Cricket*. As a result of these new arrivals the old gunboats *Bee* and *Mantis* went to shipbreakers at Shanghai but *Cricket* was saved from disposal by the war. The deck logs add some further technical information; *Grasshopper*'s quotes a displacement (full load) of 690 tons and a figure for full speed of 17.8kts at 1.687 tons of fuel per hour obtained on trials; while *Dragonfly*'s has a displacement of 585 tons (standard) and an unambiguous statement of the armament as two 4in MkV, one 3.7in MkII and two

0.5in quad MG mountings.

The *Dragonfly* sailed for Shanghai via Foochow on 14 June, then spent a week in Shanghai during which period hands were employed 'putting up bullet-proof plating on the forecastle'. In July she was 'Below Barrier Guardship' for a spell and tried out her minesweeping gear. Following this she was at Nanking for a month.

The *Grasshopper* sailed for Shanghai on 23 June. A spot of bother at Foochow caused her to be sent back there for a day but after that she spent a week in dockyard hands at Shanghai, during which time 'hands placed fore bullet-proof screen'. 'Below Barrier Guardship' duties followed, when a deep load draught of 6ft 6in forward and 6ft 5in aft was entered in the deck log. In the latter half of August she joined her sistership at Nanking. The *Scorpion* made a final inspection trip to Hankow at this time and thus, on 18 August 1939, all three new gunboats were together briefly upriver at Nanking. Three weeks later war broke out in Europe.

Withdrawal from China

The situation on the Yangtse was in any event less than satisfactory, as the Japanese had eliminated all but their own trade and, with the outbreak of war, were hinting virtuously that the warships of the belligerents should be withdrawn to avoid 'incidents'. The gunboats were reduced to a static role of safeguarding lives and property at ports, as well as serving as W/T links for consulates. As the larger gunboats could be better employed elsewhere and some of the smaller gunboats were actually trapped up rivers, the Admiralty quickly made the decision to disband the flotilla to release the ships for other purposes. In the main, the West River ships were withdrawn to the defence of Hong Kong, while the remainder of the *Aphis* class migrated west to play havoc with the enemy in the Mediterranean. Those smaller ships marooned up rivers were eventually turned over to the Chinese; and the new arrivals were sent straight off to reinforce Singapore.

The *Dragonfly* and *Grasshopper* sailed from Shanghai for the last time on 3 October 1939, bound for Hong Kong. The *Dragonfly*'s deck log takes up the tale quite succinctly. At Hong Kong all Chinese personnel were discharged. The ships sailed south via Saigon on 12 October, arriving at the Singapore Naval Base on the 19th. The following day *Dragonfly* embarked 10cwt of grey paint and the next few days were spent repainting ship. Early in November the Commander-in-Command left for a new appointment, the First Lieutenant taking over as commanding officer, and Malay ratings began joining for service or training. At this time the 3.7in howitzer was dropped from the armament list. From 18 November *Dragonfly* began her new role, patrolling at the eastern entrance to the Johore Strait – the only entrance to the Naval Base – where a boom, minefields and loops had been laid; as a general rule she worked two days on, two days off, alternating with *Grasshopper*. On 23 November she disembarked all 3.7in ammunition and embarked depth-charges in lieu. The after 0.5in quadruple mounting was removed from the ship at the end of December, thereafter her armament being quoted as two 4in MkV and one 0.5in quad. A Lieutenant RNR assumed command in February 1940.

The appointment of Rear Admiral Yangtse ceased early in 1940. The *Scorpion* accordingly sailed from Shanghai in January 1940 for the last time, arriving in Singapore three weeks later. In February she was taken in hand for conversion to an A/S vessel 'dependent on receipt of gear'. (She had another refit in September 1940 when asdic may have been installed. *Dragonfly* was quoted as having asdic fitted

The Locust *in February 1943. Note the 0.303in turret in the bridge wing, shielded quad 0.5in mounting just below the rangefinder, quad pom-pom abaft the funnel, emergency triple steering wheel abaft that, single 20mm Oerlikon on the shelter deck and the depth-charge throwers and 20mm Oerlikon aft. Bullet-proof plating has been removed from around the 4in mountings and shelter deck but is retained on the lower and upper bridge. (IWM, FL1677)*

by 1942). During 1940 she spent some months as a guard-ship at Penang, a task which may have continued into 1941.

By the end of 1941 HMS *Peterel* was the only British gunboat left on the lower Yangtse, having been sacrificed to provide a W/T link at Shanghai.[1] She was to be the first British war loss after Pearl Harbor.

Singapore

Following the Japanese invasion of Malaya in December 1941, Penang became an early casualty and the enemy's control of the air ahead of the battle front would have tied the three new gunboats to patrol duties close to the guns of Singapore. Nevertheless when the army ran into trouble at Batu Pahat, some 80 miles up the west coast, *Dragonfly* provided covering fire on the night 25–26 January and, together with *Scorpion* and other craft, carried out a major evacuation of encircled troops a few nights later. In due course *Grasshopper* oversaw the final withdrawal of troops across the Johore Strait on to Singapore Island, after which the Johore Strait and the Naval Base would have been untenable for shipping.

The final days before the fall of Singapore on 15 February 1942 are confused. Evacuation of surplus key personnel began from Keppel Harbour in the south of the island. The *Scorpion* had been damaged by air attack on the 9th and sailed to Batavia on the following day with fifty-eight passengers, mostly communications personnel. However, she was having mechanical problems and obviously suffered engine breakdowns, as late on the 13th she was encountered by Japanese naval forces in the Berhala Strait, only 150 miles south of Singapore, and was sunk with heavy loss of life.

The *Dragonfly* and *Grasshopper* survived a day longer. They were sailed south from Keppel Harbour early on the 14th in company with other, smaller ships, all laden with passengers, but were soon spotted by Japanese aircraft and later attacked. Despite fire from the 4in, multiple 0.5in, Lewis and Bren guns they were quickly overwhelmed. About midday *Dragonfly* took three hits and capsized, while *Grasshopper* was beached in flames.

The experiences of America's five remaining modern *Panay* type gunboats were curiously similar. One was turned over to the Chinese at Chungking, one was lost to the Japanese while acting as a W/T link at Shanghai and three were sunk in defence of Corregidor.

Summary of the Armament and Armour

The design for the main armament followed the pattern established for the contemporary *Halcyon* class mine-sweepers. Two old single 4in Mk V on CPII 30deg mountings of Great War vintage were to be fitted initially; and plans of the *Dragonfly* show them thus with half shields and loading trays. The gun supports were to be made suitable for 4in HA replacements, one or two of which could be fitted later if required, or as available. Nonetheless, the single 4in MkV LA actually fitted had more suitable full length shields and no loading trays.

The main armament was controlled by a 3m rangefinder with a TS (transmitting station) positioned immediately below it. A 24in searchlight was fitted forward of the rangefinder (it was planned to fit a rangefinder director). The 3.7in MkII howitzer was a modified army model on a pedestal mounting.

The two quadruple 0.5in MkIII mountings were fitted in positions which are not entirely obvious from photographs. The after position was on the quarterdeck in an octagonal gun-tub with hinged bullet-proof flaps. The latter provided protection against snipers, and presumably allowed one gun to be used singly, firing over the top. The other position was on the upper bridge, designated on the plans as the 'machine gun platform', forward of the rangefinder and the searchlight, and was enclosed and practically entirely hidden from view by the hinged bullet-proof flaps which made up the plating at the forward end of the upper bridge.

The *Dragonfly* and *Grasshopper* were equipped with eight Lewis guns, primarily for surface fire through the gunports provided, two on the bridge wings, and eight on the battery deck. A mortar was to be carried if trials were successful. Bullet-proof plating was fitted to the wheel-house (non-magnetic in the vicinity of the compass; with shutters with sighting slots over the ports) and aft, at the bridge level, to the W/T office, sickbay and TS. It was also fitted to the 0.5in positions, battery deck and 4in gun positions. Two davits (port and starboard) were fitted on the quarterdeck for a MkV minesweeping outfit, comprising two single leg sweeps.

At Singapore the 3.7in howitzers were removed and no doubt added to the fortress arsenal and depth-charges were installed. The after 0.5in mounting was also removed, either because of the addition of depth-charges and racks or because of a shortage of close-range AA mountings elsewhere. (It may be no coincidence that when the monitor HMS *Terror* emerged from her refit at Singapore in January 1940 and sailed for home waters, she had had two 0.5in quadruple mountings added to augment her close range armaments)[2]. Likewise *Scorpion*'s saluting 3pdrs were probably appropriated to help arm Singapore's rapidly growing fleet of auxiliaries. Otherwise the only additions to the ships' fixed gun armament are likely to have been Lewis guns in the 3.7in and after 0.5in positions. On the other hand it seems likely from various references that all three ships had asdic fitted sometime during 1940, although no provision had been made for this in the original plans.

The Last Three Ships

The next two replacement gunboats, *Mosquito* and *Locust*, were announced in the 1938 Naval Estimates and the confusingly repeat-named *Bee* the following year. The latter was cancelled in 1940.

The *Mosquito* and *Locust* were laid down at Yarrows at the end of 1938, being launched the following year, after the declaration of war. Although the contract had called for them to be delivered to Hong Kong, other plans had obviously to be made for their employment after the break-up of the Yangtse Flotilla. Alterations and additions during building included the fitting of depth-charges, and the re-

Table 1: *CONSTRUCTION DATA*

Ship	Estimates	Builder	Laid down	Launched	Commissioned	Completed
Scorpion	1936	White	–**	20 Dec 1937	8 Nov 1938*	14 Dec 1938
Dragonfly	1937	Thornycroft	29 Dec 1937	8 Dec 1938	6 June 1939	5 June 1939
Grasshopper	1937	Thornycroft	29 Dec 1937	19 Jan 1939	14 June 1939	13 June 1939
Locust	1938	Yarrow	Nov 1938	28 Sep 1939	?***	May 1940
Mosquito	1938	Yarrow	5 Dec 1938	14 Nov 1939	15 Apr 1940	19 Apr 1940
Bee	1939	White	Cancelled	–	–	–

* Dates differ; ** Ordered Nov 1936; ***CO appointed 9 Apr 1940.

Table 2: *SHIP DATA*

	Scorpion	Dragonfly class
Standard displacement:	670 tons	585 tons
Deep displacement:	780 tons	690 tons*
Length oa:	208ft 9in	196ft 6in
Length oa, ex rudders:	–	190ft 6in
Beam:	34ft 8in	33ft
Draught, standard:	5ft 2in	5ft
Draught, deep (fresh water):	6ft	6ft
Draught (Yangtse – actual):	6ft 7in	6ft 6in
Machinery:	2 shaft, Parsons geared turbines, 2 Admiralty 3-drum boilers, 4500shp	2 shaft, Parsons geared turbines, 2 Admiralty 3-drum boilers, 3800shp
Speed:	17kts	17.5kts
Oil capacity:	130 tons? (see text)	90 tons
Fuel consumption:	2.2 tons/hour at 16.9kts; 0.53 tons/hour at 9kts	1.7 tons/hour at 17.75kts
Endurance:	?	c900 miles at 17.5kts
Complement:	93	74

* Yarrow quotes 750 tons max for *Mosquito* and *Locust*

moval of the bullet-proof plating, except around the bridge. Asdic may have been installed at this stage. The 3.7in howitzer was omitted, a quadruple 2pdr being planned in lieu.

The *Mosquito* was the first to be completed, in April 1940, and was promptly sailed to the south coast. A collision on leaving Greenock caused a fortnight's delay at Devonport for docking and repairs, with the result that she did not arrive at Sheerness until mid May, when she was 'allocated temporarily for anti-MTB defence of the convoy anchorage'. A fortnight later she sailed to assist in the evacuation of Dunkirk, where her shallow draught was an obvious asset. However, on 1 June she was hit by a bomb whilst off Dunkirk, set afire, abandoned, and sunk in shallow water. Two days later her stranded hulk was blown-up with two depth-charges by a demolition team from her sister ship. Her operational life had been just six weeks but, during her brief spell at Dunkirk, *Mosquito* had succeeded in evacuating over 1000 troops.

The *Locust* sailed from Greenock on 19 May 1940, arriving in the Channel just in time for Dunkirk. Apart from towing the damaged sloop *Bideford* back to Dover, she evacuated over 2000 troops and was present off Dunkirk for the final evacuation of French troops during the night 3–4 June (during which period she prudently took the opportunity of destroying the wreck of *Mosquito*). She arrived at Sheerness on 4 June for damage repairs 'and the fitting of pom-poms'.

For the next two years *Locust* was based at Chatham as a 'gunboat'. The addition of a quadruple pom-pom made her a formidable little warship, and she appears to have continued *Mosquito*'s role of guardship to the convoy anchorages. In October 1940 a mine exploded immediately astern of her, disabling her engines, with the result she was in hand for repairs at Tilbury for three months. Nevertheless, apart from being attacked by enemy aircraft in April 1941 her life seems to have been comparatively uneventful until the middle of 1942, when she was reassigned to Combined Operations at Portsmouth.

The *Locust*, together with a group of Free French *chasseurs*, carried the RM commando contingent on the ill-fated Dieppe raid in August 1942, where the intention had been to land the commandos in the harbour. She suffered damage from gunfire, which was repaired at Portsmouth and where she remained based. Some of the ships assembled for the Dieppe raid were kept as the nucleus for a permanent Combined Operations force known as Force 'J', with shore headquarters at Cowes, IOW; and *Locust*, now listed as a 'Special Services Vessel', was actually the mobile Headquarters Ship for the south coast. This role she continued until November 1943 when she went into refit at Portsmouth, being relieved by the much larger LSH(L) HMS *Hilary*. It is possible that during this refit *Locust* was equipped with her navigational radar Type 970 or 971 as, just before D-day, she was certainly fitted with the IFF interrogator and transponder Types 253 and 242.

Force 'J' went on to form the assault group for Juno

The Locust, *in March 1946, after being refitted for the Far East. A quad pom-pom has replaced the after 4in gun. The hinged bullet-proof flaps on the lower and upper bridge still remain and the remainder of the bullet-proof plating has been restored. The line of eight oval Lewis gunports is just visible in the shelter deck plating (left from the triple wheel), with a further two in the bridge wing plating. Awning ridge ropes make up most of the rigging.* Locust's *draught marks now show her to be drawing about 7ft. (IWM, FL1682)*

Beach on D-day. The *Locust*, now designated a LSH(S), went north to Inverness on completion of her refit in February 1944 where the 9th Infantry Brigade was beginning training. In due course she became the flagship of the assault force S1, 9th Infantry Brigade, at Sword Beach on 6 June 1944, and later was once again damaged by shellfire. On 28 June she was redeployed as HQ ship of the Support Squadron Eastern Flank, a floating barrier of some eighty small ships set up to stop penetration of the invasion anchorages by German suicide craft. She was relieved of this duty early in August 1944.

Postwar Service

For the next 12 months *Locust* was retained in support of forces operating from Harwich and Sheerness, even though desired in the Mediterranean. 'Locust is at present employed as HQ ship for Coastal and M/S operations on the Army's flank in northwest Europe, and will be made available for use by SBNO Danube when released from present duty'. As the war in Europe slowly drew to its close other plans were made. 'Locust is to be brought forward and taken in hand in preparation for sailing to Singapore. Ship is required to leave... by mid February 1946'. In July 1945

approval was given for her to reduce to a nucleus complement, and she went into refit at Sheerness for reconversion to a river gunboat; as it was intended that she should become the flagship for the reinstated Rear Admiral Yangtse.

In March 1946 *Locust* completed her long refit, emerging painted in the traditional China Station scheme of white with buff funnel. Preparations were put in hand to sail her on the long passage to Hong Kong (CO – Lt Cdr NJ Parker, DSC, RN). The newly installed bullet-proof plating was to be removed and sent by cargo ship, as had happened with her predecessors in 1938; *Locust* herself was to sail independently but would be escorted from Aden by an RFA. In the event the US Government decreed that there were to be no warships based permanently on the Yangtse, with the result that at the last moment *Locust's* sailing was cancelled and she was paid-off into reserve instead. (Similarly the last three operational *Aphis* class, after a hectic Mediterranean war, had been taken out of well-earned care and maintenance at Taranto and sailed for the Far East in January 1946; only to be placed back in reserve on arrival in Singapore late in April 1946).

Without a role, no further operational employment could be found for a redundant China gunboat, despite her long refit. In 1951 *Locust* was sent to Bristol for the Severn RNVR, where she spent her last 16 years of life as a static drill ship, the sole survivor of the *Dragonfly* class gunboats. She was broken up locally in 1968.

Summary of the Armament

Yarrow records show that *Mosquito* and *Locust* were completed with an intended armament of two 4in MkV, one quadruple 2pdr MkVII, two quadruple 0.5in and four Lewis 0.303in. However, the pom-poms may not have been available at the time of the ships' rushed completion, as *Locust* had hers fitted at Sheerness, after Dunkirk. (This operation would have involved the removal of the mizzenmast, which would otherwise have effectively masked a large area of the field of fire.) It is not clear whether *Mosquito* had been equipped with her pom-pom before she was sunk.

Furthermore, the 0.5in may have been resited during building to more convenient positions either side of the bridge, thus leaving the quarterdeck, and the upper bridge in particular, unencumbered. (The illustration above *Locust* in the wartime editions of *Jane's Fighting Ships* was in fact of *Dragonfly* running trials.)

Over the next couple of years *Locust* had her armament augmented with two Boulton and Paul quadruple 0.303in turrets, and three single 20mm Oerlikons. In February 1943 she is shown with the 0.5in positioned either side of the bridge, two 0.303in B and P turrets on the bridge wings, two single 20mm on the battery deck, one 20mm on the quarterdeck, two DCTs and depth-charges. It seems likely (from a rather indistinct long-range photograph) that she was so fitted for the Dieppe Raid.

By March 1946, after her long refit, the quadruple pom-pom had been moved aft to replace the after 4in, enabling the mizzenmast to be restepped for the W/T aerials; and the bullet-proof plating had been installed. At some stage the two 20mm from the battery deck had been repositioned on the bridge wings, replacing the 0.5in and 0.303in, and the depth-charges and DCTs were removed.

Particulars

Construction dates are listed in Table 1, while ship's data is tabulated in Table 2. There are some anomalies. Thornycroft and Yarrow quote a length for the *Dragonfly* class of 190ft, and 190ft 6in overall, respectively, which is at variance with the 196ft 6in or 197ft overall given in reference books. The explanation is that the shipbuilders' figures were for hull length, disregarding the protruding rudders, and these figures have been included in that light. The tonnages of the *Dragonfly* class (585 tons standard and 690 tons full load) appear correct, given 90 tons oil fuel, $9\frac{1}{2}$ tons of diesel oil and $6\frac{1}{2}$ tons of reserve feed water. However, the stated tonnages for *Scorpion* (670 tons standard and 780 tons full load) do not permit of the 130 tons of fuel oil given in reference books. Either her fuel and reserve feed water capacity was approximately the same as that of the *Dragonfly* class (eg 90 tons of oil fuel, 10 tons of diesel and 8 tons of reserve feed water) or her deep load displacement was greater than that quoted.

Notes
[1] Not for the last time on the Yangtse, however. Even after the war the W/T communications at the British Embassy at Nanking were poor. This was one of the reasons why a destroyer or frigate guardship was kept at Nanking, and which in turn led to 'The Amethyst Incident'.
[2] See *Big Gun Monitors*, Ian Buxton (UK 1978) p140.

Primary Sources
Ship Movement Registers, King Alfred Library, HM Dockyard Portsmouth.

ADM187 – Pink Lists, Public Record Office, Kew.
ADM53 – Ships' Logs 1938–Feb 1940, Public Record Office, Kew.
ADM179-336 – Composition and location of Force J, Public Record Office, Kew.
Admiralty drawings and specifications for *Dragonfly* class, part specification for *Scorpion*, National Maritime Museum, Greenwich.
Residual records for *Scorpion*, Cowes Maritime Museum.
Records of particulars of *Mosquito* and *Locust*, Yarrow Shipbuilders.
Correspondence with Lt Commander N J Parker, DSC, RN.
K C Barnaby, *100 Years of Specialized Shipbuilding and Engineering*, John I Thornycroft Centenary 1964, Hutchinson (London, 1964).

Secondary Sources
Jane's Fighting Ships, various editions, Sampson Low (London).
Conway's All the World's Fighting Ships, 1922-1946, Conway Maritime Press (London, 1980).
H T Lenton and J J Colledge, *Warships of World War II*, Ian Allan (London, 1964).
M H Brice, *The Royal Navy and the Sino-Japanese Incident, 1937-41*, Ian Allan (London, 1973).
A Cecil Hampshire, *Armed with Stings*, William Kimber (London, 1958).
Gregory Haines, *Gunboats on the Great River*, Macdonald and Janes (London, 1976).
Kemp Tolley, *Yangtze Patrol*, Naval Institute Press (Annapolis, 1971).
China at War (1939), The China Information Publishing Co (China, 1939).
John Campbell, *Naval Weapons of World War II*, Conway Maritime Press (London, 1985).
Adrian Stewart, *The Underrated Enemy*, Kimber (London, 1987).
Richard Gough, *The Escape from Singapore*, Kimber (London, 1987).
Geoffrey Brooke, *Singapore's Dunkirk*, Leo Cooper (London, 1989).
Peter C Smith, *Hold the Narrow Sea*, Moorland (Derbyshire, 1984).
R Plummer, *Ships that saved an Army*, Patrick Stephens (Northants, 1990).
A D Divine, *Dunkirk*, Faber and Faber (London, 1945).
Charles Messenger, *The Commandos, 1940-46*, Kimber (London, 1985).
Ronald Atkin, *Dieppe 1942*, Macmillan (London, 1980).
D G Chandler and J L Collins (editors), *The D-Day Encyclopedia*, Helcon (New York, 1994).
Invasion Europe, HMSO (London, 1994).
Commander K Edwards, *Operation Neptune*, Collins (London, 1946).
British Naval Vessels Lost at Sea, 1939-1945, HMSO (London, 1947).
John Lambert and Al Ross, *Allied Coastal Forces of World War II*, Conway Maritime Press (London, 1990).
Malcolm H Murfitt, *Hostage on the Yangtze*, (USA,1991).
HMS Locust, RNVR News Sheet.

GERMAN AUXILIARIES AT WAR 1939–45

Minesweepers, submarine chasers and patrol boats

During the Second World War the German Kriegsmarine employed well over one thousand auxiliary minesweepers (M), submarine chasers (UJ) and patrol boats (V)[1] a considerable number of which were lost to mines and air attack. Pierre Hervieux describes the surface and anti-submarine actions in which these vessels were involved, with particular emphasis on those actions that are less well-known.

The first auxiliary to fall victim to a British submarine was the *V209* which was torpedoed and sunk by HMS/M *Sturgeon* in the Heligoland Bight on 20 November 1939. A few weeks later, on 7 January 1940, during anti-submarine operations in the Heligoland Bight, HMS/M *Undine* fired a torpedo at the auxiliary minesweeper *M1204*, which missed. In company with *M1201* and *M1207*, *M1204* counterattacked with depth-charges, heavily damaging the submarine which was forced to surface. The *Undine* was then scuttled by her crew, who were rescued by their intended victim – *M1204*.

Reports on the loss of the patrol boat *V1507* are contradictory, there being two possibilities; firstly that she was torpedoed and sunk by HMS/S *Triton* off the southern coast of Norway in April 1940 and secondly that she was sunk by a mine off Frederikshavn in the summer of 1940. In either case she was salved in the autumn of 1940 and recommissioned but was again sunk, by a mine near Cap d'Antifer, on 12 June 1944.

Norway

The submarine chasers, *UJ125*, *UJ126* and *UJ128* depth-charged and sank HMS/M *Sterlet* in the Skagerrak on 18 April 1940 and, in the same month, during the operations in Norway, the *M1701* and *M1702* were sunk by HMS/M *Snapper*. Also in the Skagerrak, on 23 April, there was a brief action between the French destroyers *L'Indomptable*, *Le Malin* and *Le Triomphant* and the patrol boats *V702* and *V709*; the former patrol boat being damaged. Three

days previously, at Herøysund, the Norwegian torpedo boat *Stegg* exploded after being hit by gunfire from the *V221* and on 5 May a second Norwegian torpedo boat, the *Snøgg*, was captured by the submarine decoy ship *Schiff 18* (ex trawler *Alteland*).

On 4 May HMS/M *Seal* was damaged by a mine in the Kattegat which resulted in her being unable to submerge and, on the following day, she surrendered to German patrol boats after an Arado 196 seaplane had taken her Captain prisoner. HMS/M *Shark* found herself in a similar position two months later, on 5 July – unable to submerge following hits from aircraft bombs, she was overtaken off Skudenes by the minesweepers *M1803*, *M1806* and *M1807* and captured. However, in this case, following scuttling measures taken by the crew, she sank while in tow on 6 July. Two more submarines fell victim to auxiliaries in 1940, the British *H49* – sunk by the submarine chasers *UJ116* and *UJ118* near Terschelling on 18 October – and the Dutch *O22* – depth-charged by the *UJ177* and *UJ1104* off the south west coast of Norway on 8 November.

The British raid on the Lofoten Islands on 3 March 1941, which involved two light cruisers, five destroyers and two assault ships, resulted, among other things, in the sinking of seven merchant ships and three small fishing vessels. More importantly, the British captured an 'Enigma' type cypher machine from the patrol boat *NN04 Krebs* – before she was also sunk.

HMS/M *Trident* torpedoed and sank the submarine chasers *UJ1201* on 27 September and *UJ1213* on 3 November, the former while escorting a convoy off northern Norway and the latter in Svaerholthavet.

On 1 October 1941 the old Norwegian torpedo boat *Draug* departed Scapa Flow with the Norwegian *MTB56* in tow. The MTB was released 120 nautical miles off the Norwegian coast and made her way to Korsfjord where she attacked a convoy consisting of the Norwegian tanker *Borgny* (3015 tons), *M1101* and *V5505*. After sinking the *Borgny* with a torpedo, causing the loss of fourteen of the tanker's crew, she returned to the *Draug* and was towed safely back to Scapa.

During a second British raid on the Lofotens in December, the patrol boat *V5904* was sunk in Vestfjord on the 26th by the destroyer *Ashanti* while, on the following day, in Maalöy Sound, the destroyers *Onslow* and *Oribi* sank the *V5108* and drove four freighters ashore and, near Vaagsöy, the destroyers *Offa* and *Chiddingfold* sank *V5102* and the German freighter *Anhalt* (5870 tons).

Break Out

At 2000 on 31 March 1942 ten Norwegian merchant ships departed from the neutral port of Göteborg in Sweden in an attempt to break through the Kattegat and Skagerrak and sail to England. These ships, few of which were to succeed, were the tankers *B P Newton* (10,324 tons), *Buccaneer* (6222 tons), *Rigmar* (6305 tons), *Storsten* (5343 tons) and *Lind* (461 tons), the cargo vessels *Dicto* (5263 tons), *Lionel* (5653 tons), *Charente* (1282 tons) and *Gudvang* (1470 tons), and the whale factory ship *Skytteren* (12,358 tons). The Royal Navy sent the destroyers *Faulknor*, *Escapade*, *Eskimo*, *Wallace*, *Vanity* and *Valorous* to meet the vessels as they emerged into the North Sea and assist their escape. The

A German flak-ship in Western France, on which three shielded 20mm AA guns are visible. In the left foreground is a twin 7mm AA machine gun mounting. (ECPA)

first vessel to be intercepted was *Dicto*, which was found at 0254 on 1 April by *V1613*, south west of Hallo. Although she managed to escape her pursuer undamaged, she was forced to return to Gothenborg.

Next the *Buccaneer* and *Lionel* were intercepted, at 0717 north east of Skagen, by *V1609*. After being hit by gunfire the *Buccaneer* was abandoned but scuttling charges, detonated at 0759, produced no immediate effect and she was finally sunk by gunfire from the V-boat at 1150. The *Lionel* managed to escape unscathed but was forced back into Swedish waters and returned to Gothenburg. The next vessel to be caught was *Skytteren*, intercepted at 0730 by the *V1612*, four miles west of Maseskär. She detonated her scuttling charges at 0749, after making an unsuccessful attempt to ram her opponent, and sank at 1250.

No further interceptions were made until the afternoon, when *Charente* was approached by *V1613* and *V1604* as she entered the Skagerrak at 1325. Ten minutes after being sighted her scuttling charges were detonated and she sank at 1441. The *Storsten* was sighted by aircraft south of Kristiansand at 1556 and attacked without result but, at 1613, she reported that she had been torpedoed – in fact she had struck a mine and sank shortly afterwards. The *Gudvang* was intercepted and sunk by the *V908* at 2130 when about 50 miles south of Kristiansand. The *Rigmor* survived until the 2 April when she was attacked by aircraft of Luftflotte 5 and sunk by an aerial torpedo at 1850, when

about 60 miles southwest of Egersund. The *B P Newton* was also attacked by aircraft of Luftflotte 5, in the afternoon of 1 April, but suffered no damage or casualties. She was later met by the *Valorous* which escorted her to Methil where she arrived on 2 April. The *Lind* also broke through, being found by the *Escapade* at 2215 about 120 miles east of the Scottish coast and similarly escorted to Methil.

Convoy Defence

Off Cap Gris Nez during the night of 17–18 January 1942, two British coastal forces units – MTBs *38, 44* and *47* and

A camouflaged V-boat armed with two 20mm AA guns

MGBs *324, 328* and *330* – intercepted a convoy proceeding from Dunkirk to Boulogne. The convoy consisted of the motor coasters *Heinrich, Rheinland, St Antonius* and *Dorothea Weber*, and the siebel ferry *No110* in tow of the tug *B126S*, escorted by the *V1806* and *V1808*. During the following action *MTB47* was hit in the engine room by gunfire from the *V1806* and disabled, the crew (ten of whom were later picked up by the *Dorothea Weber*) abandoned ship after setting their vessel on fire.

In Seine Bay on 19 June 1942, the escort destroyer

The patrol boat Bisam *in Norwegian waters. She is probably an ex-Norwegian ship – the guns she carries are not of German origin.* (ECPA)

A former tug off western France, armed with an ex-French 75mm gun forward and a 20mm gun aft.

A former whaler, operating as a UJ or V-boat, off western France. (ECPA)

Albrighton, with *SGB7* and *SGB8*, attacked a convoy proceeding from Le Havre to Cherbourg and consisting of the motor ship *Turquoise* (810 tons) escorted by the *RA1*, *RA2* (ex French *CH19* and *CH20* respectively) and *M3800*. The *Turquoise* was torpedoed and sunk by *SGB7* and the *M3800* was heavily damaged. However, gunfire from *M3800* disabled *SGB7* which had to be scuttled – the crew were picked up by *RA2*. A somewhat larger convoy, consisting of the tug *Océanie*, *V1520*, *RA2*, *M3800*, *M3820*, *M3821*, *M3824* (in tow of *M3800*) and *M3827*, proceeding in the opposite direction was attacked off Barfleur on the night of 6–7 August by MTBs *232*, *237* and *241*. The only casualty was *MTB237* which, having penetrated the screen and fired her torpedoes without success, was heavily hit and set on fire forward and in her petrol compartment. With the fires out of control her crew was taken off by *MTB241* which then depth-charged the burning wreck

A UJ sub-chaser, operating west of France, armed with a 40mm Bofors forward and two non-German 20mm AA guns – note the depth-charges aft. (ECPA)

A newly completed M-boat, her armament still incomplete and probably running trials off western France. (ECPA)

but, although completely gutted, this failed to sink. It is probable that the gunfire which damaged the MTB came from *V1520* but it is also possible that further damage was inflicted by *Océanie*.

A few days later, during the night of 17–18 August, two groups of British MTBs (*24, 43* and *204*; *38, 218* and *219*) made a similar assault on a convoy consisting of the steamer *Fidelitas* (5700 tons) escorted by the R-boat depot ships *Brommy* and *Von Der Gröben*, and the V-boats *1501, 1505, 1506, 1511* and *1809*, proceeding from Boulogne to Dunkirk. Again the only casualty was British – *MTB43* which was hit by gunfire and had to be abandoned, heavily on fire, north of Gravelines.

Operation 'Jubilee', the British raid on Dieppe, which took place on 19 August 1942, involved 252 vessels, including the landing craft, among them eight escort destroyers and a large number of coastal forces craft. At 0448 the eastern landing group – twenty-three landing craft and their escorts – encountered a small German convoy of five coasters escorted by *UJ1404, UJ1411* and *M4014*. The landing craft were carrying No3 Commando for an assault on Berneval and Belleville. A brisk exchange of fire took place resulting in considerable losses among the commando force and the sinking of several British small craft, while *SGB5* was set on fire and the *UJ1404* was sunk. As a result of this action the British were unable to subdue the German coast defence batteries six miles east of Dieppe which contributed to the failure of the operation.

During the night of 30 September–1 October 1942, two British units, consisting of MTBs *230* and *234*, and MGBs *18, 21, 82* and *86*, operating from HMS *Mantis*, were ordered to sweep along a suspected convoy route between Texel and Terschelling. Shortly after midnight the force was illuminated by starshell from convoy No348, en route from Cuxhaven to the Hook of Holland. The convoy consisted of the Swedish steamers *Oswin* (1325 tons), *Born* (1215 tons), *Thule* (2325 tons) and *Narvik* (4250 tons), the Danish steamers *Skotsberg* (1450 tons), *Viborg* (2027 tons) and *Elisabeth Mærsk* (1893 tons), the German steamer *Monsun* (6590 tons) and an escort of the V-boats *1313, 2003, 2007, 2008* and *2011*. In the course of the following action, *MGB18* was heavily damaged by gunfire from the *V2003* and *V2007* and, out of control, collided with *MGB82*. Her mess deck and wheel house flooded, and down by the head with her propellers out of the water, *MGB18* was unable to move. *MTB234* went alongside the stricken vessel and took off the entire crew, without casualties, and the boat was then set on fire by her commanding officer. All the British vessels were hit during the action but only *MGB18* was fatally damaged; the commander of *MGB86* was killed and the convoy lost the *Thule* and *V2003* to torpedoes.

A British unit consisting of the MGBs *60, 77, 78* and *81* was patrolling off the Dutch coast in the early hours of 3 October 1942 when *MGB77* sighted what was thought to be four enemy trawlers but were, in fact, the V-boats *1330, 1339, 1340* and *1341*. In the action which followed contact with *MTB78* was lost at about 0230 and a search was made in gathering fog, without result. The vessel had actually received a number of hits, probably from *V1340*, had lost two of her propellers and had been abandoned by her crew and blown up. Apart from her commander, who had been killed, the crew were rescued by the German vessels.

During the night of 27–28 February 1943, off the Hook of Holland, an attack on a convoy by the British MTBs *77, 79, 81* and *111* was frustrated by defensive fire from the escorting vessels *V1304, V1305, V1309, V1313, V1314*, a Type 40 minesweeper and a flak-ship; *MGB79* was sunk. During the night of 10–11 March, the Free French MTBs *94* and *96* attacked a German convoy off Morlaix, Brittany, and sank *M4620* (ex *M1201*, ex German *Harvestehude*).

Soviet Assaults

On 20 August 1941, near the Kolka lighthouse in the Baltic, a skirmish took place between the *M3137* and four Soviet MTBs, one of which, the *TKA82*, sank on the following day. On 12 September the MTBs *TKA11* and *TKA12* attacked a German convoy, escorted by the *NT05 Togo* (ex Norwegian minesweeper *Otra*), off Petsamofjord in the Arctic. This attack, the first to be made by Soviet MTBs on a convoy, was unsuccessful. On the 22nd of the following month two Soviet MTBs were in action with the *V103* and *V314* and two days later, off Orengrund Island, the *V308* was torpedoed and sunk by two Soviet MTBs, one of which, the *TKA12*, was sunk by a second V-boat.

In the Baltic, on 21 August 1942, the *UJ1216* was torpedoed and sunk by a Soviet MTB while guarding a mine barrage (earlier in the month two Soviet submarines had been lost to mines in this same area – the *M97* on the Seeigel barrage and the *Shch405* on an old Soviet barrage).

Not fully equipped and probably running trials, this is a UJ boat, again off western France. (ECPA)

In an attempt to repeat the success three MTBs attacked the *UJ1206* and *UJ1207* on 1 September but without result.

On 20 January 1943, the Soviet destroyers *Baku* and *Razumny* carried out a sortie against the northern coast of Norway and had a brief, indecisive engagement off Syltefjord with the minelayer *Skagerrak*, on her way to lay a mine barrage in company with the *UJ1104*, *UJ1105* and two Type 40 minesweepers. The speed of the German ships was, at best, half that of the attacking destroyers, they were out-gunned and there was no shelter nearby but, according to the German War Diaries, the Soviet ships fired a few salvoes at extreme range and then retired – no German ship was hit.

On 12 September 1943, the *UJ1217* was sunk off Pylterfjord by the Soviet submarine *K1*.

On 12 December 1943, in Varangerfjord, five Soviet

The UJ1403 *which, on 3 December 1941, was attacked by the Soviet submarine* K3 *while escorting the German steamer* Altkirch – *see* Warship 40. (Drüppel)

MTBs attacked a German convoy, first with torpedoes, which missed, then with gunfire. Three of the MTBs were sunk (one of which was *TKA14*) and five crew members were rescued. In the same area and on the same day another group of Soviet MTBs sank the *V6106*.

A close-up of the fore end of a flak ship somewhere in western France, showing a single 37mm gun forward with a shielded single 20mm abaft it. (ECPA)

A flak ship armed with a quad 20mm (Vierling) forward, a single 20mm forward of the mast, three 13mm or 7.9mm machine gun mountings amidships and in the bridge wings (abreast the funnel), a single 20mm on the after superstructure and a 37mm mounting in the stern.

On 10 April 1944, during an operation against a German convoy off Kirkenes, Soviet MTBs sank the German collier *Stör* (665 tons) but *TKA212* (ex US *PT275*) was sunk by gunfire from the escort. Soviet MTBs attacked another convoy near the entrance to Petsamofjord on 22 April but launched their torpedoes at too great a range and all the ships turned away unharmed. On 8 May, in Varangerfjord, the *V6107* and *V6108*, while under attack by three Soviet MTBs, sank the *TKA217* (ex US *PT291*) and damaged another.

On 15 July 1944, south of Busse Sound in the Arctic, a German convoy was attacked by the Soviet MTBs *TKA12*, *TKA13*, *TKA238*, *TKA239*, *TKA240*, *TKA241*, *TKA242* and *TKA243*, which had been brought to the scene by two Yak9 reconnaissance aircraft. The escort managed to defeat the attacks – *UJ1211* sinking the *TKA239* (ex *PT412*) and taking two of her crew prisoner, although her attempt to take the burning boat in tow failed. On 19 August, off Persfjord, *V6102* and the German freighter *Colmar* (3946 tons) were sunk by Soviet TKA motor torpedo boats and two TKAs were sunk by two Type-35 minesweepers.

Operations in the Mediterranean

In the Aegean on 16 November 1942, between the islands of Andros and Euboea the *UJ2101* and *UJ2102* were escorting a convoy from Piraeus to the Dardanelles when *UJ2102* depth-charged and sank the Greek submarine *Triton*, which had initially been located by the destroyer *Hermes*; the submarine's crew was taken prisoner.

A UJ or V-boat under way. (ECPA)

In the western Mediterranean the UJ boats had become quite active by early 1943. These vessels belonged to the 22nd Flotilla of sub-chasers and began their operations with a success when, at 1050 on 27 February, six miles southeast of Capri, the *UJ2210* obtained an underwater contact while escorting a convoy. At 1114, she dropped fifteen depth-charges and, at 1135, a further fifteen which brought a great quantity of air and oil to the surface. She regained contact at 1200 and attacked with a further fifteen charge pattern which, again, brought air and oil to the surface. Finally, at 1225, she obtained contact once more and ten minutes later, for the fourth and last time, dropped another fifteen depth charges. This resulted in the appearance of a large air bubble, about 60m long and 3m wide, which was followed by a large oil slick. It is probable that the submarine attacked was the British *Tigris*, which had left Malta on 18 February to operate in the area south of the Gulf of Naples but had been ordered to leave this area on 6 March and sail for Algiers.

During February and March 1943, *UJ2209*, *UJ2210* and *UJ2220* escorted supply convoys to Tunis and Bizerta in support of the operations of the Afrika Korps and the Italian Army. Similar duties were carried out during late March and April by the UJ-boats *2202*, *2203*, *2204*, *2205*, *2207*, *2208* and *2210* which escorted several supply convoys to Tunisia. On 29 March the *UJ2201* and *UJ2202* were torpedoed and sunk by HMS/M *Unrivalled* in the Bay of Picarenzi. On the following day, east of the Tyrrhenian Sea, the *UJ2203*, together with a second sub-chaser and a torpedo boat, was escorting an Italian merchantman bound for Bizerta when, at 0735 an underwater contact was obtained. She dropped ten depth-charges and a large oil slick appeared on the surface. The *UJ2203* explored the area for about 15min but was unable to regain contact so rejoined the convoy. Her target had been HMS/M *Tribune* which, although damaged, succeeded in reaching Algiers.

On 14 April 1943 the *UJ2206* was carrying out an anti-submarine sweep between Genoa and San Remo when, at 0725, a submarine suddenly surfaced about 3500m away. For about ten minutes the two vessels exchanged an intense fire – the submarine using her 102mm gun and the sub-chaser her three 37mm weapons. The *UJ2206* suc-

ceeded in hitting the submarine with a few rounds and, after firing about forty shells, the enemy vessel ceased fire and submerged. Almost at once an underwater contact was obtained and *UJ2206* managed to maintain this almost continuously until 1221. During a little under five hours she dropped eleven depth-charge patterns (eighty-one charges in all) and observed several signs which led her to believe the submarine had been damaged. Her target was HMS/M *Trident* which was having a particularly unlucky patrol. From 3 to 12 April the submarine had launched sixteen torpedoes against five targets and all had missed and then came the incident with *UJ2206*. In fact her commander had surfaced in the belief that the German vessel was a small tanker – she survived, with only slight damage, and reached Algiers on 18 April. On 15 May there was some compensation for the British when the *UJ2213* was torpedoed and sunk by HMS/M *Sickle* in the western Mediterranean.

Early in September 1943 the Greek submarine *Katsonis* sailed on a special mission to land agents on the coast of Euboea in the Aegean. On completion of this mission she was to carry out a patrol off Nicaria but, shortly after 2000 on 14 September, she was sighted on the surface in the northern entrance of the Euboea Channel by *UJ2101*. The sub-chaser opened fire and heavily damaged the submarine which was then rammed and sunk as she lay stopped in the water. The *UJ2101* picked up fourteen survivors, including the captain and wireless operator – the only British members of what was otherwise an entirely Greek crew.

A few days later at 0017 on 18 September, off Stampalia, the *UJ2104* was escorting the Italian cargo ships *Pluto* (3830 tons) and *Paula* (3754 tons) when they were attacked by the British destroyers *Eclipse* and *Faulknor* and the Greek destroyer *Vasilissa Olga*. The merchant vessels were sunk with gunfire and torpedoes and the *UJ2104*, heavily damaged, was run ashore – where her crew were later taken prisoner. On the 7th of the following month, again near Stampalia, a convoy consisting of the German freighter *Olympus* (852 tons), seven ferry barges and the

UJ2111 was completely destroyed by a British force comprising the cruisers *Penelope* and *Sirius* and the destroyers *Faulknor* and *Fury* – 1027 survivors were picked up by German ships and aircraft.

During the night of 16–17 October, near Kos in the Aegean, the British escort destroyer *Hursley* and the Greek destroyer *Miaoulis* sank the *UJ2109* and the Italian freighter *Trapani* (1855 tons).

In the Gulf of Genoa, on 3 October, HMS/M *Usurper* was sunk by the *UJ2208* and, on 17 October, near Calino, HMS/M *Trooper* was sunk by the German Q-ship *GA45*. However, *GA45* was sunk in turn by the British destroyers *Penn* and *Pathfinder* on 7 November (*Trooper* had left Beirut on 26 September for a patrol west of the Dodecanese and, later, west of Leros). Off Leghorn, during the night of 2/3 November, the US motor torpedo boats *PT207* and *PT211* sank the *UJ2206* (ex French trawler *Saint Martin Legasse*). On 29 December 1943, the UJ2208 sank a second submarine, the French *Protée*, off Toulon

On 22 and 28 December respectively, the French submarine *Casabianca* torpedoed and sank the *UJ6076* and damaged the German cargo ship *Chisone* (6168 tons). On the latter occasion the *Casabianca* was counter attacked by the *UJ2220* which dropped three depth-charge patterns, all of which detonated close to the submarine but, despite damage, the boat escaped. A few months later the *Casabianca* was again engaged with a sub-chaser, when she came across the *UJ6079* proceeding independently from Toulon to Nice on 6 June 1944. The submarine opened fire with her 3.9in and 20mm Oerlikon guns at 0140 but the German vessel initially thought this was coming from shore batteries and only realised her mistake when she could elicit no response to her recognition signals. Consequently, it was ten minutes before she returned fire and even then she thought she was under attack by a group of four MTBs and a gun vessel. In the course of the action both vessels claimed hits and reported their respective enemy as

A UJ or V-boat armed with a single 88mm and three single 20mm guns. (ECPA)

stopped and on fire. The *Casabianca* had been closing her target as the action progressed and with the range down to 1200m decided to make a torpedo attack, firing her forward tubes at 0156 and diving two minutes later. Only three of the four torpedoes left their tubes but shortly *Casabianca* heard an explosion, followed by another about five minutes later. Periscope observation apparently revealed an increase in the smoke coming from the target and, after a second, the vessel was no longer visible. However, all the torpedoes had in fact missed, *UJ6079* having taken avoiding action, although she actually saw the track of only one torpedo as it passed astern. The sub-chaser had opened fire again with her entire armament from immediately after the torpedo attack until 0205 when she retired to the west. Ten minutes later *Casabianca* surfaced, concluded that her target had been damaged by gunfire and probably sunk by torpedo and similarly retired from the scene. In fact, *UJ6079* had suffered no casualties and had received only superficial damage – one Oerlikon hit to the hull and some splinter damage to the after deck and bridge. The poor observations of the crew of *UJ6079* can probably be put down to inexperience, this was their first action and they had only received a very brief period of training; in addition conditions close to the shore were misty with visibility down to 1.5 miles.

British MTBs sank the patrol boats *GR02* and *GR94* near Kos in April 1944 and on the 27th of that month, south of Toulon, *UJ6075* (ex French trawler *Clairvoyant*) was torpedoed and sunk by HMS/M *Untiring*. In the Ligurian Sea, on 24 May, a group of American PT boats, *PT202*, *PT213* and *PT218*, attacked a German naval force, sinking the *UJ2223* and badly damaging *UJ2222*, which later reached Leghorn. The PT boats were rewarded with another success during the night of 27/28 May, when they torpedoed and sank the *UJ2210* (ex French trawler *Marcella*) off La Spezia (the *UJ2210* had sunk HMS/M *Tigris* on 27 February 1943). On 10 June, the *UJ6078* (ex French armed trawler *La Havraise*) was torpedoed and sunk by HMS/M *Untiring* and, in the Aegean, on 23 June, *UJ2106* was torpedoed and sunk by the HMS/M *Unsparing*.

A former whaler operating as a UJ boat off Brittany – note the depth charge armament at the stern. (ECPA)

In the Gulf of Genoa, during the night of 13–14 September 1944, *UJ2216* (ex-French yacht *Eros*, formerly owned by the banker Rothschild) and a number of lighters were sunk by the American *PT559* and the British *MTB376* and *MTB422*. Meanwhile, in the Aegean, British naval forces were engaged in interfering with German evacuation movements and, on 15 September, the light cruiser *Royalist* and the destroyer *Teazer* sank the gunboat *Erpel* (ex-*KT26*) and the submarine-chaser *UJ2171* (ex-*Heidelberg*, ex-*KT29*) off Cape Spatha. On 30 September a German convoy, consisting of the German freighters *Zar Ferdinand* (1994 tons) and *Berta* (1810 tons), escorted by the torpedo boat *TA18* and the harbour patrol boats *GK92* and *GD97* sailed from Piraeus for Salonika. On 2 October, the *Zar Ferdinand* was torpedoed and sunk by the French submarine *Curie* (ex-HMS *Vox*) and, on the following day, the *Berta* by HMS/M *Unswerving*. The last German ships in the Aegean moved from Piraeus to Salonika during 6–13 October, and on the 7th the *UJ2101*, the harbour patrol boat *GK32* and the torpedo boat *TA37* were sunk in action with the British destroyers *Termagant* and *Tuscan* southwest of Kassandra-Huk.

During the night of 20–21 November, off Sestri Levante, south-east of Genoa, two British and one American (*PT308*) MTBs attacked a German convoy and sank the sub-chaser *UJ2207* (ex-French trawler *Cap Nord*).

Biscay Offensive

Early in 1943 a number of American submarines were deployed in the Bay of Biscay but had limited success due to problems with their torpedoes. On 4 January the USS *Shad* torpedoed and sank the *M4242* (ex French *Odet II*) and, on 25 January, torpedoed and damaged the iron ore ship *Nordfels* (1214 tons). The latter vessel was indirectly connected with another attack by an American submarine, the USS *Blackfish*, a few weeks later:

On the afternoon of 19 February two patrol boats, *V408* and *V414*, were proceeding from St Jean-de-Luz to a position off Bilbao, where they were to rendezvous with the iron-ore ship *Nordfels*, which they were to escort to the Gironde. At 17.55, in 43.29N/02.57W, torpedo tracks were sighted by *V414*, who was leading, and the alarm raised, whereupon both boats proceeded to take avoiding action. *V414* succeeded in making two torpedoes miss astern, but *V408*, although also missed astern, was struck aft by a second, and she sank in seconds. *V414* immediately altered towards the direction from which the torpedoes had come, and, on reaching the estimated position of the submarine, dropped six depth-charges before stopping to initiate a hydrophone hunt. No contact was obtained. *V414* continued dropping depth-charges for the next ten minutes, until her stock of twelve depth-charges was exhausted, when she returned to pick up *V408*'s survivors.[2]

On 5 July 1944, Allied destroyers began Operation 'Dredger', an assault on the German escort vessels which operated at the U-boat assembly points, to the west and south of Brest. During the night, the Canadian destroyers *Qu'Appelle*, *Saskatchewan*, *Skeena* and *Restigouche* attacked three patrol boats and *V715* was sunk following a courageous defence in which the first two destroyers received many small-calibre hits. The survivors were rescued by two S-Boats. Ten days later, during the night of the 14–15 July, the destroyers *Tartar*, HMCS *Haida* and the Polish *Blyskawica* made a sortie into the area of the Île de Groix, near Lorient, and sank the submarine-chasers *UJ1420* and *UJ1421*.

On 6 August, north of the Île D'Yeu, near St Nazaire, a British force, consisting of the light cruiser *Bellona*, the destroyers *Ashanti*, *Tartar*, *Haida* and HMCS *Iroquois* sank the patrol boat *V414*, two type-40 minesweepers and a coastal launch – *Haida* was slightly damaged. On 12 August, the Canadian destroyers *Assiniboine*, *Qu'Appelle*, *Skeena*, *Restigouche* and the escort destroyer *Albrighton* sank a force of three armed trawlers, south of Brest and, during the night of 22–23 August, the cruiser *Mauritius* and the destroyers *Ursa* and *Iroquois*, sank the patrol boats *V702*, *V717*, *V720*, *V729* and *V730* off Audierne, Brittany.

Battle in the Narrow Seas

In an engagement off the Somme Estuary during the night of 17/18 April 1943, the British MGBs *38* and *39* sank the *V1409* and, during the night of 27–28 April, the British escort destroyers *Goathland* and *Albrighton* sank the *UJ1402* and a 5100 ton steamer when they attacked a German convoy 60nm NNE of Ushant. On 1 May a naval engagement took place off Terschelling, between the British *MTB624*, *MTB630*, *MTB632*, *MGB605*, *MGB606*, *MGB610* and *MGB612* and four boats of the 12th Patrol Flotilla in which the *V1241* was sunk.

Near Dunkirk, during the night of 28–29 May, British coastal forces, were covering a mining operation by *MTB219*, *MTB221* and motor launches, when they became engaged with four German patrol boats near the West Dyck Bank. The *MGB110* was sunk by gunfire but five of her crew were rescued by the Germans; of the remaining British MGBs – *108*, *118* and *116* – only the latter was undamaged and an attack on the German vessels by the MTBs of the escort – *607*, *628*, *629* and *632* – failed.

During the night of 26–27 September 1943, a convoy proceeding from Le Havre to Dunkirk was attacked by Allied coastal forces off Fécamp and Berck-sur-Mer. The British MGBs *108*, *117* and *118* engaged the convoy's

The former Norwegian torpedo boat Snøgg *in German service after capture by* Schiff 18. *She was renamed* Zack *by the Germans and classified as patrol boat* V5504 *(later* V5502*) and was lost when she ran aground, north of Bergen, on 6 September 1943. (ECPA)*

escort of patrol boats and motor minesweepers from the seaward side, while the Dutch MTBs *202*, *204* and *231* attacked from the landward side. The *V1501* and the German freighters *Madali* (3019 tons) and *Jungingen* (800 tons) were sunk.

On 15 October 1943, off the Dutch coast, five British MTBs of the 11th Flotilla (*348*, *349*, *352*, *356* and *360*) were engaged in a sweep from the Hook to Ijmuiden and back when, at 2338, an enemy patrol which appeared to consist of two large trawlers and two armed coasters was sighted on a southerly course. In fact, the vessels sighted were *V1303*, *V1304*, *V1307*, the gun ferry *AF42* and the *M3406*, which were providing an anti-MTB screen for minesweepers of the 34th Flotilla. Deciding to decline action, the MTBs turned away to the north west but they were sighted by the German vessels and challenged. Shortly after midnight the Germans opened fire, first with starshell and then their main and secondary armaments. *MTB356*, the senior officer's boat, was hit in the stern at which point the senior officer reversed his earlier decision and decided to counter attack. While his boat was increasing speed to carry out this manoeuvre, *MTB356* received a direct hit in the starboard engine room from an 88mm shell, which blew a large hole in the vessel's side, destroyed most of the starboard engine, blew out the bulkhead to the petrol compartment and burst open at least one of her petrol tanks. With her engine controls jammed the boat quickly lost way and began to settle by the stern; she was soon abandoned and destroyed with scuttling charges, her crew being taken off by *MTB349*. Both *AF42* and *V1304*, the only two German vessels firing 88mm shell, claimed the MTB but it is impossible to be certain which of the two fired the fatal round.

Seven British MTBs of the 55th and 50th Flotillas (*606*, *617*, *621*, *630*, *632*, *650*, *671*) were dispatched on the night of 3/4 November for a special operation off the Dutch coast followed by an anti-shipping sweep northward along the convoy route to the Hook. On arrival off the Dutch coast at 2104, radar was switched on and, almost immediately, the unit was challenged and fired upon. By chance the MTBs had fallen in with two S-boats which, after a brief exchange of fire, disengaged at 2117 and headed toward the shore under cover of a smoke-screen. The British boats hauled

The auxiliary minesweeper M3800 *which disabled* SGB7 *with gunfire on 19 June 1942.* (Bilddienst)

out to seaward and, at about 2200, after obtaining several confused radar echoes, decided to abandon the special operation. At this point *MTB617*, the senior officer's boat, parted company with the unit, command being transferred to *MTB606* (which was not fitted with torpedo tubes), and the unit then set course for the Hook. At 2304, when about three miles north of the Hook, large shapes were sighted ahead and the MTBs deployed for a gun action. One minute later they illuminated their targets – the German buoy layer *Main*, screened by *V1401*, *V1419* and the flak ship *FJ23* – and opened fire. A heavy gun fight ensued and within a few minutes *MTB606* was hit by an 88mm shell from the *V1401* which wrecked the bridge, temporarily knocking-out all the bridge personnel and wounding the senior officer, the commander and another member of the crew. A second 88mm shell, again from *V1401*, hit the boat aft bringing the two port engines to a stop, starting a fire, jamming the steering gear and leaving her to career round in a tight circle. The second in line, *MTB621*, led the unit past *MTB606* and, in so doing, was also crippled when she received the full force of the German fire. The rest of the unit was led away to the east by *MTB630* and, at 2322, she altered course and began searching for *MTB606* which she soon found. Coming alongside she passed a tow line to the stricken boat but just after this another burst of fire hit *MTB606*, set her after petrol compartment alight and holed her on the water-line. It was decided to abandon her, demolition charges were placed and, about ten minutes after *MTB630* had cast off, *MTB606* blew up.

In the North Sea, on 15 February 1944, an engagement between three German auxiliary minesweepers and British coastal forces, resulted in damage to MTBs *444* and *455* and the loss of *M3411* which sank after a collision while trying to evade the enemy. Two days later, south of Jersey, MTBs *415* and *431* were engaged with the escort vessels

of a German convoy and damaged the *M4618* which later reached Jersey.

In Northern Waters

Off Askøy, near Bergen, on 28 July 1943, the Norwegian *MTB345*, after an engagement with German forces, was captured by the *V5301* and subsequently towed to Askevold by the motor minesweeper *RA202*. Another capture took place on 2 November when the *V1606* intercepted the British blockade runner *Master Standfast* (ex *MGB508*) close to the Swedish coast. The British vessel had just left Sweden on her return journey to Britain and it seems that the German patrol boat deceived her into the belief that *V1606* was Swedish. *Master Standfast* was found in Kiel after the war, having been renamed *RA11*.

On 1 November 1944, during attacks on German shipping in Sognefjord, Norway, the Norwegian *MTB709* and *MTB712* torpedoed and sank *V5525* and *V5531*. During the night of 12–13 November, a British naval force, consisting of the cruisers *Kent* and *Bellona*, the destroyers *Myngs*, *Verulam*, *Zambesi* and HMCS *Algonquin*, attacked the German convoy KS357 off Listerfjord, southeast of Egersund and sank two of its four freighters – the German *Greif* (996 tons) and *Cornouailles* (3324 tons). Of the six escort vessels, the submarine-chasers *UJ1221*, *UJ1223*, *UJ1713* and one type 40 minesweeper were also sunk, while a second minesweeper, damaged during the action, was sunk by aircraft the following day. Also on this day, 13 November, the Norwegian *MTB627* and *MTB688* attacked a German convoy in the southern exit of Krakhelle Sound in the Sognefjord. They fired four torpedoes, which were avoided by the two steamers in the convoy, but slightly damaged the escorting *UJ1430* before being driven off by *UJ1432* and *V1512*. Two other Norwegian MTBs, *623* and *715*, made a similarly unsuccessful attack, off Sognefjord, on the night of 27/28 November against a patrol boat force consisting of *V5514*, *V5527* and a motor minesweeper. On the same night, a second pair of MTBs, *627* and *717*, attacked a German convoy escorted by *V5303*, *V5312* and one motor minesweeper. The MTBs torpedoed the German freighter *Welheim* (5455 tons), which had to be beached, but they were in turn hit by gunfire from the escort. On 8 December, off Korsfjord, the Norwegian *MTB653* and *MTB717* attacked a convoy consisting of two steamers escorted by the patrol boats *V5113* and *V5114*, and sank the German freighter *Ditmar Koel* (670 tons). Early on 26 December, near Fröysjoen, MTBs *627* and *717* attacked another convoy, consisting of two steamers escorted by *V5102* and *V5114*, and sank the German tanker *Buvi*. On 16 January 1945, off Trondheim, the Norwegian submarine *Utsira* (ex-HMS *Variance*) torpedoed and sank the patrol boat *V6408*.

The Black Sea

In the Black Sea on 28 August 1943 an unidentified submarine was depth-charged by the *UJ2304* and *UJ2306*, following the sinking of the German rail ferry *Hainburg* off Cape Lukall. The submarine, probably the *M111*, was seriously damaged but escaped. Soviet submarines were to become particularly active in the last three months of the year and the UJ boats retaliated in kind. On 16 October, off Cape Tarkhankut, the sub-chasers *UJ2302*, *UJ2303*, *UJ2306* and *Schiff 19* claimed to have sunk a submarine but it seems likely that this was *Shch205* which survived her depth-charging; however, on 4 November, off the Tendra Peninsula, *Schiff 19* sank the Soviet submarine *A3*. On 25 November, west of the Crimea, the Soviet submarine *L6* torpedoed and sank the German tanker *Wolga-Don* (965 tons) which was being escorted by *UJ2301*, *UJ2309*, the Romanian gunboats *Stihi* and *Dumitrescu*, and the German motor minesweeper *R205*. On 4 December, off Yevpatoria, *UJ102* reported depth-charging and sinking a submarine but this was in fact *Shch201* which, although damaged, escaped (Western publications have recorded the Soviet submarine *D4* as being sunk on this day but it is probable that she was actually sunk by a mine early in December 1943).

On 23 December, following an unsuccessful attack on a steamer, the Soviet submarine *M117* was depth-charged

The M1201 *which, together with the* M1204 *and* M1207, *sank* HMS/M *Undine on 6 January 1940.* (Bilddienst)

by *UJ103* off the Crimea but escaped. There was greater success for *UJ103* on 16 February 1944, when she sank the submarine *Shch216* 18 miles west of Cape Tarkhankut after the latter had successfully attacked convoys on 9 and 10 February.

From 12 April to 13 May 1944, there was heavy German and Romanian transport traffic between the besieged fortress of Sevastopol and Constanza, which soon attracted the attention of Soviet naval forces. On 18 April the submarine *L6* attempted to attack the disabled Romanian steamer *Alba Julia* (5700 tons), which had been set on fire by bomber aircraft, but in so doing was sunk, north of Constanza, by *UJ104*. On 22 April the *Shch201* attacked *UJ103* but was herself attacked by her intended target being straddled by depth-charges before escaping. Soviet MTBs made a number of torpedo attacks on German traffic between 16 and 27 April and in the last succeeded in torpedoing *UJ104*; however, the vessel survived and was brought safely into Sevastopol. In further attacks, during 3–4 May, the wreck of *UJ104*, together with *UJ2304*, a tug and seven lighters, was destroyed. On 9 May, while escorting the German tanker *Dresden*, *UJ103* was hit by a heavy shell from Soviet land artillery which put her engine out of action; she had to be scuttled after her crew was taken off.

By late 1944 the naval fighting in the Black Sea was coming to an end. However there was still one short, but indecisive, engagement between *TKA221*, *TKA223*, *TKA227* and *TKA233* (all ex US PT boats) and two UJ submarine-chasers, east of Constanza, on 22 August.

Actions off the Channel Islands

On 8 May 1944, the Free French MTBs *91*, *92*, *227* and *239* attacked a German convoy heading toward the Channel Islands and, between Jersey and Guernsey, sank the steamer *Bizon* (750 tons) – *MTB227* was damaged by patrol boats of the 2nd Flotilla. Off St Helier, during the night of 26–27 June, *M4620* was lost in an attack by four British MTBs and, during the following night, *M4611* sank off Jersey after an engagement at very short range with the destroyers *Eskimo* and *Huron*. The *Eskimo* was, however, hit by two 88mm shells from the *V213*, which penetrated No1 and No3 boiler rooms and left her steaming in circles without power to her switchboard, steering, guns, radar and searchlights. Her speed was reduced to 6kts, at which rate she crawled back to Plymouth, while *V213* escaped to Jersey to celebrate her victory, persuaded that *Eskimo* had

The patrol boat V1507 *(ex-*Rauvi*), probably taken during the first two months of 1940 – the circumstances of her loss are not clear.* (Bilddienst)

been sunk. Also off the Channel Islands, a few days later, during the night of 7–8 July, the destroyers *Tartar* and *Huron* attacked boats of the 46th Minesweeper Flotilla and sank *M4601* and *M4605*.

In the area of the Channel Islands, the British *MTB676*, *MTB677*, *MTB716*, *MTB717* and *MTB720*, had engagements on 5–6 August with auxiliary minesweepers of the 46th Flotilla and auxiliary patrol boats of the 2nd Flotilla. Two days later, during the night of 8–9 August, a second assault was made on these flotillas by the American destroyer escort *Maloy* and the motor torpedo boats *PT500*, *PT503*, *PT507*, *PT508* and *PT509*. The *PT509* was sunk and of the crew of seventeen, only one wounded survivor was rescued by the Germans – he was found in Jersey, nine months later, having recovered and been very well looked after. Another boat, *PT507*, was damaged on the same occasion.

Normandy

During the night of 14–15 March 1944, British MTBs attacked two groups of the German 36th Minesweeping Flotilla off Gravelines and sank the leader, *M3630*, with a torpedo. On the following night two units of British MTBs – Group A consisting of MTBs *207* and *211* and Group B of MTBs *362*, *417*, *418* and *433* – were deployed with the object of attacking German shipping on passage between Calais and Boulogne. At 2000, shore-based radar reported five or more vessels of trawler size leaving Calais southbound and Group B was ordered to intercept. During the approach, MTBs *362* and *433* lost contact with the rest of the force and only MTBs *417* and *418* intercepted the

German ships, five miles off Cap Griz Nez at 2042. The enemy vessels – *V1802*, *V1803*, *V1804*, *V1810*, *V1811*, *V1815* and the *Brommy*, on passage from Calais to Boulogne – heard the engines of the approaching MTBs and, after challenging them, opened fire, initially with starshell. While turning to port to engage the enemy *MTB417* was hit by 88mm fire from *V1810* and *V1811* which set her on fire. *MTB418* attempted to close the boat, which was burning fiercely, but was deterred by the concentrated fire of the German vessels and shore batteries. As a result *MTB417* sank before help could be provided and a subsequent search found only charred wreckage. Between Dieppe and Calais, on 29 March, during an attempt by the British MGBs *40*, *204*, *611*, *613*, *614* and *615* to attack a German force consisting of three patrol boats, three gun ferries and eleven minesweeping cutters, MGBs *611* and *614* were damaged.

During the night of 19–20 May, the *V208* and *V210* were on their way to assist *V205* in rescuing the survivors of *V211* (earlier sunk by the French *MTB90*), when they became involved in a short action with vessels of their own side – S-boats of the 5th Flotilla, fortunately without loss.

On the eve of the Normandy invasion, the night of 5–6 June 1944, the three patrol boats *T28*, *Jaguar* and *Möwe* sailed from Le Havre to attack approaching enemy ships. They later ran into part of the invasion force and Korvetten-kapitän Hoffmann of the *T28* has recalled the following as his ship retired after launching torpedoes against the approaching enemy:

when we emerged from the other side of the smoke screen, I saw a sight which touched me by the tragedy of its simplicity: three armed trawlers were proceeding steadily at 8kts toward the cannon fire! No longer having radio, I could not warn them, but the British gunfire, with the help of radar, followed me across the smoke, and soon came upon the leading trawler. All three turned away. I passed in front of them and tried to draw the enemy fire, but one of the trawlers was hit by a 15in shell from the battleship HMS *Warspite* and sank.[3]

The vessel observed by Hoffmann was the patrol boat *V1509* and, when one considers the thousands of ships on the other side of the smokescreen, its loss neatly sums up the inequality of the forces present on that day, off the Normandy coast in June 1944.

Off Normandy, in the night of 8–9 July, four MTBs attacked a group from the 13th Patrol Boat Flotilla comprising *V1301*, *V1306*, *V1310* and *V1313* and in the following action *MTB434* and *V1306* were sunk. A month later, in the night of 8–9 August, patrol boats of the 15th Flotilla had an engagement with two British SGBs off Fécamp, in which *V241* was sunk. During the night of 19–20 August, boats of the 38th Minesweeper Flotilla beat off attack by the British coastal forces craft *MGB321*, *MGB322* and *MTB473*, *MTB474* and *MTB479*, off Cap de la Hève.

The Germans began to evacuate Le Havre on the night of 23–24 August; the 15th Patrol-boat Flotilla, consisting of two V-boats, a UJ boat, sixteen KFK patrol craft and two motor minesweepers (with two more in tow), departing for Dieppe. Off Cap d'Antifer and Fécamp this group were attacked first by the British frigate *Thornbrough*, escort destroyer *Talybont* and MTBs *692*, *694* and *695*, and then by the British frigate *Retalick*, escort destroyer *Melbreak* and the MTBs *205*, *208* and *212*. Despite the number of ships sent against them only *V716* and a motor minesweeper were damaged. On the following night, in company with the 38th Minesweeper Flotilla, the 15th Flotilla moved on once more, this time from Dieppe to Boulogne – the entire force consisted of twenty-one V- and M-boats (five trawlers, sixteen drifters), three MFKs, a motor minesweeper and a naval ferry barge. In succession the German vessels were attacked by the American PT boats *250*, *511*, and *514*; the British frigate *Seymour*, with MTBs *252*, *254*, *256* and *257*; the British MTBs *447*, *452* and *453* with the escort destroyer *Talybont*; the frigate *Retalick* and MTBs *205*, *209* and *210*; and finally the British escort destroyer *Bleasdale*. Again, despite all this activity, the only results of these engagements were the loss of one escorting S-boat and the *M3857* and damage to the *V243*.

On 28 August, two UJ boats escorted a group of motor minesweepers (which had been minelaying in the Seine Estuary) to Fécamp and, off Cap d'Antifer, were engaged by the frigate *Thornbrough*, *MTB447*, *MTB450* and *MTB482* and then the French escort destroyer *La Combattante*, with British *MTB692*, *MTB693*, *MTB695* and the American *PT512* and *PT519*. The Submarine-chaser *UJ1433* was sunk and a motor minesweeper was damaged. On the following night, one UJ boat, one KFK patrol boat, nine motor minesweepers, one MFL minesweeper, six gun

ferries and one tug moved from Le Havre to Fécamp under the escort of S-Boats. The group was attacked by *Retalick* and the escort destroyer *Cattistock* but the assault was unsuccessful and the escort destroyer was damaged.

Sweeping the Dutch Coast

On 11 May 1944, British MTBs sank the *V1311* off the Hook of Holland. During the night of 9–10 June units of the British 58th MTB Flotilla – *666*, *681*, *683*, *684*, *687* and *723* – were engaged in an offensive sweep between Texel and Ijmuiden. At 0115 they sighted a German convoy escorted by seven boats from the 13th, 14th and 20th V-Flotillas – *V1314*, *V1315*, *V1317*, *V1419*, *V2020*, *V2021* and *V2022*. Visibility was very poor and at 0131 the MTBs were able to make their attack unobserved so it was not until two of the V-boats were hit by torpedoes that the Germans realised they were under attack. They immediately opened fire, despite not having seen a target, but nevertheless managed to hit *MTB681* as the British force was retiring. The MTBs made a second attack, in which *MTB681* (having caught fire) and *MTB684* did not participate, before setting course for home. En route, the fire in *MTB681* gained the upper hand and, at 0430, she blew up and disintegrated, with the loss of two of her crew. Of the German ships, three – *V1314*, *V2020* and *V2021* – had been torpedoed and sunk.

Off the Dutch coast, during the night of 3–4 July, the German freighter *Weserstein*, escorted by the 20th Patrol Boat Flotilla, consisting of *V1315*, *V1317*, *V2016*, *V2019* and *V2022*, was unsuccessfully attacked by four MTBs. On the following night the British MTBs *666*, *684*, *687*, *723* and *729* of the 58th Flotilla were engaged in an anti-shipping sweep off Ijmuiden when, at 0047 radar contacts were obtained, which the unit closed until, at 0132, it was only $1\frac{1}{2}$ miles from Ijmuiden. At 0214, a German patrol consisting of *V1411* and *V1415* with the gun ferries *AF41* and *AF47* sighted the MTBs' silhouettes, whereupon they challenged and opened fire with their 20mm and 37mm armament. The MTB unit responded by illuminating the German vessels with rockets and then closed to attack. As, however, the latter failed to present a viable torpedo target, the MTBs turned north, whilst continuing to fire, and a circling action ensued. At about 0225 *MTB666* was hit in the engine room by a 37mm shell from *V1415* and caught fire so she was ordered to retire in company with *MTB684*. Shortly afterwards *MTB666* reported that the fire was out, but that she was stopped. Meanwhile, another two V boats *V1401* and *V1418* were approaching with the intention of joining the action when, at about 0340 they saw *MTB666* and briefly opened fire on her with their 88mm guns. As they closed the MTB, her crew abandoned ship, after first opening the sea-cocks, but the Germans succeeded in boarding her, closed the sea-cocks and took her in tow. They also rescued the MTB's crew. Although *MTB666* was making water, the two V-boats managed to bring her into Ijmuiden but, at 0735, in the fishery harbour, an internal explosion occurred and the captured vessel capsized and sank.

On 14 July, the British MTBs *455*, *457*, *458*, *467*, *468*,

469 and *470* made a sortie into the area off Ijmuiden where an engagement took place with three German patrol boats in which *V1412* was sunk and three MTBs damaged. Again, off Ijmuiden, on the night of 30 September–1 October, British MTBs *347*, *349*, *350*, *351* and *360*, attacked the German convoy 1291, towing vessels from Rotterdam to Borkum. The escort, under Korvetten-kapitän Fischer, comprised *V1301*, *V1310*, *V1313*, *V1317*, *V2017*, *V2019*, *M3824*, *M3827*, *M3832*, *M3838*, *MFL675* and seven motor minesweepers. The British attacks were unsuccessful and *MTB347* and *MTB360* were sunk by gunfire. The convoy put into Den Helder during the night of 2–3 October and then continued on its way; it was subsequently attacked by aircraft off the Dutch coast and one of the vessels under tow was sunk.

During the night of 8–9 October, off the Hook of Holland, a patrol boat unit, consisting of *V1303*, *V1306*, *V2004* and *V2007*, was repeatedly attacked by British MTBs and *V1303* was sunk; later, a further assault by MTBs near Texel failed. These events were repeated in the same area on the following night – with MTBs *472*, *473*, *475*, *476* and *480* attacking patrol boats and badly damaging one of them – and again on 15–16 October – when *V2016* was sunk. On 2 November, there was an engagement in the North Sea between British MTBs and German patrol boats, in which *V2016* (II) was sunk by two torpedo hits.

Finale in the Baltic

In the Baltic, the Soviet submarine *Lembit* torpedoed and sank the minesweeper *M3619* off Brüsterort in October 1944. On the east coast of the Sworbe Peninsula, during the night of 20–21 November, the patrol boats *V302*, *V1713* and two type 40 minesweepers had engagements with Soviet gunboats and coastal forces, during which the Germans claimed to have sunk an MTB. During an evacuation operation on 22 March 1945, the *V2022* was sunk by the Soviet submarine *L21*.

One of the last operations carried out by the auxiliary patrol vessels of the Kriegsmarine was to assist in the evacuation of refugees from the Baltic. On 5 May *V303* and *V2002*, together with four destroyers, five torpedo boats, three freighters, one auxiliary cruiser, one type 40 minesweeper and one training vessel, embarked 45,000 refugees in Hela and, after beating off Soviet MTB attacks from Kolberg, arrived safely off Copenhagen on 6 May. So ended one of the less well-known chapters of the war at sea, a collection of actions fought largely in obscurity by small, unglamorous ex-fishing boats. Their work was, nevertheless, indispensable to the Germans and I think that their best epitaph, one that can be applied equally to the S-boats, is to be found in the words of the official naval historian of one of the countries against which they fought – Captain S W Roskill, DSC, RN:

> The S-Boats proved skilful and stubborn fighters, and the German convoy escorts defended their charges with devotion, and often with success.

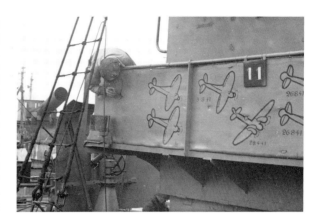

A flak ship displays her successes – several Spitfires and a Blenheim shot down on 28 April, 3 August and 28 August 1941, with more in the process of being added. (ECPA)

> Their guns' crews were excellently trained and provided with good weapons, and it was mainly they who succeeded in keeping the enemy's coastal traffic moving, in spite of the unremitting and very varied offensive which we were now waging against it.[4]

Addenda

German auxiliary minesweepers, sub-chasers and patrol boats operating in the west ('M', 'UJ' and 'V' boats combined, large 'M' minesweepers, 'R' motor minesweepers, gun ferries and sperrbrecher excluded) on 1 January 1943:

Trawlers (80 large, 58 small)	138
Whalers	13
Motor luggers	71
Motor fishing vessels	17
Sardine and lobster boats	15
Paddle vessels	4
Total	258

The 'west' extended from the coast of Holland to the southern coast of Biscay, about 900 nautical miles (1700km). Before the assault on the Soviet Union in June 1941, all the auxiliary sub-chasers (UJ) and about 25 per cent of the large armed trawlers (M and V) left the western theatre.

Notes:

[1] Other designations were used for these vessels, including KFK for local defence vessels and harbour boats, and GD, GK, etc for former German or captured drifters, trawlers, whalers, yachts, etc.

[2] Ministery of Defence, London.

[3] German captains eyewitness report.

[4] *The War at Sea*, HMSO (London, 1954–61).

WARRIOR AND MAGNIFICENT

Postwar Canadian carrier aviation 1945–1957

Following the Second World War the Canadian authorities, after some debate, decided that their navy should operate a single aircraft carrier. The first of these, the light fleet carrier *Warrior*, proved less than satisfactory and was soon replaced by the *Magnificent* which had a comparatively long and active career. Thomas G Lynch describes the operational histories of these two carriers and the background events that led to their being taken over by the Royal Canadian Navy.

The desire of the RCN to operate aircraft carriers after the Second World War, had its roots in a joint RCN-RCAF committee's recommendations made in October 1943, after which 'The Naval Staff, after considering the question in relation to the RCN's planned contribution to the war in the Pacific, then proposed "in principle" the acquisition of two fleet carriers.' It was next mentioned at a Cabinet War Committee meeting on 12 January 1944, when the Minister for the Navy reported that no carrier would be available to the RCN before January 1945. Consequently approval was given for the taking over of *Nabob* and *Puncher* (see *Warship 94*).

The first indication to the Admiralty that the RCN wanted to operate light fleet carriers came in an *aide-mémoire* to the CNMO (Canadian Naval Mission Overseas), dated 17 July 1944. This stated that Naval Service Headquarters envisaged the employment of 'two escort carriers, subsequently to be exchanged for two light fleet carriers' in the Pacific war and that the Admiralty was to be so informed. The British naval authority made the next move by passing, through the CNMO, two official messages, dated 28 and 31 August, indicating that the allocation of two light fleet carriers was under consideration and that *Ocean* and *Warrior* had tentatively been ear-marked. Negotiations dragged on through the fall, with the Canadian Government putting flies in the ointment with their decisions to allocate only 13,000 naval personnel to the Pacific theatre and not to get involved in the Indian Ocean operations. With nearly 2000 men needed for the carriers, plus aircrews, support personnel, etc, this threw a damper on Admiralty hopes that Canada would provide up to 30 per cent of the escort requirements and also a substantial commitment in repair ships. In addition they wished to have the flexibility to deploy the forces as needed, without theatre restrictions.

Finally, in November, the Admiralty approved the Canadian proposal and submitted it to the British Cabinet. It was decided that *Ocean* and *Warrior* would be provided and their completion dates were consequently moved up to July and September 1945 respectively. However, Canada was suffering from its own manning problems and indicated that it would not be able to man the first carrier until September, which effectively eliminated *Ocean*. Just before New Year's Eve 1944, it was agreed that *Warrior* and *Magnificent* would be made available with completion dates of September and November 1945, respectively.

The formal offer of transfer came from the UK on 14 January 1945, with the suggestion that they commission as RCN ships, there being no Lend-Lease complications as there had been with *Nabob* and *Puncher*. However, Canada stood by its decision of theatre restrictions, and reiterated these in its reply of 14 February, which the British Cabinet finally accepted on 23 April 1945, along with a proposal for the transfer of a flotilla of fleet destroyers. This was further revised and refined in a letter to Ottawa, dated 13 December 1945 (after the feasibility of forming Canadian air squadrons had been addressed) stating the terms for the loan of two light fleet carriers and two *Crescent* Class destroyers. On 19 December 1945, the Canadian Cabinet, faced with the peacetime realities of reduced defence spending, approved in principle the formation of a Naval Air Component, as the Admiralty had recommended. At this time, Canadian planning was based on the assumption that the peacetime complement of the RCN would be about 10,000 of which the air component would be 11 per cent, or approximately 1100 officers and men to man one carrier,

two TBR and two fighter squadrons, and one air station.

Warrior

The *Warrior* was commissioned into the RCN at Belfast on 24 January 1946 and, after crossing the Atlantic, arrived in Halifax on 31 March, with the twenty-eight Seafires and Fireflies of 803 and 825Sqds. However, it soon became clear that *Warrior* was unsuitable for winter operations in eastern Canadian waters and the ship was sent to Esquimalt, BC, on 5 November. In January 1947, she was taken in hand for a refit, periodic overhaul and repairs to the hull, the latter the result of a grounding the previous August off Pointe St Antoine, Quebec, when the rudder had jammed hard to port during a visit to Montreal.

While in refit, important decisions were being made in Ottawa as to her future. During the previous summer, when *Magnificent*'s commissioning date had been provisionally set for July 1947, the ambitious carrier plans made prior to the end of the war had to be revised. Given the manning ceiling imposed on the RCN, it could only contemplate manning one carrier at a time. Various schemes were proposed to the Admiralty but a decision was forced upon

The newly completed Warrior *being towed out of the Harland and Wolff fitting-out yard in January 1946. The 'false hull' camouflage pattern was to be painted out within a year as the RCN standardised its postwar paint schemes*. (Kealy/Lyncan collection)

the RCN when, early in 1947, the Canadian government made substantial reductions in the armed forces estimates for the forthcoming fiscal year. Accordingly, any idea of retaining *Warrior* in reserve was scrapped and, because she was unsuitable for year-round operations in the Atlantic, the Canadian government proposed that *Warrior* be returned to the RN when *Magnificent* commissioned. This was agreed by the Admiralty and, with a firm delivery date of March 1948 for *Magnificent*, *Warrior* was to spend the next year in exercises, good-will tours and 'show the flag' trips.

HMCS Warrior *on route to Canada's west coast in November 1946. Built to RN standards, her heating systems proved less than equal to the harsh weather of the Canadian Atlantic coast and she was moved to the more temperate climate of the Pacific coast for the winter of 1946–47.* (Marcom Museum)

The Warrior *returns to Halifax, NS, on 28 August 1947 after visiting the UK. Her armament reflects the transitional phase of British-built carriers at this time, most of the equipment dating from 1944–45.* (H Rule/Marcom Museum)

The *Warrior* visited Vancouver early in February 1947. With her aircraft embarked later in the month, she began the long voyage to Halifax, in company with the destroyer *Crescent* and light cruiser *Uganda*. The trio reached Balboa on 9 March where *Crescent* and *Uganda* parted company. The *Warrior* proceeded through the Panama Canal, which was particularly harrowing, since some of the narrower locks of the Canal only afforded the carrier some 8.5in clearance on each side. She was then met, in Colon, by the destroyers *Nootka* and *Micmac* which accompanied her to the Greater Antilles and Cuba. They arrived in Havana on 15 March, the first Canadian ships to pay such a visit since HMCS *Vancouver* in 1929. They departed on the 18th for Grassy Bay, Bermuda, with the hopes of further training opportunities but strong winds and high seas caused their cancellation, and the ships sailed on for Halifax, arriving on 27 March.

In Halifax, the two air squadrons, 803 and 825, were formed into the 19th CAG (Carrier Air Group) and embarked in *Warrior* from lighters. In April she sailed for Bermuda escorted by *Nootka*, for joint exercises with the RN's North America and West Indies Station warships, *Kenya* and *Sheffield*, two sloops and a frigate. The *Warrior* returned to Halifax in May, where the ship was taken in hand in HMC Dockyard for repairs to the main manoeuvring valve which were not completed until the first week in June. She then took two short cruises, the first a trip along the Canadian Atlantic coast and the second another exercise which was completed by 24 June, when the ship returned to Halifax for annual leave.

The Warrior *in the Strait of Juan de Fuca, off the coast of British Columbia, in February 1947. A Fairy Firefly FR1 is landing-on and, in the background, the destroyer* Crescent *is towing a Baldwin hydrofoil target, which the Fireflies used in practice rocket attacks.* (Kealy/Lyncan collection)

The *Warrior* sailed once again on 2 August for the UK, taking part in a trooping trip. On board were 27 officers and 179 men of the 19th CAG going on a training course and re-equipping with Firefly MkIVs and Sea Fury fighters. She arrived at Greenock on 8 August, discharged her passengers and, three days later, steamed back down the Clyde, bound for home. The deck cargo included two RN aircraft for cold weather trials at Namao, Alberta. She arrived in Halifax on 28 August.

Meanwhile 826 and 883Sqds had been reformed at Dartmouth on 15 May 1947 to become the 18th CAG. Equipped with Seafires and Fireflies, formerly flown by 19th CAG, they were ready for at-sea training by mid-November. The aircraft were flown aboard off Halifax, where deck landing and navigation exercises were conducted until the 21st. On that day, *Warrior* completed her flying commitments to the RCN and the aircraft were flown off to the Eastern Passage. Thereafter, until the end of the year, all hands were occupied in storing, provisioning and the loading of some 3000 packing cases intended for the *Magnificent*. She sailed on 7 January 1948, accompanied by the destroyer *Haida*, for Bermuda where she swung at the Flagship Buoy in Grassy Bay for the next five weeks, while the ship was prepared for paying off.

The *Warrior* departed Bermuda on 12 February 1948, arriving in Belfast Lough on 20th. The transfer of stores to *Magnificent* was begun immediately, being completed on the 27th, and the first advance party of seventy-six men were drafted to the new ship. On her last voyage, *Warrior* departed Belfast, passed through the Needles Passage on 1

This midship view of Warrior *on 28 August 1947, illustrates well the details of her folding W/T masts, rig and the sponsons for her single 40mm guns. Note the quad 2pdr mounting fitted at the after end of the island superstructure and the raised platform carrying its director, with Type 282 radar, between it and the funnel. Radar aerials visible include for Type 279B, with Type 242 IFF 'pitchfork' above, on the stump mast at the after end of the island; Type 281, with Type 243 IFF 'candelabra' above, on the foremast head; and the cheese aerial of Type 293M on the platform projecting forward of the tripod mast. The YE homing beacon is on a telescopic mast welded to the side of the funnel casing.* (Marcom Museum)

March and anchored off Spithead, where her aviation fuel was pumped out prior to her being moved into dry-dock. The main draft, of five officers and 238 men, departed for *Magnificent* on 22 March and, on the following day, the Broad Pennant of Commodore DeWolf was struck and the ship was returned to the RN.

HMCS Magnificent

After the Cabinet decision of January 1947 to return *Warrior* and keep only one borrowed light fleet carrier in commission, the future hopes of the air arm became centred on *Magnificent*. She had been launched at Harland and Wolff's

A Fairy Firefly MkIV of the RN's Fleet Air Arm aboard Warrior *in August 1947. This was one of two aircraft being transported to Canada for cold weather evaluation at Namao, Alberta.* (DND/Lyncan Collection)

A Seafire of 803 Sqd, with hook down, lands on Warrior's *flight deck.* (DND/Lyncan)

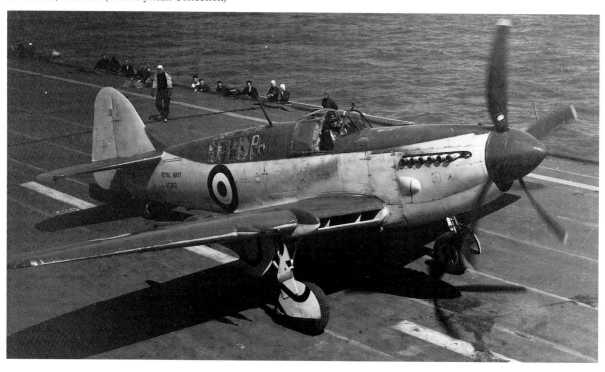

yard in Belfast on 16 November 1944 but construction had ceased shortly after VE-Day. Work recommenced in 1946, with the decision by Canada to accept two light fleet carriers, but slowed in mid-1946 until the Canadian government made its decision of January 1947, at which point work to complete the ship became frenzied. When the large party from *Warrior* arrived in March 1948 they found the ship alongside in Musgrave Channel with dockyard workmen putting on a final spurt to complete the ship for the projected commissioning date. This took place on time, on 7 April, with Commodore H G DeWolf assuming command. Unlike her predecessor, the new *Majestic* class carrier was prepared for cold weather service and incorporated various Canadian requirements, particularly in respect to messing arrangements.

The *Magnificent* put to sea for the first time on 15 April 1948, successfully completing acceptance trials of her main machinery prior to proceeding to Portsmouth for her remaining trials. In May she began the work for which she was built; aviation fuel was embarked at Spithead and the next day aircraft from Royal Air Station Ford rendezvoused with the ship off the Isle of Wight for flying tests, which again were successful. Returning to Portsmouth, the embarkation of stores and ammunition occupied all hands until the middle of the month when course was shaped for Belfast. There, the aircraft of 19th CAG and those of 806Sqd, RN, were hoisted aboard.

The ship sailed for Canada on 25 May, arriving in Halifax on 1 June, in cloudy, rainy weather which prevented all but two of her aircraft from flying off to the Dartmouth Naval Air Station. After a brief shake-down cruise in June and the clearing of the hangar decks of air department stores, the carrier began flying operations in August with the aircraft of 19th CAG. During ten days of flying, 171 deck landings were made and two ditchings occurred, the crews being retrieved by the plane guard destroyer *Haida*. When the cruise completed, command of the ship was assumed by Commodore GR Miles, OBE, RCN.

The ship departed Halifax on 2 September 1948, accompanied by the destroyers *Haida* and *Nootka,* for exercises off the Atlantic east coast. These included full-scale practice strikes against the Magdalen Islands and joint exercises with the RCAF, but were terminated abruptly when contamination of her aviation fuel was suspected. The ship

FR1 Fireflies of 825 Sqd await their turn at the Warrior's *catapult during exercises in the Caribbean with the RN's North America and West Indies Squadron in April 1947.* (Kealy/Lyncan)

proceeded through Hudson Strait and visited Wakeham Bay, where the two destroyers were refuelled and provisioned by *Magnificent*, the latter then departing for Halifax, leaving the two destroyers anchored in the bay. The weather improved on the way back and, with the contamination problem resolved, the aircraft of 19th CAG resumed exercises with aircraft of the RCAF, before flying off for Dartmouth as the carrier neared Halifax Harbour. The air crews and unserviceable aircraft were landed in Halifax and the ship departed for Saint John, NB, for a refit.

HMCS Magnificent *in 1951, with the new Grumman AS3 Avengers spotted forward and Hawker Sea Furies aft.* (Quinn/Marcom Museum)

The 'plane guard' destroyer Micmac *moves up to refuel from* Magnificent *in February 1950, framed by the propeller blades and folded wings of a Hawker Sea Fury FB11.* (Quinn/Marcom Museum)

Training exercises with other ships of the RCN resumed when the ship re-entered service in early 1949, as well as with ships of the RN's North America and West Indies Station, being particularly intense in March and April 1949. She departed for the UK in January to ferry her Firefly MkIV aircraft back to the UK to exchange them for newer MkVs and Sea Fury fighters. On the way back she encountered a series of severe gales, sustaining damage forward and losing one of the deck cargo propellers intended as spares for the Canadian *Tribal* class destroyers. Somewhat shaken up by the loss, and the seemingly unending storms, the grateful crew of *Magnificent* saw the ship berthed in Halifax on 25 February 1949.

Caribbean Cruise

The aircraft were landed during the following week and the ship prepared for a cruise to the West Indies, with the newly formed 18th CAG (consisting of 828 and 826 Sqds flying Firefly MkI and V aircraft). The ship departed in early March, accompanied by *Haida* and *Nootka*. Two days out, deck landing training was commenced northeast of Bermuda but was terminated after a barrier crash in fresh-ening south-easterly winds and rain squalls.

Arriving in Bermuda, she anchored at Five Fathom Hole and awaited the formation of Task Group 215.8, which sailed that evening to gain sea room in light of gale warnings. In the process, *Haida* lost her starboard anchor and five shackles of cable. In face of the inclement weather in the area, *Magnificent* and *Nootka* set out for the Cacaos Islands, while *Haida* remained to retrieve her anchor and cable. Off Jamaica, flying training resumed, highlighted by the crashes of a Firefly MkI and a Sea Fury into the sea, the crews being rescued by *Nootka*.

A Firefly V of 825 Sqd, BD-H, after sliding off the Magnificent*'s flight deck and onto the starboard sponsons during landing, August 1950.* (Wales/Marcom Museum)

After catching its tail wheel in No 2 arrester wire this Firefly V slammed into the Magnificent's *flight deck and broke off its starboard undercarriage. The second photograph was taken a few seconds later, after the aircraft had come down hard on the port wheel, which broke off the strut, causing the aircraft to make final contact on its belly. All three of the aircraft's crew walked away from the incident.* (Wales/Marcom Museum)

Using HMS *Jamaica*, which was in transit from the Canal Zone, as a target, a successful practice strike was made by nine planes at a distance of 162 miles from the carrier. The *Magnificent* then rejoined Task Group 215.8 outside Colon, where they were joined by TG 215.9, consisting of HMCS *Ontario, Athabaskan* and *Antigonish*, which had transited the Canal the previous day and were at anchor. The resulting formation, dubbed TF 215, under the command of Commodore Miles sailed back to the West Indies two days later to join the ships of the RN's North America and West Indies Squadron, which were spotted by aircraft of the *Magnificent* and used as practice targets by the ship's aircraft before the two forces met. Command of the overall force then passed to the C-in-C, North America and West Indies, and the fleet steamed to St John, Antigua, for a two-day layover. The new combined force was called TF 73 and sailed in mid-March, with day/night exercises en route, to Guantanamo, Cuba.

Aircraft from the carrier next took part in a convoy drill during 30–31 March, in which the carrier was part of Blue Force under the orders of the Senior Canadian Naval Officer Afloat (SCNOA). The combined fleet then dispersed, but the Canadian ships remained together until 1 April when, in honour of Newfoundland becoming Canada's tenth province, the ships were dressed overall. Shortly thereafter, TG 215.9 was detached for the Panama Canal and returned to the Pacific, while TG 215.8 maintained its flying schedule and then, after a visit to Bermuda, sailed for Halifax. All serviceable aircraft were flown off *Magnificent*'s pitching deck on 7 April, while some 225 miles from home, while the carrier, with her two attendant destroyers, arrived in HMC Dockyard on 8 April.

Repair and Refit

With the prospect of a busy summer of flying training, operations commenced in local waters during May, everything going according to plan until the last dog-watch of 4 June. On this day *Magnificent* was approaching the entrance to the harbour of Port Mouton when, at 1937 local time, she took the ground on the tip of White Point as she

was passing through the channel between the Point and White Point Rock. Luckily, sea and swell were slight and four hours later, with the aid of her escort destroyers, she floated off and slowly made her way back to Halifax. In the early hours of the 5th, *Nootka* was detached to return to Port Mouton for the recovery of cable and wire, while *Magnificent* and *Haida* berthed at Halifax shortly after noon. After preparations for docking, *Magnificent*, accompanied by the navy tug *Riverton*, departed Halifax on 14 June and, although delayed by heavy fog, entered the dry-dock at Saint John, NB on the 18th. Repairs and refit kept her there until mid-October.

Shortly thereafter, Commodore KF Adams assumed command and the ship departed for Halifax to resume her operations. However, the refit period had been put to good use, an alternative deck-landing control officer's position having been fitted for use with USN landing techniques. However, the necessary instruments for the latter were not fitted, since instructions had been received that the 18th CAG would continue to use British deck-landing drill during the autumn cruise.

Air Search

Early on 17 November *Magnificent*, with *Haida* and the frigate *Swansea* as escorts, was steaming into the wind off the Nova Scotia coast while her aircraft were practising deck-landing training, when she was directed by signal to carry out an air search for a missing US B-29 aircraft. Although hampered by bad weather, vast areas were searched by the carrier's aircraft, and *Swansea* was dispatched to a position where a flare had been observed, but with little result. On the 19th, a search flight of eight aircraft were being recovered when a US B-17 was reported to be circling 14 miles off the carrier's port beam. However, owing to a severe fuel shortage in the returning Fireflies the landings had to continue but as soon as the last touched down, *Haida* was detached to investigate. Within the hour the destroyer picked up survivors from three life rafts, and upon returning to the vicinity of the carrier, the ship's medical officer was transferred to *Haida* to attend to the

Having just turned into wind, the first Firefly lands on the Magnificent *in waters off Bermuda on 26 November 1950. Note the mixture of single and twin 40mm mountings in the sponsons.* (Lyncan Collection)

airmen. The *Magnificent* and *Haida* then made best speed for Bermuda, while *Swansea*, hove to during the heavy weather with trouble to her starboard main circulating pump, proceeded independently back to Halifax as the weather permitted.

Arriving in Bermuda, *Haida* discharged her survivors, and TG 211.1 continued on to Guantanamo, arriving on 24 November. They sailed on the 27th for San Juan, Puerto Rico. The ships returned to Halifax on 6 December, after flying off part of the 18th CAG and landing the rest by lighter. The rest of the year was given over to domestic duties and leave periods for the crew.

Thus the pace and routine of a peacetime carrier in the RCN was established. Hereafter, only highlights will be presented, as training routines largely followed this set pattern.

February 1950 saw a long cruise for *Magnificent*, with maximum air exercise time utilised to hone the 18th CAG's skills to the maximum. One Firefly was lost during the cruise, *Micmac* recovered the aircraft's observer but the pilot was never found. Ports of visit included Charleston, North Carolina, Guantanamo, Havana, and New York before returning to Halifax on 14 April.

Diplomatic Cruise

In the third year of her commission, *Magnificent* became the flagship for a squadron that sailed on a 'diplomatic cruise', designed to consolidate ties of friendship with European members of NATO and secondly, to let them see

something of Canada's navy. In company with *Micmac* and *Huron*, and carrying the 19th CAG, composed of 803, 883 and 825 Sqds, *Magnificent* departed Halifax on 22 August 1950 – the first port of call being Ireland (destroyers to Londonderry; carrier at Moville). While there, on 19 September, Rear Admiral E R Mainguy assumed command, shortly after which the ships proceeded to Rosyth and then on to Oslo, before departing, on 2 October, for Gothenburg, Sweden. The *Magnificent* had the honour of being the longest warship ever to enter the latter port where she was secured between head and stern buoys – an interesting hour was spent in turning the ship in the narrow harbour when it came time to sail for Copenhagen.

Upon departure from Copenhagen, the ships headed into the Baltic, then the North Sea, where the destroyers were detached for a port visit to Amsterdam while *Magnificent* entered the Maas River at the Hook of Holland, and securing between buoys at Rotterdam. The following day, there was a considerable traffic of self-propelled barges passing the carrier as she lay in mid-channel, one in particular having great difficulty in making headway against an estimated 3kt current. Another barge, *Shell 25*, having more power, attempted to pass the labouring barge to starboard, close to *Magnificent*'s port side, when she too was gripped by the current and struck the carrier's port side just forward of the accommodation ladder: her stern then swung towards the carrier and, in so doing, crushed the captain's barge and motorboat, which had been secured to the lower boom. (The barge owners, Shell Nederland NV, subsequently paid C$12,586.54 to the Canadian government.) The carrier departed on 16 October with an irate captain and minus one crucial motorboat.

The next port of call was Portsmouth, on the 17th, and then Cherbourg, where she was rejoined by her escorts. Four days later she sailed for Lisbon, mooring first off Caxis before berthing astern of her escorts at Alcantara.

Two Hawker Sea Fury FB11 fighters of the 18th CAG in 1951. The Sea Fury proved a much more robust carrier fighter than the Seafire, although its radial engine made it susceptible to torque-stalling at low speeds when landing. (DND/Lyncan)

The group departed on 4 November and entered Gibraltar Bay two days later. On 9 November she sailed with a large element of the British Home Fleet for Exercise Maple Leaf. She left the Home Fleet elements on 11 November for Bermuda, where Task Group 215.1 was augmented by the Canadian frigates *Swansea* and *La Hulloise*. On the return leg to Halifax, the TG was 'attacked' by a recent addition to the Canadian naval aviation fleet, Grumman AS3 Avengers of 826 Sqd based in Dartmouth, NS. This flight set a new duration record for RCN aircraft, since the pilots had spent 14 hours out of 24 in the air during their search for the TG, the whole being part of a joint RCAF-RCN exercise.

The *Magnificent* flew off her serviceable aircraft on the 25th, shortly after which the weather deteriorated and speed had to be reduced to 8kts, delaying her arrival in Halifax until the 27th.

After de-storing, *Magnificent* entered refit at Saint John, NB in December. Work during this refit included a new four-blade propeller for the starboard shaft, replacing the three-bladed one in an effort to reduce the vibration experienced at the high speeds required for aircraft launch and recovery. This modification was successful in large measure, as was proven by subsequent trials. She undocked near the end of December and celebrated the arrival of the New Year in Halifax. Meanwhile, some 14 hours before, the Korean War had started with a bang but, although Canadian destroyers would be heavily engaged in operations off Korea over the next four years, *Magnificent* was to steam thousands of miles in cruises to the Mediterranean, Euro-

pean and Caribbean waters, destined never to serve in what was then being described as 'armed intervention' in Korea.

Task Group

Task Group 215.1 reformed, with the destroyer *Crescent* replacing *Micmac* as plane guard between 5 February and 9 March 1951. The TG was to have sailed on 5 February but the discovery of sabotage in the form of sand and filings in the lubrication pumps and main gearbox of the carrier caused a day's delay, before setting out for the Caribbean. On 28 February, one pilot of the 18th CAG was killed and three aircraft lost, the first occurring at 1312 when a Sea Fury stalled into the sea, the pilot being recovered. Three hours later, another Sea Fury stalled during take-off, turned over on its back, and plunged into the sea, disappearing with its pilot. Finally at 1615, an Avenger, coming in to land, had a power failure just short of the 'round-down' of the flight deck, stalled and ditched off the starboard quarter of the carrier. The pilot, having climbed out, walked along the wing, then returned to the cockpit for his dinghy, walked out again, inflated the raft and then calmly climbed in – a most encouraging demonstration for the other pilots and observers of the comparative lack of danger involved in ditching an Avenger.

The *Magnificent* returned to Halifax for 10 days in March and then returned to Bermudan waters on the 23rd for further flying evolutions. Ports of visit were King's Wharf, Port of Spain, Barbados and Boston, with the aircraft being flown off for the Dartmouth Air Station on 27 April. The 30th CAG undertook refresher courses in carrier duties in *Magnificent* during brief trips in May and June and, after a spell ashore, rejoined the ship in early August for a trip to the Mediterranean. During the journey, flying evolutions were uneventful, other than one ditching, with

The Magnificent *enters Grand Harbour, Malta in September 1951.* (Quinn/Marcom Museum)

A visiting USN 'blimp' lands on Magnificent's *after elevator off the coast of Nova Scotia in May 1952. Two such craft were visiting* HMCS Shearwater *on a goodwill tour at the time, and this exercise was intended to demostrate the 'blimps' maneuverability.* (Quinn/Marcom Museum)

A Sea Fury crash on Magnificent, *resulting from the collapse of the aircraft's starboard wheel strut on touchdown. The mobile crane, known as the 'beast', is moved into postion to move the aircraft onto the elevator so that landings can resume.* (Lyncan)

the pilot recovered after 45mins by *Micmac*. Ports of call were Grand Harbour, Malta; Naples, Saint Raphael, Salins d'Hyeres and Golfe Juan, before departing for Canada on 14 October in a full gale. She arrived in Halifax on 24 October.

On 29 October, the Broad Pennant of Commodore Adams was struck and Captain K S Dyer assumed command. That evening the ship sailed with the officers and men of 410 Sqd, RCAF for passage to Glasgow. However, the *Magnificent* initially sailed to Norfolk, Virginia to collect forty-eight Sabre jets, which were lashed to the flight deck. On route to Scotland, rough seas made it necessary to heave-to on two occasions to re-secure aircraft but eventually the Sabres were off-loaded at the King George V Dock and replaced by Sea Furies before the ship departed for Canada. Upon arrival, she destored for a long refit at Pier 7, Halifax Shipyards Ltd, Halifax.

The *Magnificent* returned to HMC Dockyard on 12 April 1952, where she spent 12 days embarking and stowing 158 tons of stores before trials could begin. By the end of the month, 881 Sqd had re-qualified in carrier landing practice. A post-refit shake-down cruise in May had an unusual beginning – Avenger aircraft spotted on the flight deck were used to pull the ship off the jetty and turn her in the harbour. At sea, with the cruiser HMCS *Quebec* acting as a rather self-conscious plane guard, *Magnificent* had a USN blimp, which was visiting Shearwater, land on her aft lift as a demonstration of the manoeuvrability of these craft. The shake-down cruise ended on 17 May, followed by a demonstration of naval air power to the Canadian Industrial Preparedness Association off the east coast on the 19th.

The 30th CAG was then ferried out to the carrier on 2 June and she sailed for a four month cruise in European waters. Ports of call were Plymouth, Portsmouth, Spithead, Malta, Navarin (leaving 18 July), Phaleron Bay (Athens), Istanbul (25-26 July), Tobruk (28 July), Malta (again), Belfast, Laggan Bay (Isle of Islay, 10 September), Rosyth and Oslo, arriving back in Halifax on 9 October. During this period, *Magnificent* and her consorts had participated in no less than three major NATO exercises, the largest being the 13 day 'Exercise Mainbrace' in which 160 ships took part. The *Magnificent* lost one Sea Fury on 8 September, with the pilot retrieved by the Portuguese frigate, *Diogo Gomes*.

Coronation Review

The *Magnificent* rounded out the year with one more southern exercise before undergoing boiler cleaning in December, in anticipation of a long refit at Halifax Shipyards Ltd commencing on 12 January 1953. At the end of April, the carrier was in a near frenzy, trying to conduct deck landing training for VS 881, a post-refit work-up and preparing the ship for participation in the Canadian Coronation Squadron.

Commodore H S Rayner relieved Captain Dyer and with the CAG aboard, the carrier joined the squadron for the voyage to England. Ships of the squadron were the cruisers, HMCS *Quebec* (flag, Rear Admiral R E S Bidwell) and *Ontario*, the destroyer *Sioux* and the frigates *Swansea*, *La Hulloise* and, of course, *Magnificent*. On arrival in the UK they carried out a series of exercises and then visited Torquay before arriving at Portsmouth on 29 May. Coronation Day was observed by the ship's company at church services, while libertymen lined the route in London. On 8 June, *Magnificent* assembled with other Commonwealth ships in St Helen's Roads before proceeding to moor in the review anchorage at Spithead – the review took place on 15 June and the fleet was illuminated that night. On the 17th the ships departed with the Australian carrier *Sydney* and, after some difficulties in recovering their CAGs due to persistent fog, the Squadron arrived back in Halifax on 25 June.

On the *Magnificent*'s return to Canada her annual docking was again due and this took place at Saint John, NB, over a two week period in July. Her CAG was re-embarked from lighters on 16 August but fog delayed sailing until the following day and then had to be aborted after trouble developed with one of the ship's turbo-generators. After another false start, the ship finally got to sea on 21 August, accompanied by the cruiser *Quebec*, for a training cruise that saw the ships visit Provincetown and Quonset Point, Rhode Island, and forming up as part of Carrier Division 14 under the command of Rear Admiral WL Erdmann, USN, before sailing to New York on 4 September. By the 9th, *Magnificent* was back as part of TG 81.4, while *Quebec* returned to Halifax.

Exercise Mariner

Upon completion of the exercise, the carrier detached for Norfolk for a four-day visit, before participating in 'Exercise Mariner', which would prove to be one of the highlights of the carrier's career. Over a 19-day period, 300 ships, 1000 aircraft and half a million men from nine NATO countries took part in co-ordinated operations which ranged over large areas of the North Atlantic, North Sea and the English Channel. The RCN ships participating were *Magnificent, Quebec, Algonquin, Swansea* and *La Hulloise*. RCN units made up part of Blue Force, while the opposing Orange Force consisted largely of submarines, land-based bombers and surface raiders.

'Mariner' began for the carrier on 16 September when she sailed as Commander Task Group 203.6 to provide ASW and air defence for ten logistic support ships forming an Iceland convoy. Avengers of 881 Sqd and Sea Furies of 871 Sqd flew an almost 'round-the-clock' schedule to prevent 'enemy' submarines and long-range, shore-based aircraft from attacking. The 'enemy' cruiser, USS *Worcester*, harassed the convoy until driven off by three of the screening destroyers, with six Avengers making a mock rocket

This Avenger AS3, No85475, having suffered the collapse of its port landing gear, slewed across the deck, over the arrester wires and came to rest in the port, after sponson. The Magnificent's *rescue helicopter, an HO4S-3 nick-named 'Angel', hovers off the carrier's stern as plane guard – 9 August 1956. (PAC)*

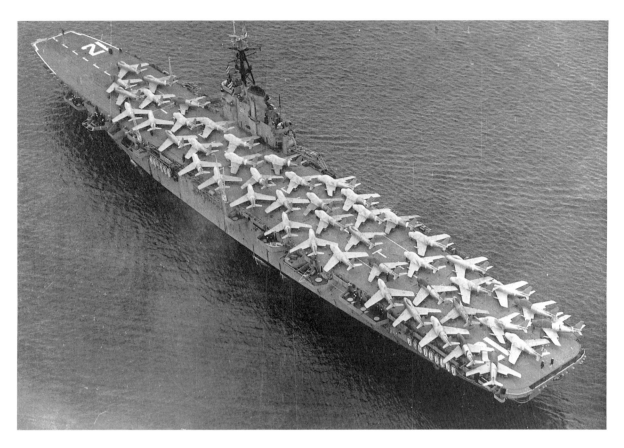

attack on the cruiser at twilight. On the 21st, a Sea Fury lost power during its final approach leg to the carrier and was forced to ditch. The aircraft was lost but in 32 seconds the carrier's Sikorsky HO4S-3 had retrieved the pilot, unhurt; this marked the first such rescue carried out by a Canadian naval helicopter.

The first phase ended off Cape Race and the convoy became a logistical support group. After at-sea replenishment of the escorts, all ships, including *Magnificent*, integrated with a fast carrier force headed by USS *Bennington*. En route to Iceland on the afternoon of the 23rd, eight Canadian Avengers and some thirty-four aircraft from the USN carriers were launched at 1330 and placed under the control of USS *Wasp* for a strike. However, shortly after, fog began to gather and the aircraft were recalled but by this time the fog had so thickened that the aircraft were unable to see the flight decks. Finally, at dusk, as the planes were reaching their reserve levels of fuel, the fog thinned temporarily and the planes were ordered to land on the nearest carrier post-haste. The *Magnificent* recovered her Avengers, plus one Skyraider from *Bennington* by 1828, the latter being returned the following day.

Later in the week the ships encountered severe southwesterly gales which precluded any flying. After forming up with an RN squadron the trip was uneventful, the support group and logistical ships safely arriving in Reykjavik. Here the support group consisting of *Magnificent* and the destroyers became a hunter-killer group, the logistical group serving to replenish the warships with fuel as they progressed through the Denmark Strait, while the force was harassed by submarines and the 'enemy' raider

The long trudge home: on 9 February 1957 the Magnificent *sails for Canada for the last time, carrying F86 Sabre jets of the RCAF that had been replaced in West Germany by the CF-100 Canuck. The aircraft had been taken on board at the King George V Dock, Shieldhall, Glasgow.* (DND/Marcom Museum)

HMS *Swiftsure*. The ships were further replenished on the 30 September when the weather moderated.

The final session of 'Mariner' had the Blue Forces steam toward the British Isles to launch air strikes against air bases. In turn, they were attacked on 1 and 2 October by Orange Forces, mainly aircraft that dropped theoretical bombs, including an atomic device, but the carriers were prevented from launching their attacks by heavy seas. When the exercise ended at 1100 on Sunday, 4 October, *Magnificent* was 180 miles WSW of Land's End and, after detaching her USN destroyers, proceeded to Belfast. After further exercises, she visited Portsmouth and then Glasgow, where she collected nine Sea Furies and one Avenger (which badly congested the flight deck so no flying was carried out for the rest of the month). A series of gales struck the ship as she returned to Canada but she finally arrived in Halifax on 2 November, having first flown off 30th CAG to Shearwater.

Training

December 1953 was occupied by the annual Support Air

Group sea-training programme, with *Algonquin*, and the *Haida* as plane guard, the former returning to Halifax with engine defects. A severe storm on 2 December prevented any flying and heavy seas caused damage to the bows, a motor cutter, and opened one of the diesel tanks to the sea. HMCS *Prestonian* took the place of *Haida* on the 3rd. After flying-off her aircraft to the RCAF Station at Summerside, Prince Edward Island, the carrier returned to Halifax on 9 December.

January and February 1954 were taken up with general repairs by the ship's company and HMC Dockyard. On 1 March she sailed for England and on the 9th began a long electronic and general refit at Portsmouth. By the time this refit ended in May, a total of 683 officers and men had attended courses at RN training establishments. Having carried out radar and radio trials off the Isle of Wight, the ship proceeded to Belfast where a quantity of stores destined for Canada were taken aboard and the ship then returned home, arriving on 11 June.

Events of 1954 followed the same pattern, with VS 881 and VF 871 carrying out carrier qualifications in July. Afterwards, VS 881 went on night training exercises, and VS 880 re-qualified later in the month. A total of 541 deck landings were successfully carried out within a 30-day period.

Exercises took place off Long Island, NY, during 10–12 August and the usual round of joint CANUS exercises were carried out through August until mid-September. Nato exercise 'New Broom II' occupied ten days in late September. The 27 September was spent shipping W/T aerials and removing sponsons in preparation for the transit of the Panama Canal, which took nine hours on the 28th. The ship visited Balboa, San Diego, San Francisco (22 October departure), Esquimalt (25–28 October), Vancouver (3–5 November), Esquimalt (6–7 November) and Balboa (27 Novem- ber). During this year she had steamed some 33,755 miles. She began her annual refit at Halifax on 15 December.

Sea-going cruises did not begin until April 1955. A total of 34,260 miles were steamed in 138 sea-days on three major exercises, 'Fogbank', 'New Broom IV' and 'Sea Enterprise', with the last two exercises accounting for 7596 miles in a single voyage. The CAG flew 4000 hours and 1975 deck landings were made, seven aircraft were lost but all crews were recovered thanks to the carrier's helicopter. Also, the first reserve training flights were carried out in August, with aircraft of VC 920 Reserve Squadron from HMCS *York*, Toronto, flown aboard on the 8th. All nine reserve pilots qualified within days. Foreign ports visited during the year included New York, Portsmouth, Trondheim, Plymouth, Rotterdam, Gibraltar, Valencia, Genoa and Marseilles.

The *Magnificent* underwent a self-refit from 8 December 1955 until 26 February 1956 and, on the day after its completion sailed with *Haida* for Operation 'Spring Tide'. The air detachments were changing too, with VS 881 aboard, as well as HS-50, the HO4S-3 Sqd, a detachment of HU 21 and No1 Drone Target Unit (with radio-controlled drones). Ports of visit were Bermuda, the US Naval Base at Chaguaramas Bay, Trinidad; Kingstown, St Vincent; Bridgetown, Barbados; Roosevelt Roads, Puerto Rico; St Thomas, San Juan; Port-au-Prince, Haiti; Havana, Cuba;

Norfolk and Portsmouth. She returned to Halifax on 7 May. Exercises had included 'Spring Tide', 'Big Hello', 'New Broom V' and 'New Broom VI'.

Exercise 'New Broom V' was of particular importance, since this marked the first time that the HO4S-3 'Horse' ASW helicopters had worked operationally off the carrier, the results were excellent. Meanwhile, Captain A B F Fraser-Harris assumed command in August, and Reserve Air Squadron VC 920 joined the ship that same month, successfully making 101 deck landings with only one accident. Operation 'New Broom VI' was *Magnificent*'s last NATO exercise, with VS 881 and HS 50 aboard, between 8-14 September, in some very disturbed weather conditions. This exercise was a milestone as well, since the newest ship in Canada's naval fleet, *St Laurent* took part in the exercise, forecasting the new era in ASW warships which was about to dawn.

Final Operations

Back in harbour in late September, *Magnificent*'s association with the Air Arm was about to be terminated too. A final three-week training period commenced 25 September when VS 880 was flown on from Shearwater. A two-day operational visit was paid to Boston followed by five days of flying and surface exercises in which *Magnificent*, *St Laurent*, *Assiniboine*, HM Submarine *Alliance* and VS 880 participated.

The last plane airborne was recovered after lunch on 10 October 1956, marked by an appropriate ceremony. Off Halifax all VS 880 aircraft were launched to Shearwater. The ship berthed at Jetty Three in HMC Dockyard and within days the complement was sharply reduced with the departure of the air facility; destoring commenced in anticipation of *Magnificent*'s last trip back to England.

Following Privy Council approval, the Admiralty had been informed in October 1951 that Canada would pay for substantial alterations to *Magnificent*, including the strengthening of the flight deck to take heavier aircraft and the fitting of new equipment such as improved lifts, arrester gear and safety barriers. It was not anticipated that the modernisation refit would take place for two to three years but, after being taken in hand, *Magnificent* would be out of service for at least another two years. To meet this situation, the Admiralty, in the course of preliminary negotiations, presented Naval Headquarters with three alternatives:

1. Borrow a carrier temporarily during the period of refit;
2. exchange the *Magnificent* for a modernised light fleet carrier;
3. purchase one of the partly built light fleet carriers on which construction was stopped in the UK in 1945 and then complete and modernise it.

During a visit to London in November 1951, Mr Brooke Claxton, the Minister of National Defence, discussed the matter with British officials and in the following April, the Cabinet Defence Committee came to the conclusion that it would be best for Canada to acquire her own aircraft carrier to replace *Magnificent*.

During the succeeding years the possibility of retaining *Magnificent*, in addition to a new carrier, as, perhaps a helicopter carrier and training ship, was closely studied but a ministerial decision in 1955 finally ruled out the idea. As *Magnificent*'s career neared its end, the retention of the ship by the RCN was suggested again in a letter from Sir Anthony Eden, the British Prime Minister to the Canadian Prime Minister, Louis St Laurent. The Canadian Naval Board was prepared to recommend placing the ship in Category C reserve, but the government decided in September 1956 that she would be returned to the Royal Navy.

Meanwhile, *Magnificent* soldiered on; sailing on 29 October 1956 she was joined by the *Prestonian* class frigate *Buckingham*, sporting a strange-looking platform over her stern. Off Chebucto Head, *Buckingham* received the first at-sea landing of a HO4S-3 Sikorsky helicopter on a small warship, with the odd-looking platform being a built-to-purpose test deck. The helicopter was provided by HU 21's Detachment 3, Shearwater, and a number of landings were made under a variety of circumstances. Little could anyone envision that these first, cautious experiments would have such a dramatic effect upon Canadian naval aviation.

Suez

Trials were conducted over a period of three months but *Magnificent* departed after the first three days, bound for Belfast, where she arrived on 4 November and began landing stores for the new carrier, (the future *Bonaventure*). By the 7th, she was lying at Tail of Bank, Greenock, waiting a favourable tide for Glasgow where some fifty Sabre jets belonging to the RCAF were to be collected and returned to Canada.

However, fate stepped in and at 2000 a bomb-shell in the form of a signal ordering the ship back to Halifax at best speed had the ship's duty watch and shore authorities scrambling to recall libertymen for immediate departure. By the morning watch on the 8th, *Magnificent* was at sea, Canada-bound, bucking gale-force winds and worsening seas, while the lightened ship breasted the conditions as

best she could. Meanwhile, preparations were made for her new role, acting as a troop ship and headquarters vessel in connection with the United Nations action in the Middle East, cordoning off the Suez Canal in light of the Egyptian/Israeli War then ongoing. The *Magnificent*, despite the weather, made the crossing in five days and eleven hours, arriving in Halifax on the evening of 13 November.

Dockyard and naval personnel swarmed aboard to prepare the ship for Operation 'Rapid Step'. Guns, ammunition, ready-use lockers, etc, were removed and landed in record time and equipment and fitting required for 500 extra men were brought on board. 'A' hangar was converted into a huge dormitory, with double-decked bunks; additional wash places and sanitary facilities were installed and the sonobuoy flat became a sick-bay annex. While this work was in progress, 'B' hangar was rapidly filled with army stores of all descriptions.

The *Magnificent* was moved to Pier 9B to embark army ammunition and 203 vehicles. In the middle watch on Sunday, 18 November the last trucks were hoisted aboard and secured as deck cargo and at 0800 the ship returned to Pier 4 to take on fourteen heavy vehicles. Except for loading the troops, Operation 'Rapid Step' had now been completed. The crew were ready to go but the Canadian government waffled back and forth over its decision to dispatch the ship and troops for the rest of November and the first 11 days of December. The ship and crew remained in limbo, the ship reverting first to eight hours notice, then 24-hours notice. The 950 officers and men of the First Battalion, Queens Own Rifles of Canada, rushed from Calgary, were in a similar state, while the UN pondered over the needs and requirements to make up its newly formed Emergency Force.

A severe tropical storm caused the Magnificent *to heave-to on the three consecutive nights of 11–13 February 1957. With waves easily topping the 37ft height of the flight deck, the cargo of Sabre jets were thoroughly soaked in salt water and on several occasions threatened to break loose.* (DND/Marcom Museum)

Table 1: *PARTICULARS OF* WARRIOR *AND* MAGNIFICENT

	Warrior	*Magnificent (CVL 21)*
Displacement:	13,350 tons standard, 18,200 tons full load	15,770 tons standard, 19,550 tons full load
Length (oa):	694 ft 6in (211.7m)	694 ft 3in (211.6m)
Beam:	80ft 3in (24.5m)	80ft (24.4m)
Draught (max):	23ft 6in (7.2m)	25ft (7.6m)
Machinery:	2-shaft, geared steam turbines, 40,000shp = 25kts.	2-shaft, Parsons geared turbines 40,000shp = 25kts.
Armament:	6 × 4 – 2pdr pom-poms, 19 × 1 – 40mm Bofors	7 × 2 – 40mm Bofors (MkV RP50 mountings), 14 × 1 – 40mm Bofors (MkVC mounting)
Aircraft:	30 (designed max = 48)	34
Radar, etc:	Type 281B air-search with Type 243 IFF; Type 279B with Type 242 IFF; Type 293M S-band target indicator; Type 282 gun control for quad 2pdrs; YE homing beacon.	Type 281B air-search with Type 243 IFF; Type 293M target indicator; two Type 277Q surface warning, Sperry Mk3, Mod1, high resolution surface/navigation set; FV5 VHF/DF; YE homing beacon.
Sonar:	Type 144	Type 149
Complement:	1076	1350

Eventually it was decided that the Queen's Own resembled too closely 'British' forces that were dug in 22 miles south of Port Said, who had not been treating the Egyptian President, Colonel Abdel Nasser, too kindly. Accordingly, they were sent home to Calgary, the equipment unloaded from *Magnificent*, and when completed, Operation 'Rapid Step II' was initiated, loading some 100 tons of supplies, 233 vehicles weighing approximately 800 tons, and four RCAF Otter aircraft, plus 406 army personnel (members of the Royal Canadian Corps of Signals, Royal Canadian Electrical and Mechanical Engineers, Royal Canadian Army Service Corps and a headquarters detachment).

The *Magnificent* slipped her lines on 29 December and Terceira in the Azores hove into view at daybreak on 4 January 1957, with a mail drop made by helicopter. This procedure was repeated at Gibraltar and two days later, the ship was refuelled at sea by the USN oiler *Mississinewa* and reprovisioned by the supply ship USS *Hyades*, both belonging to the USN's Sixth Fleet. This evolution took five hours, with the ships steaming at 12kts, line abreast. Ahead of schedule, *Magnificent* shaped course for Malta for a short visit but on the 8th a signal was received that the ship was to proceed to Port Said with all due haste. Accordingly, speed was increased to 17kts and course altered to comply, with the ship encountering a short but intense storm on the 9th, with Port Said entered on the 10th.

The unloading of the ship began on the 12th, and by the 16th, all the deck cargo and stores from 'B' hangar had been landed, doing in eight days what had been projected as a 20-day task. The ship was externally painted, cleaned throughout and liberty parties of up to 120 landed for conducted tours of Cairo and the Pyramids. Limited night leave for Port Said was also granted but by 20 January the ship had fulfilled all obligations to UNEF and set sail once more, visiting Naples, and entering the Firth of the Clyde and Glasgow on 2 February, where she commenced loading fifty-nine Sabre jets being returned to Canada for use by Reserve RCAF squadrons. As the ship departed, the ship's helicopter departed for the final time, assigned to the new carrier, *Bonaventure*.

Consecutive low pressure areas and severe storms across the Atlantic caused the carrier to heave-to on three consecutive nights during the trip back to Canada, with the loss of some of the deck cargo Sabres a very real possibility. However, by the 14th the weather had moderated and the wind abated, allowing the carrier to work up to 24kts. The ship entered Halifax Harbour for the last time, flying Rear Admiral Bidwell's broad pennant.

The month of March was spent in destoring and on 10 April, *Magnificent* sailed for the last time from Halifax, bound for Plymouth, England, where further work was done to prepare her for paying-off. The ship reverted to the RN on 14 June 1957, with the main draft of personnel still aboard then sent to Belfast for passage home in the new carrier *Bonaventure*, which had commissioned in January. The *Magnificent* was relegated to the RN's Reserve Fleet at Plymouth where she remained until 1965 when she was moved to Faslane for breaking-up.

SIR ROWLAND BAKER, RCNC

In the view of the author, David K Brown, RCNC, the three greatest British naval constructors were William White, Stanley Goodall and Rowland Baker. He never met the first two but had the unforgettable experience of working for Baker and wishes to leave some record of this brilliant, versatile and fearless man, and to provide some idea of why his staff worshipped him. Unattributed quotations are from personal letters from Sir Rowland to the author c1979 while writing the history of the RCNC.[1]

Rowland Baker was born[2] at Upchurch, Sittingbourne, on 3 June 1908; he has written – 'My father was a sailing bargeman. It must be from him that I inherit an almost infinite degree of patience. His father was a ship's carpenter in the days of declining sail and I [learnt] from them both perhaps a feel for floating objects...' Some may doubt the infinite patience but he did inherit a command of the English language unique amongst senior civil servants. At Upchurch Village School he was always top of the class and was successful in cricket and football. He entered Chatham Dockyard as a shipwright apprentice where, after four gruelling years of the Dockyard School[3], he was selected as a constructor cadet. He joined the Royal Naval College in September 1928, together with Alfred Sims and Vic Hall and two private students. Sims was a very hard working student and set the pace but Baker's more light hearted approach won him second place, just missing the coveted 1st class certificate.

He then went to the Mediterranean Fleet for a year as a Constructor Lieutenant, serving in *Sussex*, *Achates*, *Basilisk* and *Royal Sovereign* and, during a visit to Rome, received a papal blessing. Returning to the UK early in 1933 he worked as Assistant Constructor, 2nd class, in Portsmouth Dockyard. On promotion to 1st class in the summer of 1934 he moved to the Admiralty, where he worked on sloops – this included the trials of *Grimsby*, *Halcyon*, *Bittern* and *Kingfisher*, and the design calculations for the *Black Swan* and later the *Kingfisher*s. 'So I had a nostalgic feeling for the sloops.'[4] There was a brief interval at Sheerness in 1937–38 before returning to the Admiralty as Constructor[5] in September 1938. He had expected to be in charge of his old sloop section but '...the section had been divided and I was given the poorer end.'

Minesweepers

The immediate task was the structural design of the minesweeping sloop *Seagull*, the first all welded ship for the RN. Externally, she looked like the riveted ships of the *Halcyon* class (except for the flush plating) but Baker had designed a radically new structure which would still have been seen as advanced ten years later. The framing was longitudinal instead of transverse and the seams in the plating were butt welded. Private shipyards were, with rare exceptions, hostile to welding and *Seagull* was built in Devonport Dockyard alongside a riveted half sister. Even though she was the first welded ship to be built in the yard, there were important savings in time of building, in weight and in cost compared with her sister.[6]

Baker was very proud of his design for the *Bangor* class and was upset by criticism of them. They were designed as very simple wire sweepers but soon became overcrowded with magnetic and acoustic sweeps, radar and more AA guns, and the men to man them. Despite their size, they were very seaworthy craft and forty-five were built in the UK with others in Canada, India and Hong Kong (modified for the IJN). Baker seems less proud of the bigger, more capable and much more expensive ships of the *Algerine* class. At this time he was also responsible for the design of the unusual, armoured, *Ranger* class of oilers, paddle-ship conversions and auxiliary minelayers but landing craft were beginning to occupy more and more of his time. Few of these vessels had a Staff Requirement 'until after trials and completion'. His assistant director was Woolard who allowed his young constructor unusual authority. The DNC, Goodall, was concerned over this delegation but Woolard assured him that Baker was worthy of it.

Sir Rowland Baker as commodore Royal Canadian Naval Volunteer Reserve. (Courtesy Rear Admiral and Professor S M Davis)

Landing Craft

'My introduction was like this. In the early '30s there were a few Motor Landing Craft [MLC]. These were nearly useless because the Staff Requirements were fouled up, partly by the Staff and partly by DNC.' The constructor responsible was retired early but Baker feels that the chief '...did not understand our business, which is basically not to agree with the Staff, or argue with them, but control them – they can only have what we [constructors] can offer'. He continues:

> The error in the MLC was quite fundamental. They were intended as ship-to-shore ferries...would be carried on board, put in the water and loaded with one or two vehicles, or some men, to take them to the shore and come back for more. Although they were and had to be specialised, custom built, their use was always to be in association with the carrier ships which were the current troopers.

This led to a weight limitation and, in turn, to low power, while low endurance was accepted. 'Worse was to come, someone (in the Army I expect) put enormous stress on

ability to unbeach. This led to the use of Gill or Hotchkiss so called jet propulsion, actually pumps.'

Thus when unloaded they had a high centre of gravity while when loaded they had a *very* high centre of gravity.[7] They were reasonably ('or was it unreasonably') boat shaped below the waterline but the vehicle deck was above the water and occupied the full beam of the craft. The area of the vehicle deck (strictly the second moment of area) was greater than that of the waterplane. They had plated bulwarks and freeing ports. Modern readers will note the similarity with Ro-Ro ferries.

'By the mid '30s a new staff look decided that landings would probably be in Europe and they wanted the MLCs to cross the channel. Someone had the bright idea that crossing the Channel at $4^3/_4$kts would be hazardous so they were tried stern first, achieving 5kts. It was then decided to tow them behind a destroyer. A trial was laid on with five boats in line behind the destroyer, bow first, and ballasted to load condition.

> At the eleventh hour I was seconded from the sloop section...and went on board a *V & W* class destroyer and off we went. We followed the track of the Portsmouth-Ryde ferry intending to pass through the Solent. I was sitting in a deck chair on the quarter deck, we got up to 14kts, when suddenly the first MLC capsized, immediately followed by the others. My explanation, spray had come over the bow ramps and flooded the vehicle deck; a sort of flash flood and the stability vanished. This finished the MLCs of the day and, I thought, my association with landing craft. I had, however, learnt that freeing ports would never deal with flash floods and that even in landing craft the load should be kept low.

While Baker was at Sheerness there were considerable developments in landing craft. The Inter Service Training and Development Centre (ISTDC) had been set up under Captain Maund and they had sponsored propeller driven Assault and Mechanised Landing Craft, both designed by Ken Barnaby of Thornycrofts. Both these craft were successful and built in considerable numbers during the War.

Baker saw service in a number of Royal Navy ships at the beginning of his career as a naval constructor in the early 1930s. One of these ships was the cruiser Sussex, *seen here at Malta in November 1932.* (Courtesy John Roberts)

On his return to the Admiralty, he had responsibility for landing craft.

> After Dunkirk it became evident to Churchill first I think that if we were ever to get back into Europe we should have to have a new look at invasion techniques. In June 1940 he demanded of the Admiralty, landing craft to carry the largest tanks then envisaged – 40 tons. The staff requirement was offered me by Capt Maund (ISTDC); it said beach slope of 1 in 35, three tanks of 40 tons and a speed of 10kts. He gave me the overall tank dimensions (of course there were no existing 40 tonners then, or for a long time) and said to land in $2\frac{1}{2}$ft of water. ... The general view was that simplicity was all, but I felt that some elaboration was essential to overcome the errors that had beset the MLC. My innovations related to features as follows – The appearance of the craft, flush decked with a hold. Floating dock type section in which the inertia of the water on deck could not approach that of the waterplane. Acceptance of the fact that the bow ramp would always leak.

It will be noted that these are almost identical to the recommendations following the loss of the *Herald of Free Enterprise*.[8] Baker continues on the subject of the bow ramp:

> I arranged the tank deck [bottom of the hold] above the hinge at the bow and fitted preventer watertight doors at the highest point. The space between the ramp and the doors drained outboard. This system worked like a charm, the little well so formed half filled with water, and it did not really matter if [the] ramp was tight or not. Most of the tank deck was below water. There was conventional close subdivision under the tank deck and in the wing spaces.
>
> For leaving the beach, there were kedge anchors, also used as normal anchors, as the LCT [Landing Craft Tank] anchored by the stern (a device worthy

The escort sloop Wren *of the* Black Swan *class in February 1943. Baker did the design calculations for the class, which were the last and largest of the prewar sloop designs.* (MOD)

of more general adoption). Propeller guards were fitted against beach obstructions.

The LCTs were flat bottomed, hard chine barges, with buttock flow, and a long run. Gawn (Superintendent of AEW – the Admiralty model test tank) could not fault the form.[9]

> The craft were powered by what we could get, two Hall Scott Defender 500bhp petrol engines, downgraded to 350bhp. John Browns and Fairfields worked on the detailed drawings and twenty boats were ordered from [the] shipbuilders; the first was delivered by Hawthorn Leslie in November 1940.
>
> This was the first heavy vehicle landing craft in the world. She did not really need trials or evaluation to prove right and in fact the concept has never been questioned. Before the first order had been completed the view gained acceptance that their first use would be from Egypt so after trials they were broken down and shipped out as deck cargo in sections.
>
> However, having got a start "everyone" found the need for improvement and this is the story of landing craft from this time on. It seems absurd now, but it was only after the first LCT was running that it was realised that not only tanks but other vehicles could be, and should be, catered for. A slight increase in beam...in the LCT(2) [meant] it could carry twice as many trucks while three engines in place of two gave a slight increase in speed. [Goodall noted in his diary that he did not believe Baker's speed estimate but the following day's entry said that he had checked the estimate and 'Baker was right'.]

The Bangor *class minesweeper* Whitehaven. *Baker was intensely proud of his design for these vessels.* (Tom Molland)

At the beginning of 1941 there was a general realisation that numbers were the name of the game. At this time CJW Hopkins, RCNC, was working in the Ministry of Supply as Director Naval Land Equipment [the fabulous trench digging machine – "Nellie"] When we were forced out of Europe the need for this equipment lapsed and the Paxman engines were adapted for LCTs. The first LCTs were built by shipbuilders but the outcry was absolutely deafening because of the riveting. So Hopkins was made responsible for LCT production under the Controller and authorised to get the actual building done by structural engineers. A vast programme was envisaged, but no shipyard labour was to be used to minimise the effect on merchant and warship building. Hopkins organised groups of structural engineers in Glasgow and in the North East coast who organised the use of disused shipyards. The technical organisation was left to me and the shipbuilder's drawings for LCT(2)s made by John Brown and Fairfields were "structuralised"...by the Stockton Construction Co. At this time Hopkins really had a marvellous way of dealing with the firms. He acted as though they were angels and he God. (But they all needed me).

The next development step was in May 1941 when the LCT(2) was stretched by 32ft, Paxman engines fitted and became the LCT(3) (a prototype had been completed as a 32ft extended LCT(1)). The basic drawings still came from the shipbuilder but all production was with the structurals...235 LCT(3) were finally built.

In late 1941 plans were made for the LCT(4):

The reasons for the change lay in the realisation that the Normandy beaches were very flat and it was unreasonable to have craft with any considerable stern trim. The LCT Staff Requirement made them expendable – a single cross channel voyage was the cry. They were built of very light scantlings and I also made a mistake. They had a sharp upward break at the poop. I thought the discontinuity would not matter for a single cross channel trip[10] – nor did it, but I should have known better than to believe that sort of limitation.

The LCT(4) had the 'same bow ramp, bow doors and side pontoon feature as the earlier boat, but the tank deck was above the waterline and the vehicles were exposed.' Fairly large propellers were essential but 'even so the draught of the LCT(4) was less than 5ft fully loaded. Construction continued until the end of the war.' In November 1941 Baker was given a special allowance of £150 – then a considerable sum – in recognition of his unusual responsibilities.

Landing Ships

In the summer of 1940 Churchill ordered a tank landing ship [LST] – this was meant to be a giant. It led to first of all the conversion of three Maracaibo tankers[11] to carry tanks and launch them over the bow direct onto the beach. These ships were chosen because of their shallow draught, but no one liked their maximum speed of 10kts. The first was completed by Greenwells of Sunderland in July 1941. She was, me thinks, the first tank landing ship in the world. Her trials proved that ships as distinct from craft could land on a beach, disembark tanks over a ramp and get off again by kedging.

Concurrently with the Maracaibo conversions a new design of tank landing ships, LST(1), the *Boxer* class, was undertaken by me. They were very elaborate even though the Staff reduced Winston's Giant to three ships to do the same job. (They were often referred to as "Winettes") This design was undertaken with no bench marks; we went from the LCT(1) direct to a ship 400ft long with a speed of 18kts, to carry 13 Churchill tanks in the hold, 27 MT on the upper deck, an army complement of 13 officers and 180 men and a naval crew of 20 officers and 143 men. We fitted a very elaborate disembarking ramp devised by Stothert and Pitt[12] and a lift to take MT up and down. ...All the systems worked. These were the first tank landing ships in the world to be specifically designed for the purpose.

Long before their completion, but before the first Maracaibo trial in 1941, the condition of the war seemed to change from the need for raids on distant beaches to the invasion of Europe. The number of tanks seemed to grow astronomically and it became quite obvious that none of our schemes were grave enough. The question was asked of me – Could LCTs cross the Atlantic under their own power? The answer was only if they were made larger – I thought 300ft. This led to two separate developments; we asked the Americans to build seven LST(1) under Lend Lease and I produced a sketch design[13] for the Atlantic LST which was a marriage of the LST(1) and the LCT(3).

A suggestion from Capt Hussey (ISTDC) led to a floating dock type LSD[14] 'which I claim as an invention of mine'. 'The idea of a "Go Between" was not dead either and Thornycrofts (Ken Barnaby) produced a proposal for a double-ended small LCT. Actually, I would not agree the double-end[15] and this proposal saw the light as LCT(5)' – the double ended version finally appearing in the USN as the LCT(6).

Visit to The USA

By the autumn of 1941 we were therefore building LCT, LCM, LCA and some LST but we were scarcely touching the fringe of the possible requirement for numbers and it was decided that only American help could enable this requirement to be met. So at the end of November 1941 I was sent to Washington with Captain Hussey and Cdr Todhunter (of DNE) to explain to the US authorities what we had in mind. They already had drawings of the LCT(1-4) and of the LST(1) and we took my sketch of the Atlantic LCT, the sketch design of the LSD and of the LCT(5).

We arrived in Washington on 20 November and on the 28 were taken by Admiral Sir Charles Little to see Admiral Stark, Admiral Robinson (the US Controller), the Chief of the Bureau of Ships and Captain Cochrane (Later Admiral and himself Chief of the Bureau). Actually, of these only Cochrane was clearly on our side. It took a week for Stark to turn us down. The curse of the situation was that we could only get building done under Lend Lease if the appropriate US Service would certify that the items met a US need.

Actually, the US Marine Corps were in conflict at this time with the Bureau of Ships, for the Bureau had a few LCMs, rather like our LCM(1) and the Marines disliked them so much that they had gone to Higgins of New Orleans to get their own version. Higgins was already in the field for he had sold his Eureka boat (originally a rum runner) to the USN and to us as a raiding craft. Hundreds of these were built during the war, and at the end they were beginning to replace the LCA generally. The LCM which Higgins produced for the US Marines was a conversion of some boats he was producing for Peru. They had a floating dock type section and a bow ramp. Finally, hundreds were built for the USN and ourselves as the LCM(3) and at the end of the

Wartime photograph of an unnamed Algerine *class minesweeper – another Baker design.* (MOD)

war we built similar craft as the LCM(7). By the time we got to Higgins, events had made me the expert and though it was nearly unbelievable, what I said went. All the LCM(3) had the bow ramp 3in wider and kedge anchors because I said so.

Someone who was at the Washington meetings said that after demolishing the USN studies, Baker 'had them eating out of his hand'.

Commander Todhunter has some wonderful stories[16] of the first meeting of 'Byker' (as he was often known in recognition of his Medway accent) and Higgins.

> Basically, Higgins and Mr Byker were from the same mould, no mincing of words, no tempering of the wind to the shorn lamb, but to start with they had some flaming rows, maybe because Higgins suspected that Byker might be a secret agent from the enemy camp (BuShips)...but once he got over that and realised that he was the one person in the world who knew as much about landing craft as he did himself, they got on like a house on fire.

Baker continues:

> Meanwhile Captain Cochrane suggested to me that while the rest of our mission was deadlocked we should get on in BuShips Preliminary Design with the Atlantic LCT. After all, Admiral Stark would not know that I was working on a bench. This period fixed all the basic parameters of the design. Cochrane also suggested that if the navy were not prepared to certify perhaps the army would so I used to walk up the road from the old Navy Building[17] to the old Munitions Building. The initial army reaction was that there were plenty of US ferries that would do so I had to go and examine some of these and reject them. Then came Pearl Harbour and we lost the Navy Department altogether. Again Cochrane sent me to the Maritime Commission for by this time it was agreed that non-warship firms would need to be brought in. The outcome of this was that the sketch design of the LST(2) was brought to the contract design stage by the Mari-

LCT(3) 398 *in 1944. Note the single pom-poms in the*
bridge wings and the stern anchor. (CMP)

time Commission who also made initial contact with
the Dravo Corporation of Pittsburgh.

It will be noted that this account differs in almost every
aspect from that given by Niedermeir.[18]

> Then at the end of December Churchill arrived in
> Washington and, in a flash, landing craft rose in
> priority from 10 to 2. BuShips took the LST(2) back
> [pace Niedermeir] and all our requirements were
> accepted, immediate orders being placed for these,
> for LSD, for LCT(5), for LCM and LCPL. I had two
> schemes for getting the LCT(5) across the Atlantic,
> as deck cargo in sections or complete on the upper
> deck of LSTs. Both worked throughout the war. The
> design of the LSD was brought to the contract stage
> by Gibbs and Cox. Nearly all of these original orders
> for us under Lend Lease were actually taken over by
> the USN.

Baker's idea of carrying LCTs as deck cargo was initially
opposed due to lack of cranes at the destination but he
suggested carrying them on inclined ramps so that they
could be launched into the water. This scheme was then
validated by a model test at Haslar.

Richard Moss[19] writes that one of Baker's most awe-in-
spiring traits was in astounding those present at a meeting
with a completely new solution. Critics said it was sheer
luck but they did not know that he sat up half the next
night checking that his hunch was sound.

> By February 1942 the programme was in full swing

and I was able to return to the UK, being relieved by
McMurray to provide continuing technical expertise. I actually made the Atlantic crossing in HMS
Delhi which had been re-armed in America. The
vulnerability of this class (C and D of World War 1)
to the smallest underwater damage almost proved
that I was the first and last Constructor officer to
take passage in one of them.

In the summer of 1942, I was promoted to Chief
Constructor and given a new title, Superintendent of
Landing Craft. I was transferred to London and took
over LCT production from Hopkins who still had an
office in Bush House (Ministry of Supply). I also
took over all production of minor landing craft from
SCW [Superintendent Contract Built Warships] (CJ
Butt). My instructions were that, under Controller,
and without stealing any shipyard labour, I was to
maintain production of all types. Unofficially, I was
supposed to be McMurray's Guide, Comforter and
Friend and the principal liaison between COHQ and
DNC. Woolard had been my ADNC throughout all
the time until now and he had supported me at every
stage. McMurray had to proceed with a lot of projects that I had started with the team that I had
nurtured and he deserved great credit[20] ...At the end
of the war the US Army awarded me the Medal of
Freedom with Silver Palms, whilst Dorling was still
depreciating my efforts.

As regards my work in the production field, I did
inherit a going concern, whereas in the design field
I had started from nothing.[21] It was also a great
asset that the design side was in stability under my
control (and very hard pressed). Later in 1942 Lord
Reith was brought into the Admiralty as Director
Combined Operations Material and my office space
was provided by him in 36 Whitehall. He really

would have liked to "take me over" but by this time DNC (rightly) could not agree for, of course, I used all DNC's facilities including the WPSs [Warship Production Superintendents], who were all very much my seniors. However, there was a rapport between Reith and me – the Mountain and the Midget.

There is a tale told by Cdr Todhunter[22] of a very high level meeting at which Baker was present but told not to speak unless called upon. However, the debate became too great for his silence and (quoting Todhunter's attempt to reproduce 'Byker's' accent): 'Excuse me Admiral [Mountbatten]. This 'ere General talks about beaches of 1 in 30. That one says of 1 in 25. Naow this one mentions 1 in 15! You'll let me know when the bloody beaches slope the other way, wontcher?'

> Mountbatten led the laughter and ensured a sensible response. At this time also Merrington (RCNC) was on the staff of COHQ and in a way DNC had three advisors there, Merrington, McMurray and me, but whenever there was any disagreement the old ISTDC element (Hussey) batted for me.
>
> I did have some rapport also with Mountbatten for he arrived on the scene just as we went to Washington and there is no doubt that Hussey even before that time together with the Admiral encouraged me at every turn.

In 1978 Earl Mountbatten was to write[23]:

> I had two constructors on my staff in Combined Operations. The senior one was Merrington and the junior one Baker. They were both excellent but Baker had a flare for designing new types of ship and craft, notably, the LSD, or Landing Ship Dock...
>
> After the war, when some one got an award for a little flap on the LCT ramp I put in a claim to the Royal Commission on Awards to inventors for some objects of the above vessels. The RCNC estab-

lishment[24] ... proved to them that all I ever did was slightly less than ought to have been expected of me. No award but the Secretary of the Commission wrote me an extraordinary letter which said in effect "Did I remember Admiral Byng?".

The question of awards to civil servants doing their job, rather better than usual, is, and remains, a difficult one but Baker certainly felt that he had been badly treated by the standards of the day.

Canada

When the War finished, the landing craft empire collapsed and Baker was appointed DNC's special design assistant. 'The scheme did not work in my time' due to lack of supporting staff but 'I did get some benefit in that I got a broad idea of what was going on and thought a lot about Design'. One product of this period was an interesting design of hull form, with nearly semi circular sections, which would remain upright no matter how much was flooded so that, as Baker put it, if the worst happened 'it may be abandoned with due decorum.'

Baker became aware that the RCNC officer in Canada was anxious to come home and that the Canadians wanted a replacement. Since he was almost the most junior (acting) Chief Constructor, he was concerned that he might be reverted in the postwar reductions and hence he decided to volunteer for Canada where his old experience in sloop design would be valuable.

> I got to Ottawa and had a weekend turnover from Harrison and then found I was expected to design

The versatility of the LCT design is illustrated by this view of LCT(R) 425 – an LCT(3) modified to carry 1080 5in rockets for shore bombardment. Conversions were also made from LCT(2), with 792 rockets, and in both cases the modifications were reversible. (CMP)

The frigate St Laurent *demonstrates her seakeeping qualities on 9 October 1957. Although there was some rivalry as to the relative qualities of Baker's design for the* St Laurent *and the Admiralty design for the* Whitby *there seems to have been little to choose between them.* (USN)

an icebreaker. I scarcely knew what the word meant and there was certainly no British experience to help me. There was also a danger, for while the RCN had got the plans and calculations for the US Coast Guard *East Wind* class, there was an opposition group in the Department of Transport, [who had considerable experience of icebreakers and did not want the navy to get involved. However, there was considerable support for the RCN] so we took the basic *East Wind* design, changed the steel (to UK DW) altered the bow shape and made a few cosmetic alterations (including missing out the bow propeller) and set off. *Labrador,* as she was called, was another success.

The Canadian Navy was clear that new escort vessels were needed and the Government had allocated funds. The original intention, backed by Harrison, was to buy the *Whitby* design from the UK, complete with working drawings, following the prewar practice of the RCN. However, the slow development of the *Whitby*s and the desire of the RCN to 'Canadianise' led to the idea of a home design. Baker says 'This encouraged my private wish to embark on a design' but there were real difficulties. The small design team was competent to tackle a sketch design but there was little experience in detail work. The naval staff wanted British sonar and A/S weapons and British machinery with which the Canadian engineer officers were familiar and gradually a team was built up.

> I [Baker] became more Canadian than the Canadians. Fundamentally, I said you cannot rely for ever on the British, you cannot rely forever on German and Milne [design consultants] what you need is to help me by strengthening the Constructor Staff at

Ottawa and setting up a central drawing office that will become competent to develop any design that I produce.

This constructor staff was originally built up from RCNC officers on loan but Baker was slowly able to recruit Canadians, often putting them through the RCNC course at Greenwich.

> I set out to please everybody, usually a recipe for disaster. The ships were all welded and built on a unit system, no plating less than 3/8in thick and, hopefully, no force fits. My philosophy regarding basic naval architecture was, at this time matured, even if wrong, and whilst some of the differences between *St Laurent* and *Whitby* could be dismissed as cosmetic, and my activity to have an appearance different from the British could be dismissed as rank Canadianisation, there were differences deliberately introduced by me to satisfy myself.
>
> – The actual form
> – The dimensions
> – Above water profile
> – De-icing scheme
> – Anti slamming (also cafeteria messing and bunks)

> I tried to please the British by making my dimensions conservative compared to the Type 12s, by having a model run at Haslar and [I] had good relations with NG Holt [designer of *Whitby*] and Gawn [Supt AEW]. As regards the form, I would not follow Holt in his fine entrance and relatively low prismatic, so the resistance characteristics of my

The St Laurent *class frigate* Margaree *in November 1957.* (USN)

ships were marginally inferior, even so Gawn committed himself to saying "A reasonable compromise" [but all design is compromise]. Also my beam was greater, my displacement greater. I had a flush upper deck and put the A/S mortar under cover. I argued that de-icing would be less of a problem if the above water surfaces were smooth. This led to plated masts, later copied by everybody. I also argued that you could not stop water coming on board so efforts should be made to let it get away as easily as possible, which led to well rounded deck edges and a turtle back fo'c'sle.[25] I very much wanted to have a rising M curve but partly lost my nerve, even so my midship section was much finer than the Type 12s and my sections much more V shaped[26] in the slamming area. (We nearly slipped up on my finer midship section because of difficulties in getting the Y100 boilers in!)

All in all I tried to incorporate the Staff Requirements in a model which included the experience of all the design work I had ever done, or wished to do, including plenty of space (as I've often said, the cheapest quality to provide).

When the first vessel was completed the Queen and the Mountbattens visited her in Oslo and on one of the Mountbatten visits to Bath the Earl said to Edwina, 'This is the young man who designed that lovely Canadian ship you were on the other day'.

There was a lot more to Baker's Canadian career, which lasted eight years. He was president of the Ottawa Cricket Club (getting a hat trick) and played golf and bridge with enthusiasm. Technically, he found that the new central drawing office had no schedule or programme for the output of drawings, which he soon remedied and proved a lesson which would stand him in good stead in his later career. He planned the modernisation of the carrier *Bonaventure* and that of the older, *River* class frigates, 'which I improved fantastically by making them flush decked'. At one meeting of the Canadian Naval Board, all members were opposed to his proposal to which he responded, 'Since all of you gentlemen disagree with me, it just goes to show that I am probably right'.[27] When he returned to England the Canadian Naval Staff wrote formally to the Admiralty (asking that their letter be shown to Baker) praising his work and saying, 'His initiative, zeal and resourcefulness

have played a major part in enabling this country to design and build major warships entirely from Canadian resources for the first time in history'. At the time of Sir Rowland's death it was apparent that he was still admired by many in Canada.

Dreadnought

I came back from Canada in the fall of 1956 to find that no one really wanted me and that the DNC had authorised a circulated memorandum proving that the *Whitby* class were superior in every way to my *St Laurent*s. His main point was that the *Whitby*s were 450 tons lighter. He could not have foreseen the *Whitby* modification which added 400+[tons].[28] When rumours of the re-organisation of Controller's department began to circulate, I found that even Sir John Lang [Permanent Secretary] was plumping for a DGS [Director General Ships, more usually known as DG Ships] much my junior. However, during 1957 Lord Selkirk who wanted to implement the re-organisation came to Bath and interviewed Sims, Palmer and me. I found this a little encouraging (and depressing). In November Sir Victor Shepherd told me he had recommended me to Mountbatten and that wheels were being set in motion to put me in charge of the nuclear submarine development. I was sworn to secrecy and told to wait.

The story of the *Dreadnought* project has been told elsewhere[29] and this account will be confined to Baker's enormous contribution and to the troubles which he experienced.

In the fall of 1957 Rickover told Mountbatten that we should never get off the ground (under the water!) unless we radically changed the organisation, but if we did change and he was satisfied that we meant it, he would sell us a reactor plant to give us a start. Of course he did not have the authority to do this nor Mountbatten that to accept. So they set about it. Note that Rickover's beginnings were incredibly humble. His attitude to Mountbatten was near idolatry; you could not just say he was a snob, he was, of course.

It was in, I think, February 1958, that Rickover came over to help Mountbatten get Board and government approval for his scheme. As promised, Mountbatten explained to him that he had set up a Project, under a Constructor, to deal with the whole thing. I went to Derby to see Rickover but he would not see me. The second time we met (in the Admiralty Board Room) he again ignored me.

Finally, Mountbatten convinced Rickover that Baker was the best choice.

My own views alternated between elation at the prospect and terror. Terror because just when they were about to sign a Government to government agreement, I realised that no one of those who would have to be on my staff (except Starks), approved of me in any way, or of the scheme. They had pottered about for several years, and now had not only a solution but a chieftain imposed on them. Of course they all hated it. There was one favourable thing, Terence Ridley had been appointed as the head of the Engineer-in-Chief nuclear element; on the whole he was happy to have me as chief, and he had no *amour propre*. My terror derived in part from the conviction that even if we had a Rickover reactor, all and sundry would want to "improve" it and feed in their national ideas throughout the ship. In fact having a *Skipjack* reactor could have opened the field that it was in my personal interest to close. I did succeed in this and still believe that in so far as our nuclear submarine programme has been a success it is mainly due, first to Rickover selling us his bit and second to me for insisting that the S5W plant be used by us in an environment similar to *Skipjack*, and that we should buy from America a complete machinery installation.

This led to a lengthy debate on whether the Dounreay prototype British reactor was still needed. Baker as Technical Chief Executive took the line that we should accept anything that Rickover could provide and build on it to create a UK expertise.

Neither the AEA [Atomic Energy Authority] nor the Treasury liked this very much and I did not get enormous support from within the Admiralty or from Rickover. Rickover was particularly sarcastic about our Dounreay activities although it originated from his Idaho experiment. However, in the end he must have supported me and my only other support came from Sir John Cockcroft. Harwell practically washed their hands of us (though not Risley) and we were warned that the UKAEA Safety rules would be applied to us with the utmost rigour. They were.

The author was responsible, under Baker, for the final nuclear safety trials and feels that he is too hard in his comments on the AEA at this point; to me they seemed firm but reasonable over the safety of a potentially hazardous installation.

In 1958 the whole of the Admiralty submarine activity was concentrated in one block at Bath and the major companies involved set up appropriate divisions. 'The fore end of *Dreadnought* was designed to take account of the sonar system then under development by DGW and was to include DNC's plans for ballast, accommodation, stability etc.'

There was, of course, an extreme subtlety in my title. I was not a Director nor a Deputy, just Technical Chief Executive and was not even promoted. No part of the organisation was directly controlled by me; not even the planning for I got a planner, WH Barnes, to whom we owe a lot.

The author joined the project about 18 months before *Dreadnought* completed and was surprised to find, for the first time in his career, that everyone in every profession was working as one to a schedule with dates for each key activity to complete. This organisation was initiated by Baker and detailed by Barnes with the result that *Dreadnought* completed on time and on cost, the first major defence project to do so for a very long time.

Success in building *Dreadnought* (and within the cost estimates) derived from the validity of such plans, their acceptance, the favourable publicity given to the project and also from the fact that US supplies often came ahead of schedule.

All the Bath departments seconded staff into my group, but as Rickover pointed out, as I did not write their "fitness reports", they looked elsewhere for reward. However, I did have access to Controller [Peter Reid], in part to Mountbatten [First Sea Lord] and I believe the geographical concentration of the group finally brought the realisation that loyalty to the project overrode loyalty to cloth.

Again, it is suggested that Baker is wrong and that his own burning determination had a great deal to do with the loyalty to the group. The annual Submarine Dinner and the Christmas Party, to both of which Baker made hilarious contributions, were a major factor in achieving group identity.

So it seemed to me that if I could keep the whole team to work to the plans which they had prepared for doing all the work – wherever – success would be assured. Regular project meetings started to show promise, but I also initiated a Change Notice Procedure which inhibited change and importantly treated all alike. ...though I could if I wished complain to Controller or 1SL [1st Sea Lord] I did not wish and my sanctions were minimal. [see final section for the terror with which it was implemented]

I wanted to order our second nuclear submarine *Valiant*, but even after the decision was made to design her on the basis of Dounreay aft and *Dreadnought* forward, there was difficulty because Dounreay was so far unproven. However the chance had to be taken and it seemed that by the end of 1962 that we had a small set pattern of nuclear submarine building; *Dreadnought* on trial, *Valiant* half completed on the slipway and DSMP [Dounreay Submarine Prototype] just beginning to move.

It was a very busy time, and the author well remembers a very difficult and rushed journey from Arran (*Dreadnought* trials) to more trials to Dounreay. 'Then came Polaris and a new set of difficulties.'

Polaris

During 1962 Admiral Le Fanu had written a memorandum outlining a possible organisation for a UK Polaris development. It included an overlord and, in fact, seemed to wish to take the whole activity away from the established set up – DGS. I wrote a paper saying we had a perfectly good submarine set up – but I did not know then that DGS (Sims) was preparing to abolish the whole *Dreadnought* project as such, arguing that with the impending completion of *Dreadnought* continuing activity could be dealt with in the 'usual way'. It is perhaps fair to point out that, though a special project is a very good way of dealing with an unusual task, it is often at the expense of delay elsewhere. The immediate consequence was that a high level mission went to the States, including two senior members of Baker's staff, and he was not even informed!

> In the meantime Le Fanu (Controller) got approval for his organisation. I was sent for and given a piece of paper and he said there you have it. Actually his organisation took the submarine activity out of DGS and me with it so what Le Fanu gave me although it included promotion was not what I had been arguing for. ...I was soon satisfied that Le Fanu's scheme was superior to mine and enabled C Block to build and outfit the submarine whilst someone else worried about the rest of the programme.

The Polaris Management Board which included me was set up before I joined and all our field activities were run by monthly meetings at which field officers reported to the Board in the PERT Milestone framework. The arrangements worked, the programme was completed on time. I attribute this to two factors apart from national priority: people and planning in depth. The time scale we were allowed five years to get a ship on station – was short but just right.

There were various ways of getting the ship. It would be possible to use the US drawings of their submarine which would mean a lot of re-tooling, one could cut *Valiant* in half and insert a missile section (as *George Washington* was produced) or to use an after end similar to *Valiant*, graft it to a missile space as in the US boats and add a new bow. The latter seemed to be the best choice. Baker concludes:

> I still feel that the resulting overall organisation and the methods used were inevitable, and an inevitable development from previous successful practice. The lesson for the Royal Corps now is that for success

we have to ensure that we give as much attention to the Sketch Design of a Programme as we do to the Sketch Design of the Artifact. Just like Marks and Spencer.

Baker – The Man and his Achievement

His technical record of success after success speaks for itself. *Seagull* and her welded hull, the Improved *Black Swan*, *Bangor*s, *Algerine*s then almost all the landing craft and the landing ships, including a major influence on USN programmes, the LST and LSD; after the War the magnificent *St Laurent*s and other Canadian work, and the *Dreadnought* and *Polaris* programmes as his crowning glory. No wonder that Earl Mountbatten wrote:

> I was instrumental in getting Baker put onto the design of the *Dreadnought* as I thought he would be just the right person to design our first nuclear submarine, and a great success he made of it, as you know. I was very happy that we were able to get him a knighthood.

He received the KB (Knight Bachelor) in the New Year's Honours List of 1968, a very unusual honour for a civil servant of his rank. He retired in September 1968 but returned to sort out some of the many problems of the MK24 torpedo.

Later he tried to develop a steel platform design, *Balaena*, for the North Sea oil industry. It was to adhere to the sea bottom like an inverted bucket, and so be very difficult to lift out of wet sand. It was to be built on its side for towing out to the site across shallow water. On arrival, it would be tilted and sunk without needing external power. The scheme failed for lack of funds and because it was a year late for the market.[30]

Working for him was terrifying until one learnt to ignore his language and appreciate his ability and loyalty to his staff. The author worked under Baker from about 18 months before *Dreadnought* completed (mainly on nuclear safety matters) until about two years after (as trouble shooter). His ability to switch from the senior civil servant to the bargee was devastating to the uninitiated.

Baker's idea of Change Notices has been mentioned earlier – the reality was very different. One would put the proposal to him in a cardboard file and a few days later one would be summoned to the Presence. As you went through the door the file would be thrown at you with a roar of 'I'm not signing this f— rubbish. What are you wasting my b— time for?' I was very proud that, after a short and noisy debate, he signed all the changes I put to him. Many years later I found that he signed virtually everything and the shouting was just to keep us on our toes. A modern Industrial Tribunal would die of shock if they were told of the language he used to lead his team. He could be kind, too. We had some problems with *Dreadnought* after completion and I had to cut corners with the financial arrangements to keep the boat running. My boss did not want to know but eventually Baker saw copies of my letters and wrote me a little note in his own (almost illegible) hand – 'Cor Mate, you ain't 'alf sticking your neck out. Don't worry. I'll back you if it goes wrong.' I had, in fact, covered myself fairly well but, even so, Baker's note was very welcome. It was acts like that which made his staff worship him – it was worship in the sense of the Greek Gods; Zeus could and would hurl thunderbolts if he was not satisfied. Perhaps his only weakness was that he took less trouble in dealing with his seniors than his juniors; even then the greatest, like Mountbatten and Le Fanu saw his merit.

He was fun, too; his ribald speeches at parties were unforgettable, more for the way in which they were put over than for their content. There are great people in every generation and there are still young men and women prepared to kick the system – and their seniors – but I do believe 'Mr Byker' is unrepeatable, the greatest man I met.

Annex – Baker's Views on Sloops

The following is taken verbatim from his letter of 10 January 1979.

> I joined the sloop section in 1933. VG Shepheard was the constructor (Shortly relieved by AWG Stanton). I relieved Ivor King who went to Sheerness. Because of financial stringency there was a period in which

The Royal Navy's first nuclear submarine, HMS Dreadnought, *shortly before commissioning on 17 April 1963 at Vickers-Armstrongs yard in Barrow-in-Furness.* (CMP)

the cheap little sloops had more activity than any other class – certainly more continuity. When I joined the *Grimsby* class was completing, they were basically cheap patrol and minesweeping vessels. They did in fact represent the end of their particular line. (1931 programme, I think.) The ships in the immediate preceding programme were (I think) 'Repeat *Shorehams*', before that *Shorehams* and before that *Bridgewater*, the first post war design.

This last was one of DNC's disasters. The data available was not good enough for the skills available and the outcome was that the profile of these little ships was destroyer like, a focsle OK, but generally low freeboard.[31] Then they came out heavy and when the first one was completed the range of stability was deficient (57deg, I think) and DNC had to go to the Board and say the focsle had to be extended aft (and ballast added) to improve the range. The outcome of this was that all the later classes had a less destroyer type look (ie longer focsles), but not ballast, that was too much for the RCNC of the time. Also Shepherd's predecessors became very weight conscious. The design work for which Shepherd and King were responsible was also greatly expanded. Original sloop Family: *Bridgewater – Grimsby*. (1) Sloop Minesweeper: *Halcyon*. (2) Escort Sloops: *Bittern, Black Swan, Repeat Black Swan.*(3) Coastal Sloops: *Kingfisher, Repeat Kingfisher.* [3]
(1) Ships of this class (*Grimsby*) got the weights right. I did the inclining experiment and trials.

The launch of Britain's second nuclear submarine, Valiant, *at Barrow on 4 December 1963.* (CMP)

(2) These were larger vessels and I think the design was successful because the pattern derived from going up in size. However S & K [Shepheard and King] deliberately over-estimated weight. The sloop section was now very successful and the *Bittern* class weights provided a 'Bible' for all subsequent escort sloop development.

(3) In *Kingfisher* S & K cut the weight after design and 'saved' 150 tons on 500! *Kingfisher* was condemned by the operators because her draught was too low for the Asdic.[32] When I did the inclining there seemed to be a discrepancy of about a foot on the draught. So I made Fairfield check the draught marks; my action so infuriated Fairfields that G W Barr, the manager, rang Sir Stanley Goodall with a view to getting me sacked, (this was a good thing for me. The draught marks were OK, the ship was just a foot light – in seven!).

In the repeat *Kingfisher*s (the end of the road for this class) I wanted ballast but Stanton and Woolard said 'No' so we reduced the block coefficient and added structural weight, we got good ships then but the war killed the type.

So the family continued only from the repeat *Black Swan*s and this is the first type for which I did the calculations. The weights were based on *Bittern* completion (she was built by John Brown and finished as the Admiralty Yacht [*Enchantress*]) the weights were fantastically accurate (for which I take all credit!)

Acknowledgements

My thanks are due to Lady Baker and other members of his family, to Richard Moss, Vice Admiral Stephens RCN, Rear Admiral Davis RCN, Cdr Todhunter and others who have enriched this account.

Notes

[1] The original letters are in the manuscript collection of the National Maritime Museum – RCNC Centenary Collection. Baker's handwriting is not easy to read and there is some guesswork in interpretation but the author has had considerable practice in reading Baker missives.

[2] Eldest son of Isaac and Lizzie Baker; he was a tiny baby and not expected to survive. He had a brother and three sisters.

[3] For an account of the Dockyard Schools see D K Brown, *A Century of Naval Construction*, Conway Maritime Press (London, 1983). In brief one half of the surviving students left at the end of each year; even reaching the 4th year was a major achievement whilst a 4th year pass was seen as the equivalent of a pass degree.

[4] Baker's views on the prewar sloops are of considerable interest and are included as an annex.

[5] During the rearmament of the late 1930s and throughout the war, most promotions were 'acting', which prefix I have omitted from the text.

[6] A Nicholls, 'The all-welded hull construction of HMS *Seagull*', *Transactions of the Institution of Naval Architects, 1939*, (London, 1939).

[7] This passage is based closely on Baker's words but has been altered slightly to clarify it for non naval-architects.

[8] The author was a member of the committee which drafted them and remembered Baker's wise words.

[9] Paragraph based on notes by Baker, largely using his words.

[10] In a lengthy passage Baker says that you could stand on the poop of an LCT(3) and watch ripples run along the steel tank deck due to the alternating loading on the low depth/length hull. The depth/length of the LCT(4) was even less and the side decks little higher.

[11] Shallow draught ships built c1937 for service in the oilfields of Lake Maracaibo.

[12] This ramp was 143ft long and took up so much space that the class was known to cynics as Landing Ships Ramp.

[13] The term 'sketch design' implies much more than a back of the envelope sketch. Whilst not fully detailed, it would have some supporting calculations.

[14] Confirmed by Colonel D P Wyckoff USMC. 'Let there be built great ships.' *US Naval Institute Proceedings*, November 1982.

[15] The double ended version appeared in the USN as the successful Mk6.

[16] Personal letter to the author. There is a tale of Higgins' dinner for Baker – gold plates and liveried servants.

[17] A disgusting 'temporary' building dating from the First World War.

[18] J C Niedermeir, 'Designing the LST', *US Naval Institute Proceedings*, November 1982. Baker is a reliable witness wherever checks can be made, willing to give credit to both US and British colleagues and his account is confirmed by Todhunter. It is not impossible that Niedermeir was working independently and reached similar conclusions to Baker.

[19] Richard Moss, RCNC, formerly Director of Ship Production and later Baker's business partner.

[20] An outstanding constructor who began in Lloyd's Register and transferred to the RCNC.

[21] Non naval-architects will not appreciate the full significance of this remark. Before computers, designers were almost forced to use an existing ship as a starting point and where there was no previous ship there tended to be a lengthy trial and error phase. Baker did start from nothing and deserves enormous credit for it.

[22] Letter to the author, 1983.

[23] Private letter to Mr Payne for the RCNC history dated 5 July 1978.

[24] Baker names some of those he thought opposed him. I have deleted these names as I am not sure he is correct in all cases.

[25] I was impressed by this argument and searched First World War records, when the RN had a number of destroyers with turtle back forecastles, and also consulted RCN operators but could not find evidence to justify the high cost of turtle backs.

[26] It would be hard to design frigates with hull forms more different than those of *Whitby* and *St Laurent* but repeated questionnaires in NATO put these two as equal best for their size as sea boats.

[27] Letter from Vice Admiral R St G Stephens, RCN.

[28] I had charge of the DNC stand at a major secret exhibition and part of my brief was to compare models of the two classes and explain the superiority of *Whitby*. One day, when I had finished, a stranger came up and asked who wrote that rubbish – and introduced himself as Baker!

[29] D K Brown, *A Century of Naval Construction*, Conway Maritime Press (London, 1983).

[30] Based on notes by Richard Moss, RCNC, formerly Director of Ship Production and Baker's partner in this venture.

[31] This low freeboard was not obvious as the main deck had bulwarks and there was a shelter deck over. The extension to the forecastle only meant filling the gap between bulwark and shelter deck.

[32] This is an interesting point. The P boats used on Asdic trials were paid off because they had insufficient draught. The Staff Requirement for the *Kingfisher* should have taken care of this.

THE 1950s COASTAL FRIGATE DESIGNS FOR THE ROYAL NAVY

Post Second World War plans for new Royal Navy frigates initially centred on 1st Rate designs which were ultimately designated Type 12 (*Whitby* Class), Type 41 (*Leopard* Class) and Type 61 (*Salisbury* Class); specialist vessels in anti-submarine, anti-aircraft and aircraft direction duties respectively. However, the cost of these ships forced the Admiralty to consider the design of cheaper alternatives in order to provide for greater numbers – initially 2nd Rate and then, when these also proved too costly, 3rd Rate frigates. In this article George L Moore examines the design history of these unbuilt 3rd Rate vessels, with particular reference to the AA frigate design.

As a result of a discussion on 'Ships of the future Navy' at a Sea Lords meeting held on 13 July 1949 the DTSD (Director of Training and Staff Duties) investigated the possibility of producing a much cheaper 2nd Rate vessel than had hitherto been considered. These studies resulted in the production of the Type 14 (*Blackwood* Class) frigates. The Type 14, however, proved to be more expensive and less simple to build than expected and it became imperative to 'devise' a ship that would be even cheaper, simpler and quicker to build. This request lead the DNC (Director of Naval Construction) Department to produce two studies which were presented to the Controller on 21 June 1950. The details of these designs are given in Table 1 which, for comparison purposes, also included the particulars of the 2nd Rate frigate.

In July 1950 Study N2/184 was taken as a basis for the Type 17 3rd Rate A/S frigate, the DTSD commenting that 'At first sight a design of this sort, cheap and easy to build with a small complement and easily manoeuvrable appears attractive as a Coastal Escort. The objection to her as such is her small and purely self defensive AA armament. Only the 1st Rate A/S frigates and to a lesser extent the Full

Conversion (Type 15) are capable of giving AA protection to convoys. If it is the intention that only these two classes of A/S frigates shall operate on the East Coast then clearly this design will not help us.'

In August 1950 the D of G (Director of Gunnery and Anti-Aircraft Warfare) went further, 'If we have to build large numbers of cheap small frigates (which seems very likely) would it be possible to have two types of 3rd Rate – an A/S and a "gun" type in spite of the well known objections to specialised ships?' At the end of September the D of P (Director of Plans) responded to the D of G's comments – 'As our requirement is for numbers, D of P considers that there is a requirement for such a ship and suggests that this matter is pursued to see if a ship on the lines of the Design N/184 could well fit part of it'. In mid October 1950 the DTSD recommended:

1. That a study of the N2/184 design of A/S frigate with endurance increased to 4000 miles should be undertaken. [There were debates later about range, the ability to cross the Atlantic having become an issue.]
2. That if successful this design should form part of a new

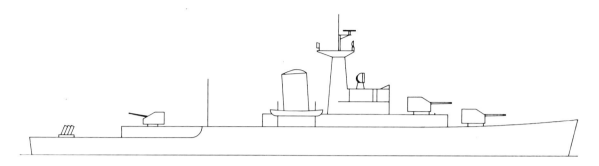

Drawing of the Type 42 based on a sketch by D K Brown RCNC, who was working in another frigate section at the time, illustrates the design at a late stage. Inevitably, with the passage of time, the recollection of the exact position of some equipment and other details are uncertain, the aft director's situation above the funnel being a case in point. The Squid may have had a handing room alongside whilst the Bofors guns were probably located on the deck extending aft from 'B' turret abreast the fore side of the mast. The funnel cap may well have been flat in the early designs but it is likely that the later versions of the ship had a funnel 'as drawn', for contemporary designs such as the ocean minesweeper, cancelled in 1955, possessed this feature.

construction emergency programme capable of producing frigates in large numbers.

3. That a similar study should be undertaken of Gunnery Coastal Frigate design (the minimum useful armament for such a ship is now being studied by the Naval Staff. A common hull with the 3rd Rate A/S frigate would clearly be desirable).

Design Studies

One official (name illegible) was not convinced that it was feasible to produce a satisfactory 'Gunnery Coastal Frigate...unless it turns out we can get a gun armament nearly as good as the 1st Rate A/S frigate so that other ships as well as itself can be protected, we may find it an incubus'. The recommendations by the DTSD were, however, approved and the DNC was accordingly requested, on 4 November 1950, to proceed with these studies at 'modest priority'. The point was made that except perhaps as a prototype these 3rd Rate designs would be for a War Emergency new construction programme only. This was the moment when both the Type 17 and Type 42 3rd Rate frigates became firm projects and, as we shall see, their development largely ran in parallel throughout the lives of the designs.

The DNC gave instructions for design studies of both the Type 17 and Type 42 to be developed in London. One immediate comment from NG Holt, ADNC (Assistant DNC) in charge of frigate design, on 20 November 1950 was that an increase in speed to say 20kts would be a better target 'particularly as a Common Hull and machinery would then be more likely to be popular for both the Anti Submarine and Anti Aircraft designs'. Quite why this comment was made is unclear for one of the requirements of DNC N2/184 was a speed of 22kts. However, Sketch Staff Requirements for the Type 17, produced in January 1951, required a speed of 19kts and knowledge of this 'aim' may well have initiated the comment.

Table 1: COASTAL AND 2ND RATE FRIGATE DESIGNS, JUNE 1950

	DNC N2/184	DNC N2/185	DNC38/463 2nd Rate Frigate
Length-wl (ft):	275	250	300
Beam max (ft–in):	31–6	31–0	33
Mean draught (ft–in)	8–9	8–3	9–9
Deep displacement (tons):	950	800	1290
Armament:	1 × Limbo (20 salvoes); 4 × fixed torp tubes (no reloads).	1 × Squid (20 salvoes); 2 × fixed torp tubes (2 reloads).	1 × double Limbo (20 salvoes); 4 × fixed torp tubes (no reloads).
	1 × twin Bofors; 1 × single Bofors; 1 × St director for twin Bofors; 2 × 2in pedestal rocket flare projectors		
Machinery:	4 ASR1 Diesels, geared to 2 shafts, 7200shp = 22kts*	2 ASR1 Diesels, geared to 2 shafts, 3600shp = 19kts*	Y101 steam turbine geared to single shaft, 15,000shp = 25kts.*
Endurance:	2000 miles at 12kts*	2000 miles at 12kts*	4500 miles at 12kts*
Approximate cost:	£500,000–£550,000	£400,000–£450,000	£650,000–£700,000

*6 months out of dock in tropical waters.

Sketch Requirements

Preliminary Sketch Staff Requirements for the 3rd Rate frigate/coastal escort (gunboat), Type 42 were produced before the end of January 1951. Details were as follows:

SECTION A

1) *Function*
a) To take her place in a mixed escort group to augment protection of coastal convoys from attack by aircraft and E boats.
b) To contribute to the protection of coastal convoys from attack by submarine to the best of their ability with limited A/S equipment.
c) To control Coastal Forces if possible.

2) *General Remarks*
a) These ships will be built under an emergency programme only.
b) They should be capable of rapid and cheap construction and require few men to man them.
c) They are to be built on the same hull as the 3rd Rate A/S Frigate Type 17.
d) Machinery shall be designed on the assumption that: 80per cent time at sea will be at 12kts; 15per cent time at sea will be at 16kts; 5per cent time at sea will be at 22kts.
e) Good manoeuvrability is essential.

3) *Speed*: To be capable of 22kts at deep load 6 months out of dock in temperate waters (Propeller silencing to be fitted but not working). Any increase above this figure would greatly improve the ship in the anti-E boat role.

The frigate Plymouth *of the* Whitby *class, in 1966. In the 1950s such vessels were regarded as too expensive to be built quickly and in sufficient numbers and generated requirements for cheaper 2nd and, ultimately, 3rd rate vessels.* (CMP)

4) *Endurance*: Sufficient oil fuel stowage for 2000 miles at 20kts in the above conditions.

5) *Deep Displacement and Dimensions*: Not to exceed 1050 tons by 275ft long.

6) *Special Features*:
a) To be fitted with propeller silencing [Note – this feature, known as 'Nightshirt', was expected to 'cost' 1–1.5kts].
b) To be fitted for service in temperate and arctic waters.

SECTION B ARMAMENT

1) *Gun Armament*:
a) GDS2, two or preferably three 3in/50 twin mountings. Mk63 Director and radar Mk34 for each mounting. As many single power worked Bofors as can be fitted in addition to the above.
b) Sufficient magazine stowage for 10 minutes fire for each 3in/50 mounting to be provided.
c) Two 2in Rocket Flare launchers.

2) *A/S Armament*: Single Squid.

3) *Asdic Sets*: Types 164,162. Note: Single Limbo and hull outfit No7 may be fitted later.

4) *Anti Torpedo Equipment*: Unifoxer.

SECTION C RADAR
Type 974, Type 293Q, American Radar Mk34 for each mounting.
Bridge to be enclosed with open wing position each side to facilitate ship handling in confined waters. Replenishment at sea not required.
At the same time Sketch Staff Requirements for the 3rd Rate A/S frigate (Type 17) were issued; it is worth recording the basic details for comparison with the Type 42:

1) *Function*:
a) To take her place in a mixed Escort Group for the protection of convoys of all types against submarines particularly on Ocean routes where threat from air attack is not great.
b) To hunt and destroy submarines.

2) *General Remarks*: These ships will supplement (but not replace) the 1st and 2nd Rate A/S frigates already planned. They will be built under emergency programme only. They should be capable of rapid production and require few men to man them.

3) *Speed*: 19kts at deep load 6 months out of dock tropics with propeller silencing fitted but not working.

4) *Endurance*: 4500 miles at 12kts.

5) *Deep Displacement and Dimensions*: Not to exceed 1050 tons by 275ft long.

6) *Special Features*: To be fitted for service in tropical and cold climates.

7) Armament: Single Limbo aft with 20 salvoes. Outfit of four target-seeking A/S weapons. One twin Bofors with S/T Director forward. A single Bofors aft.
Asdic Sets: Hull mounted No7 (Types 170, 176 & 180).
Radar: Type 974.
Replenishment at sea facility required.

When comparing the two preliminary sketch requirements there are clearly significant differences which work against the use of a common hull and machinery. Weight of armament, speed and endurance are noteworthy examples.

In comments attached to the Type 42 Sketch Requirements, the DTSD described the vessel as 'in effect a modernised "Hunt" of relatively low endurance capable of economical production and fitted to deal with air, submarines and E Boats as well as can be expected on a 1000 ton hull.' He felt the design 'would appear to be a suitable ship for production in quantity by France, Italy and Holland.' In February 1951, the D of P agreed that 'there is a need for a ship of comparatively low endurance for the protection of coastal convoys and that such a ship should form the backbone of the coastal escort group.' He suggested that 'as soon as the Sketch Requirements receive Board approval they should be tabled by our representative on the Standing Group.' Whether this suggestion to promote the design to NATO was followed up is not known. The design never went into production as a NATO project; individual countries evolved their own ideas. France for example produced

the *Le Corse* (E50), a frigate with some features similar in concept to the Type 42 which it predated.
The DTSD made further pertinent comments on both the Type 17 and Type 42 at this point:

> The sketch requirements are intended to present the minimum armament considered worthwhile in a new construction ship. The dimensions given are considered the maximum to which these designs are worth building – if they have to be increased the saving in money and effort over the 2nd Rate (Type 14) would largely disappear. The cost must also be carefully watched and though propulsion has been specified as diesel machinery on two shafts, Engineer-in-Chief and DNC are requested to consider whether some other arrangement giving the same performance at less cost could be devised..... It is intended that if the design study shows that the Staff Requirements can be met within the present dimensions the design should be frozen and used for an emergency programme. These ships will not be built under a normal peacetime programme.

Design Progress

The request to proceed with the design on a 'modest priority basis' seems to have been taken to heart. NG Holt put forward the following suggested programme for both the Type 17 and Type 42 in September 1951:

Final Staff Requirements available:	April 1952
Additional staff available:	June 1952
Drawings to Board:	December 1952
Orders placed and specification available:	April 1953
Fabrication commences:	October 1953
Lay down:	January 1954

This schedule shows slippage on earlier tentative plans when the Sketch Estimates for 1952/53 were being prepared. At that time the projected programme included prototypes of both the Type 17 and Type 42 to be ordered in September 1952, with construction commencing in December 1952 and completion in March 1955.
In mid November 1951 those responsible for the projects were clearly concerned about the lack of progress as it was suggested that the Type 17 design be moved from London to Bath, where the Type 42 was based, if the projects were to be seriously pursued. At this time results of a study into machinery installation were available; propulsion methods investigated were:

a) Geared Steam Turbine (utility).
b) Geared Lightweight Diesels (Deltic).
c) Geared ASR1 Type Diesels.
d) Free Piston Gas Generators.
e) Geared Gas Turbines.

For a variety of reasons all these alternatives failed to meet requirements: a) because it was too heavy; b) because it was too expensive; c) because it was too large for the Type 42; and d) and e) because they were insufficiently developed. It was then decided that the most satisfactory installation would be two ASR1 on a single-shaft for the Type 17 and a geared steam utility turbine installation on a single-shaft for the Type 42. The conclusion reached was that a lack of standardisation would involve increased design, installation and maintenance effort and it was unlikely to effect any saving in the cost of production in comparison with the 2nd Rate frigate. It was then decided to investigate the possibility of using 'Utility' steam installations in both the Type 17 and Type 42 with the Type 17 having one shaft and one boiler and the Type 42 two shafts and two boilers (both Y101 type). The Naval Staff now questioned the viability of the 3rd Rate A/S frigate in view of its increasing displacement, now approximately that of the 2nd Rate A/S frigate, the possible intention being to build more 2nd Rate vessels. In the event, development of the 3rd Rate Type 17 continued.

In the case of the Type 42 the possibility of designing the vessel on the hull of a 2nd Rate frigate was briefly considered, the Naval Staff still wanting three US 3in/50 twin mountings. They soon received the reply that the 2nd Rate hull was far too fine to carry a reasonable armament weight proportional to its displacement. A hull of greater beam than that of the A/S frigate would be required, with a tentative displacement of about 1300 tons deep. This assumed a single-shaft set of steam turbine machinery developing 10,000shp which was slightly less weight than a twin-shaft installation. The idea was not pursued.

According to a note made by the DNC in January 1952, particulars of the Coastal Escort (Gunboat) Type 42 were now as shown in Table 2.

Table 2: *PARTICULARS OF TYPE 42 COASTAL ESCORT, JANUARY 1952*

Length (wl):	300ft
Beam:	35ft
Deep draught:	9ft 3in
Moulded depth (to forecastle):	25ft 6in (long forecastle ship)
Deep displacement:	1300 tons
Armament:	Three twin 3in/50 with Mk63 director, one twin Bofors with STD, two single Bofors, GDS2 in operations room, single Squid with 10 salvoes.
Machinery:	Single-shaft utility steam turbine, 10,000shp = 22.5kts, endurance 2000 miles at 12kts.
Weights (tons):	
Armament:	160
Equipment:	137
Machinery:	230
Fuel:	140
Hull:	610 (mild steel)
Board Margin:	23
Total:	1300 tons deep

Armament Problems

Having overcome the 'difficulties' surrounding the planned machinery installation a further hiatus occurred at the end of January 1952 when the D of G minuted – '3in/50 mounting and Mk63 US Fire Control...It is now fairly certain that

we shall not obtain more of these equipments from America during peacetime other than the "eight" which have already been given us. It is also doubtful if we should be able to get any in emergency. They should therefore be eliminated from the list of equipment for consideration'. The proposed armament suggested for the 1300 ton ship was three single 4in Mk25, three SGS Mk1 fire-control systems, two single Bofors Mk10 (DNC quotes Mk9 single), one GDS Mk2, a single Squid and Asdic Types 164/162. This brought its own problems, as the DNC understood the 4in mounting would not be available for fitting before 1955. If the Naval Staff wanted to build the ship before this date the only alternative was a 4in twin mounting with ST director, however, the development of the design continued with the three 4in Mk25 single as main armament. (In April 1953 the prototype of the Mk25 was being manufactured by Vickers at Elswick. In November 1953 Vickers submitted details of a private venture 4in single naval gun intended for foreign sales, for possible use in the Royal Navy. The Director of Naval Ordnance however doubted its ability to meet requirements owing to a lack of water cooling. The Chilean *Almirante* class destroyers mounted a single 4in gun designated N[R]. It would be surprising if the two guns did not possess some common features.)

At this time the future direction of the Type 17 design was unclear and two alternatives were being evaluated (see Table 3). There was now little in common between the Type 17 and 42 designs. It was also becoming clear that the characteristics of the Type 42 were far from settled, no doubt due to the escalating cost of the project which was leaving its austerity role behind. In February 1952, a smaller version of the ship was being investigated with the approximate legend given in Table 4.

The D of G suggested that the smallest acceptable ship could mount two 4in Mk25 mountings, each with SGS Mk1 fire-control, two Bofors Mk10 and one GDS2. Designs with two 4in mountings were short lived. Prototypes of the Type 17 and Type 42 were included in the projected 1952/53 programme, the tentative dates being September 1952 for ordering, December 1952 for construction to commence and March 1955 for completion. This schedule was ambitious given the flexibility which still remained in the design process and showed greater optimism than the aims set out in September 1951. In the event the project was not included in the final version of the 1952/53 programme.

Weights and Dimensions

During the following months the design was further developed but matters were far from settled. By August 1952 the length was 260ft (wl) and the beam 35ft, while the weights had been adjusted as follows:

Hull:	663.4 tons
Equipment:	140.3 tons
Machinery:	230 tons
Fuel:	140 tons
Reserve feed water:	10 tons
Armament:	155 tons
Board margin:	25 tons
TOTAL:	1363.7 tons

Table 3: *ALTERNATIVE TYPE 17 DESIGNS, JANUARY 1952*

	A	B
Length wl (ft):	285	270
Beam (ft):	32	31
Deep draught (ft–in)	9	8–6
Depth to upper deck (moulded), short forecastle ship (ft–in):	18	17–6
Machinery:	Single shaft Utility steam turbines (standardised with Type 42), 10,000shp = 23kts, endurance 2000 miles at 12kts.	Single-shaft Utility steam turbines, 5000shp = 19.75kts
Armament:	As for Type 14 frigates but with single Limbo (20 salvoes); four A/S torpedoes with four tubes; three single Bofors.	
Weights (tons):		
Armament:	74	74
Equipment:	103	92
Machinery*:	230	180
Fuel:	125	107
Hull:	548	490
Board margin:	20	17
Total deep displacement:	1100	960

* Including reserve feed water.

The hull weights were based on the Hunt Type 1. The 4in mountings had by this time had their amunition stowage reduced from 400 to 300rpg. The specified machinery was for 12,500shp but by November this had been reduced to 10,000shp, while the length and beam were reduced to 250ft (wl) and 37ft 5in respectively. In this design numbers 1 and 2 – 4in guns were described as 'rather forward'; weights were modified as follows:

Hull:	640 tons
Equipment:	133 tons
Machinery:	220 tons
Fuel:	144 tons
Reserve feed water:	10 tons
Armament:	134 tons
Board margin:	23 tons
TOTAL:	1304 tons

By this time various combinations of dimensions and power were under consideration, details of which are given in Table 5, and by February 1953 a decision had been made on a hull form with the following dimensions:

Length (wl):	260ft
Beam:	37ft
Mean draught:	10ft 6in
Freeboard (for):	20ft
Freeboard (aft):	10ft
Depth of hull:	26ft 3in*
Displacement:	1350 tons

* at centreline amidships, from keel to forecastle.

By June 1953 both the Type 17 and Type 42 were to have machinery producing 10,000shp on one-shaft. A firm decision was also made to add the Type 147F Asdic set (which had been under consideration in February) to the equipment specification. The funnel was based on the design of that fitted to HMY *Britannia*; the DNC, Sir Victor Shepheard, was very proud of the work which had gone

Table 4: *PARTICULARS OF REDUCED TYPE 42 DESIGNS, FEBRUARY 1952*

Length (wl):	290ft
Beam:	34ft
Deep draught:	8ft 9in
Moulded depth (to upper deck):	25ft (long forecastle ship)
Deep displacement:	1140 tons
Machinery:	Single-shaft utility steam turbine, 8,000shp = 22kts.
Weights (tons):	Version 1
Armament (incl. radar):	120
Equipment:	107
Machinery:	192
Reserve feed water:	8
Fuel (incl. diesel oil):	130
Hull:	563
Board margin:	20
Total deep displacement:	1140

Loss of length in the above design meant the omission of one of the proposed three single 4in gun mountings and N G Holt suggested a better answer was a slightly larger ship with the following weight breakdown (speed in this design was estimated to be 21.75kts with 8000shp).

Weights (tons):	
Armament (incl. radar):	138
Equipment:	110
Machinery:	192
Reserve feed water:	8
Fuel (incl. diesel oil):	135
Hull:	580
Board margin:	22
Total deep displacement:	1185

into this funnel and wanted it perpetuated on everything!

Modified Staff Requirements

In June 1953 the following modified Staff Requirements were produced for the Type 42:

1) *Function*:
a) To contribute to the protection of Coastal Convoys from attack by Aircraft and E Boats.
b) To contribute to the protection of Coastal Convoys from attack by Submarines.
c) To provide limited control of Coastal Forces in defence of Coastal Convoys.

2) *Speed*: At least 21kts.

The Blackwood *class, 2nd rate A/S frigate* Duncan *is launched at Thornycroft's yard, Southampton, on 30 May 1957.* (CMP)

3) *Endurance*: 2000 miles out of dock in temperate conditions.

4) *Armament*: Three 4in Mk25, single mountings. Two single Bofors (Mk10/70 type)

General Remarks:
a) The ships will be built under an emergency programme only and must be capable of rapid and cheap construction.
b) Good manoeuvrability is essential.
c) Main machinery to be standardised if possible with the 3rd Rate A/S frigate (Type 17).

Table 5: *VARIATIONS OF FORM AND POWER FOR TYPE 42 DESIGN.*

Length (ft)	Beam (ft–in)	Deep displacement (tons)	Speed (kts)	
			10,000shp	12,500shp
260	35–0	1300	22	22.75/23
280	35–0	1300	22.75	24
250	37–5	1350	21	22

Note:
Machinery of 7500shp was also investigated.

Armament:

1) Main gun armament – see above.
2) Main gun control – 3 SGS Mk1 fire-control systems.
3) Close-range armament and control – see above.
4) Gun direction GDS Mk2* (Mk2* = Mk2 modified).
5) Ammunition – normal outfit.
6) Illuminants – 2in rocket flare rails on foremost 4in mounting shield.
7) A/S Weapon – single Squid.
8) Asdic Sets – Type 176 in Hull Outfit No7. Type 164, Type 162, [Type 147F added later].
9) A/S Ammunition – 10 salvoes.
10) A/T equipment – To be fitted with latest towed and projected decoys.

Radar: Type 974, Type 293Q, three Type 907 (for SGS).

Protection:

a) 10lb plating in way of bridge – operations room and Asdic control room.
b) Degaussing to be fitted.
c) Propeller silencing to be fitted.

Boats: 25ft motor cutter, 27ft whaler.

Complement: 10 officers, 180 ratings (approx).

Abbreviated Staff Requirements for the Type 17 were now:

1) *Function*:
a) To augment the protection of convoys against submarines.
b) To hunt and destroy submarines.

2) *General Remarks*: These ships will supplement (but not replace) the A/S Frigates Type 12 and 14. They should be capable of rapid production and complement kept as small as possible to man them.

3) *Speed*: $21\frac{1}{2}$kts at least at deep load, 6 months out of dock, in temperate waters with propeller silencing fitted but not working.

4) *Endurance*: 4000 miles at 12kts.

5) *Armament*: A/S – Single Limbo sited aft with 20 salvoes – provision for four A/S Torpedoes and TGSF2 in place of Limbo. Guns – Two centre line power operated single Bofors (L70), 1500 rounds per gun. Visual gun direction only.

Asdic: Hull outfits 5 and 7a, Types 170, 176 (interim 174), Type 162.

Accommodation: 9 officers, 140 ratings.

It was planned to substitute A/S Mk10 for the Limbo and Asdic 170b for Type 170.

Construction Policy

According to the D of G, by August 1953 the planned completion date for the Type 42 prototype was December 1956, which represented a further slippage said to be twelve months. As there was no possibility of ordering prototypes before December 1954 it was agreed that no provision should be made for them in the 1954/55 Navy Estimates. Early in November 1953 the Chairman of the Ship Design Policy Committee reviewed the Future Frigate construction programme and it is worthwhile setting out his memorandum on the subject in full:

> We have under construction Type 12, Type 14, Type 41 and Type 61 and have planned Type 17 and Type 42.
> 2) The 1st Rate A/S, A/A and A/D Frigates are complicated ships, highly efficient and designed to carry maximum armament in a limited tonnage. They are expensive and slow to build.
> 3) Since we could not afford the large number of 1st Rate frigates required the 2nd Rate was designed as a simpler edition of the 1st Rate, less expensive and less difficult to build. The 2nd Rate has, however, proved more expensive and less simple to build than was originally expected.
>
> **Third Rate Frigates**
> 4) It became imperative therefore to devise a ship that would be even cheaper, simpler and quicker to build. This was the 3rd Rate Frigate initially intended for A/S role only.
> 5) This ship, as visualised in 1951, was to be one which could be built and engined quickly, without interfering with the current re-armament programme, if a heavy demand for escort vessels arose. This type of ship was to be of comparative short endurance, with a hull which called for no special structural steels and could be riveted or welded to suit the practice of any particular builder. It was also the intention to fit simple commercial type engines which would be manufactured by firms not normally engaged in the more advanced types of naval machinery.
> 6) Since then the situation has changed fundamentally. The Naval Staff rejected a short endurance vessel, which meant that the tonnage would have to be increased considerably. The welding capacity of the Country which was limited in 1951 has now increased enormously while riveting capacity has been falling rapidly and will shortly be negligible.
> 7) There is further now no cheap simple engine available in this Country which will go anywhere near meeting the Staff requirements. A special design by YARD would therefore be required and that could not be undertaken for at least eighteen months to come. On the other hand the Y100 engine has now proved itself. Eight firms are now tooled-up for making the engine and others could be very quickly tooled-up in emergency. Moreover, considerable potential exists amongst the firms which normally build for land purposes and works for building this engine have been completed in Canada.
>
> **Coastal Escort**
> 8) Another type planned is the Coastal Escort. This ship is of comparable size with the 2nd and 3rd Rates and should therefore be taken into account when considering a new frigate design.
>
> **Future Frigate**
> 9) Now while I accept the necessity for a limited number of 1st Rate A/S (Group Leader ships) and a

The Tribal class, Type 81, general purpose frigate
Gurkha in April 1963. This ship and her sisters
represent the final outcome of the Admiralty's post-war
attempts at a cheap utility escort and were directly
inspired by the work on the Type 42 coastal escort. (CMP)

moderate programme of special A/A and A/D Frigates, it seems to me to be imperative in the light of our financial limitations and in the interest of simplicity, that we should try to rationalise the hull and general conception of the mass of our smaller escort craft for the future.

10) To do this we may have to accept certain shortcomings. Some types of ship may have to have larger hulls than is strictly necessary for their particular function, others may have to be overpowered and some will perhaps be slightly less well armed than the staff would like. But to achieve uniformity of design and build these deviations from perfection may well be cheerfully accepted.

11) It would be axiomatic that the hull design would be as simple as possible and, in order to enable us to build widely, as close to normal merchant practice as can be arranged. The propulsion machinery must be common to each type, even accepting some under or overpowering as the case may be. The hulls, at least up to the upper deck and as much of the superstructure as possible, must be nearly as possible common to all types. The design would make provision for alternative armament for this is highly desirable when the emergency comes and we cannot always obtain exactly what we want. Furthermore we will almost certainly find that the character of the new war will make new and special

demands in a particular direction and the value of having a hull into which different armaments could be placed must be manifest to all.

12) I think it is fair to claim that in this ship we should have:

a) Designed the simplest craft to build at speed in time of emergency – and at less cost too.

b) Build a ship easily adaptable to whatever particular class of ship was in special demand.

c) One common instead of several different types of ship in which Officers and Men would have to be trained.

d) Enormously simplified the supply of spares.

e) Reduced the pressures on design staff who are now sorely strained.

13) To sum up my proposals are:

a) To continue a limited programme of the present A/A, A/D and 1st Rate A/S Frigates.

b) To allow the present 2nd Rate design to lapse as soon as the present programme is completed.

c) To design a ship, as simple as possible to build, with common propulsion units capable of being armed for one or other of the several duties which escorts are required to fulfil.

This will leave us with four types of frigate only in any future building programme.

Final developments

Work stopped on the 'Coastal Frigate' Type 42 on the 11 November 1953. No further units of the 2nd Rate Type 14 were ordered for the Royal Navy, design work started almost immediately on the 'Common Hull Frigate' with the

Ship Design Policy Committee deciding, on 16 December 1953, that Y100 machinery would be used. The story was not, however, over for the Type 42 'ideas' were soon resurrected as the following memorandum from the DTSD on 11 June 1954 indicates:

Coastal AA Frigate (in lieu of Common Hull AA Frigate).

Design studies prepared so far by DNC indicate that it is not possible to mount an acceptable armament in the gun version of the Common Hull Frigate of about 1600 tons.

The DTSD has therefore drawn up the attached staff requirements based on the Type 42 Coastal Frigate but with two twin 4in mountings in lieu of three single 4in, with Y100 single-shaft machinery. It is hoped that this will result in a ship of about the same size as the Common Hull A/S Frigate (1600 ton version) currently under investigation by DNC.

Set out below is an abbreviated version of the Sketch Staff Requirements for Coastal A/A Frigate. [Note the marked similarities with the Type 42 Preliminary Sketch Requirements as set out in January 1951]

1) *Function*:
a) To contribute to the protection of coastal convoys from attack by aircraft and E Boats.
b) To contribute to the protection of coastal convoys from attack by submarine.
c) To provide limited control of Coastal Forces in defence of coastal convoys.

2) *Construction*: These ships must be capable of rapid and cheap construction.

3) *Speed*: At least 21kts at deep load six months out

The Type 14 frigate Palliser *in September 1958, operating as a fishery protection vessel during one of Britain's many disputes with Iceland over fishing rights. In many ways this was a role ideally suited to a 2nd class vessel, although it was not one envisaged when the ships were designed.* (CMP)

of dock in temperate conditions. 23/24kts desirable.

4) *Endurance*: 2000 miles at 12kts.

5) *RAS fitted*.

6) *To be winterised*.

Armament: Two 4in Mk19 twin mountings. Two Bofors Mk10 (Single L70). Single Squid, 10 salvo's.

Asdic: Type 164/176 in HO7, Type 147F, Type 162.

Radar: Type 974 or replacement, Type 293Q, Type 262, Radar for TOM.

Protection: 10lb plating – bridge, operations room and Asdic control room.

Machinery: Single shaft Y100.

Boats: one 25ft motor cutter, one 27ft whaler.

Complement: 10 officers, 203 ratings.

At this time 'abbreviated' requirements for the 'Common Hull Frigate' – A/S (1600 ton version) were:

1) *Function*: To contribute to the protection of convoys of all types against submarines.
To hunt and destroy submarines.

2) *General Remarks*: These ships must be capable of rapid and cheap construction.

3) *Speed*: At least 21kts at deep load 6 months out of dock in temperate conditions. 23/24kts desirable.

4) *Endurance*: 4000 miles at 12kts 6 months out of dock in temperate conditions.

5) *RAS fitted*.

6) *Winterised*.

The Type 81 frigate Tartar *in 1977.* (C & S Taylor)

Armament: Single A/S Mortar Mk10 with 20 salvos. As many A/S torpedoes as can be accommodated in fixed tubes with a minimum of four.

UCSF 2.

Asdic: Type 170B/176 in HO7a with HO5a, Type 177 in HO10, Type 162.

Guns: two Bofors Mk10 (Single L70).

Machinery: Single shaft Y100.

The breakdown of any commonality within the two Common Hull Frigate specifications seems to have rapidly led to its demise and a further reappraisal of requirements for, by October 1954, the main characteristics of the Type 81, *Tribal* Class, had been agreed. Twenty-six ships of this class were planned at one stage. With the abandonment of the Coastal AA Frigate the story of the Type 42 Coastal Frigate finally closed, as did any thoughts of rapidly producing 3rd Rate vessels in large numbers in an emergency programme.

Both the Type 42 and the Common Hull Frigate envisaged defending Coastal Convoys against E boats and aircraft. The need for this requirement would seem to indicate that, in the event of Soviet aggression, the coasts of Denmark, the Low Countries and probably Northern France would be lost, for how else could the British coast be threatened by E boats at that time? The thinking behind the evolution of both designs was very much a 'carry over' from the Second World War. It was ended by the realisation that the era of the hydrogen bomb was upon us.

Acknowledgements
Many thanks are owed to the staffs of the Public Record Office and the National Maritime Museum for their help. In particular I am most grateful to David Topliss of the latter institution. D K Brown, RCNC, is especially thanked for checking through the text and providing a practical insight to the subject.

Sources
National Maritime Museum:
Ships' Cover 825, Coastal Frigate Type 42 (AA frigate 3rd Rate). (Note: Covers for the Type 17 and the Common Hull Frigate are not yet held by the National Maritime Museum.)
Public Record Office:
ADM1/21695, Ships of the Future Navy: Notes on sketch requirements for 5in light cruisers, 1949.
ADM1/22001, A/S Frigates for NATO: design 1950/51.
ADM1/25127, Design of 4in single naval gun by Vickers Armstrongs for Foreign Sales: Possible interest for service use, 1953/54.
ADM1/25807, The Supply of Two Destroyers to Chilean Government, 1954/56.
ADM1/26040, Main gun armament in General Purpose (Type 81) Frigates: Comparison between 4.5in Mk5 single mountings and 4in twin Mk19 mountings, 1955/56.
ADM1/27156, Type 81 General Purpose Frigate, Staff Requirements, 1955/59.
ADM256/53, Naval Ordnance Department Reports, April 1953.

WARSHIP NOTES

This section comprises a number of short articles and notes, generally highlighting little-known aspects of warship history.

GUNS FOR THE ALABAMA

Andrew Bowcock describes his research into the pivot gun mountings of the Confederate warship Alabama, *which resulted in the production of the accompanying drawings.*

The *Alabama* was built by Laird Brothers of Birkenhead and launched in 1862 for the Confederate States during the American Civil War. The ship was built as a warship, or commerce raider, but no armament or ammunition were placed on board the ship while she was in the Mersey. Both the ship and her armament had been ordered by James Dunwoody Bulloch on

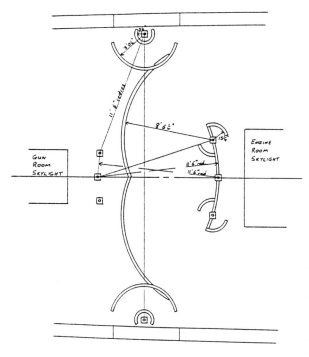

Figure 1: Detail plan of the deck sweeps for the pivot gun mounted between the engine room and gun room skylights. This arrangement agrees with the available photographic evidence showing this area. The arrangement of the other sweeps is shown in Figure 2. (All drawings are by the author).

behalf of the Confederate States. She sailed on 29 July 1862 just in time to avoid being seized and, according to the report of the Surveyor of Customs dated 30 July '..left this port without any part of her armament on board. She had not so much as a signal-gun or musket'.[1] Bulloch sailed from Liverpool on 13 August 1862 aboard the *Bahama* with the man who was to become the *Alabama*'s captain, Raphael Semmes.[2] The *Bahama* met up with the *Alabama* off the Azores where two guns and stores were transferred. The rest of the guns had been transported earlier by a ship called the *Agripinna* which had sailed from London.[3]

The armament consisted of six 32pdr in broadside and two pivot guns. The after pivot was an 8in smooth bore (112cwt) and the forward one a 100pdr rifled Blakely.[4] These two pivot guns worked on traverses, or sweeps, which were laid down while the ship was coaling and taking on stores off the Azores.[5] After a few days the armament was on board and in place and the ship ready to be commissioned as a warship.

A contemporary description was made by the captain of one of the ships captured by the *Alabama* which describes the guns carried and says she also had tracks laid forward for a pivot bow gun and aft for a pivot stern chaser.[6] All the guns are described as being of the Blakely pattern. Another description says that the guns were of English make and some bore the name of '....Preston & Co'.[7]

The ship was eventually sunk in battle with the USS *Kearsarge* off Cherbourg in 1864. The wreck was discovered a few years ago and excavation and recovery of some items has been carried out.

There are a number of original plans (or copies of original plans) available but only one shows the guns. This is part of a book published by the University of Alabama[8] and shows six 32pdr and two pivot guns, an 8in Blakely and a 9in smooth bore. It is assumed that they are a diagrammatic, not an actual, representation based on the photographs taken on board the ship.

There are two good models of the ship: one, in the Mariners' Museum, belonged to Bulloch and shows four sets of sweeps for pivot guns but no guns; the second was at Cammell Laird Shipbuilders (successors to Laird Brothers) and, since the closure of the yard, has been in a local

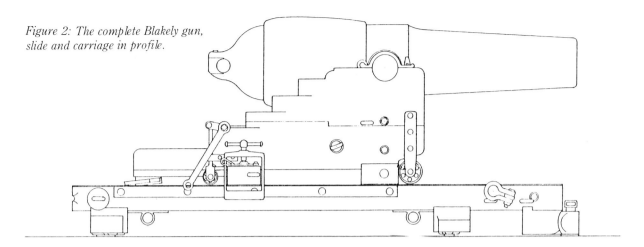

Figure 2: The complete Blakely gun, slide and carriage in profile.

museum – this model shows the same basic layout and position of four sets of sweeps for pivot guns. The Laird model also shows eight identical guns, all mounted on pivots, which are different to those shown in photographs – the whole model has therefore been condemned as inaccurate by some people, which is not a fair judgement.

The best list of sources of information on the ship is given in an article by Jim Bacon[9] but he was unable to give any additional help over details or plans of the guns. Photographs taken on board the ship in South Africa in 1863 provide excellent views of

Figure 3: General arrangement of carriage and slide for the 7in rifled gun.

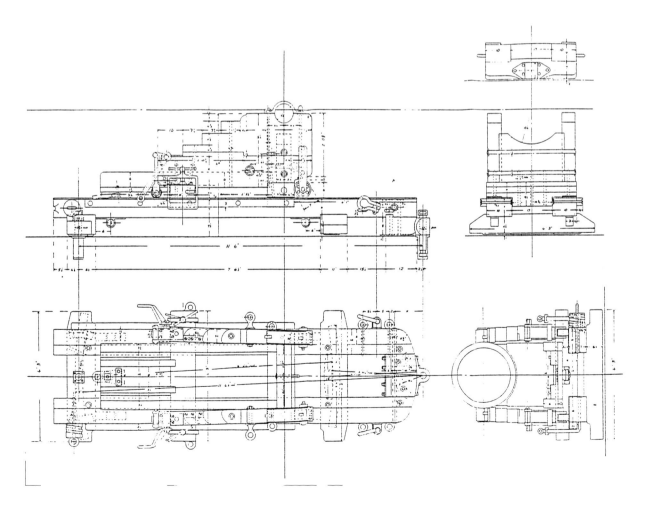

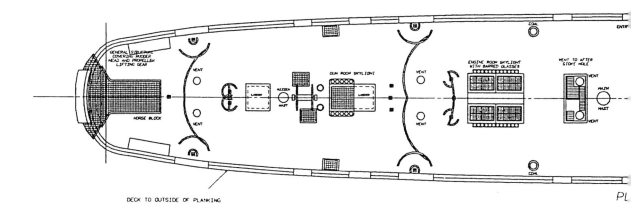

DECK TO OUTSIDE OF PLANKING

the upper deck and include some of the guns. The 8in smoothbore appears

Figure 4: The reconstructed profile and plan of the 7in Blakely rifled gun.

in two photographs which show the breech of the gun and part of the carriage but not much of the slide. Part of the deck sweeps can be seen in one of these views. There is no photograph that I know of showing the rifled

Blakely but there is what could be part of the left cheek in one photograph. A shell from the Blakely lodged in the stern frame of the *Kearsarge* during the battle off Cherbourg but failed to explode. This shell is now

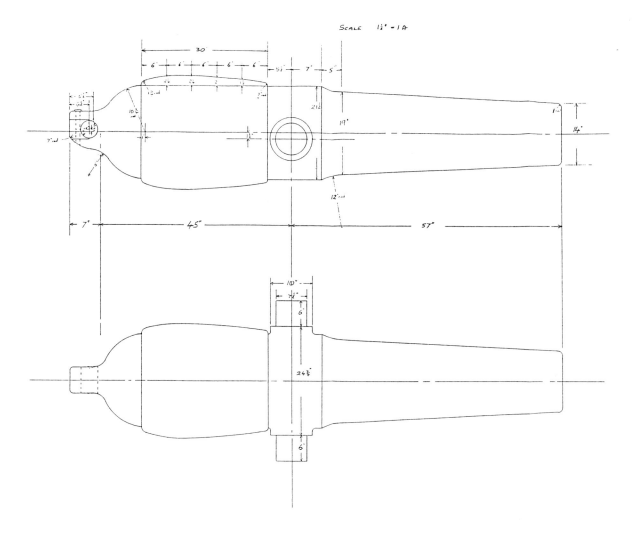

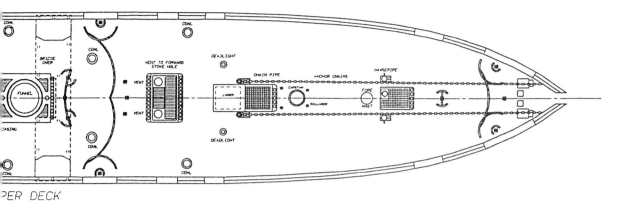

on display, in part of the stern frame of *Kearsarge*, at the Washington Navy Yard.

Researching the *Alabama* included starting from scratch with the guns. It was thought by some people that the guns were made by Fawcett Preston and their archive seemed the best place to start (Fawcett Preston also built the engine for the *Florida*, the first ship Bulloch ordered when he ar-

Figure 6: The carriage and slide for the 8in smooth bore.

rived in Liverpool – the *Alabama* was the second). I was told, on making preliminary enquiries, that the archives (now in a museum in Liverpool) contained no plans of the *Alabama*'s guns. However, I decided to examine the archive for general information on guns and amongst the plans found one showing four sets of deck sweeps on an unnamed ship. Written on the plan is – 'The Original (drawing) of this sent to I.D.B. August 8th, 1862'. It took me a long time to realise that I.D.B. is in fact James Dunwoody Bulloch and the date is just five days be-

Figure 5: Plan of the Alabama's *upper deck showing positions of deck sweeps.*

fore he sailed with Semmes and the last of the guns and equipment to join the *Alabama*. The plan of the deck sweeps gives the numbers of the two pivot guns they were designed for and all that was required was to see which guns these referred to and examine the plans available for them.

The main plans for the first gun listed, an 8in smoothbore, are the gun, the carriage and slide and the wrought

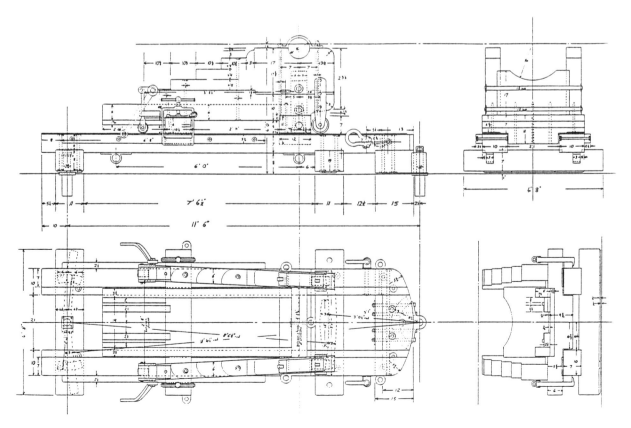

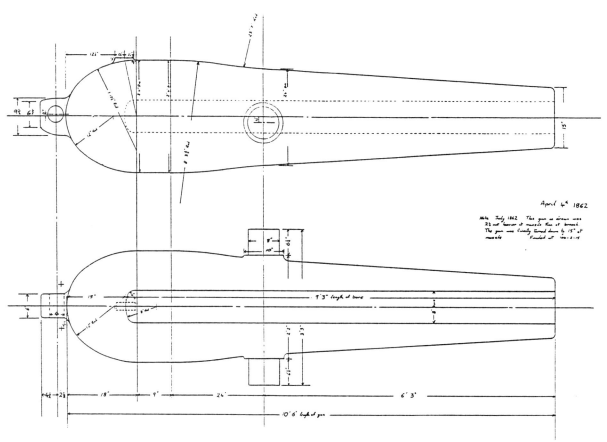

Figure 7: Profile and plan of the 8in smooth bore gun.

iron work. There is also a preliminary drawing for the carriage and slide. The main plan for the second gun, a 7in rifled gun, is the carriage and slide and there is also an unfinished preliminary carriage and slide. There is no plan of the 7in gun but it is shown in outline on the carriage. There are several other small drawings which show things that are common to both carriages, for example the front and rear carriage rollers are of the same diameter but different widths.

The original drawings of the Blakely rifled gun are in a poor state, and for convenience I decided to redraw them. I started with the complete carriage and slide for the Blakely and this is reproduced as Figure 3. All the main dimensions are given on the original but checking with a scale rule shows there can be considerable differences due to the condition of the plan and things like the paper stretching over the years, therefore, care is required when scaling off the original. In addition, smaller items, such as the compressor frames, would have been drawn in de-

tail and fully dimensioned on separate drawings which are now missing. Where there were significant differences the drawing of the wrought iron work for the smoothbore gun could give guidance.

The gun is only shown in outline on the original carriage drawing and only two dimensions are given, the trunnion diameter and the distance between the centrelines of the gun and the trunnion, so all other dimensions had to be scaled off the drawing. By reference to other drawings of Blakely guns it has been possible to produce the reconstruction shown as Figure 4. The chamber and bore have not been drawn as there is insufficient information available on these areas at present, this also applies to the details of the rifling. Excavation of the gun from the wreck should provide this information. The gun on the carriage and slide are given as Figure 5.

I found the plans for the 8in smoothbore carriage and slide some considerable time after the other plans, but in the meantime had attempted to reconstruct it using the photographs and the plan of the wrought iron work. The slide was assumed to be basically the same as that for the Blakely, ex-

cept for the width, because the pivot points on all four sets of deck sweeps have the same spacing. The resultant drawing, when compared to the plans found later, was similar, the most noticeable difference being that the reconstructed carriage was too long (by about 3in).

The major difference between the two original drawings is in the height of the carriage. The quoin has been changed so that it is the same as that of the Blakely: this resulted in the height of the carriage increasing by just over 4in, with an extension added to the rear. The new quoin also resulted in the cascabel having to be changed and it is shown in the drawing as having a similar shape to the Blakely.

The drawing of the wrought iron work is based on the first carriage and therefore the length of the capsquare bolts has been increased to the second. The other items appear to be the same except that some of the carriage and slide loops have the words 'not used' written across them. Comparing the plan with available photographs, the carriage loops are different and it appears that the upper loop of the two has been replaced with a lower one similar to that shown on the Blakely plan.

Two small scraps of the same plan, each about 4in square, proved to be sections of a carriage and slide. I had come to the conclusion that these were from the 8in gun, or one very like it, and comparison with the complete carriage and slide confirmed they were all part of the same plan. This carriage and slide have been redrawn and are shown in Figure 6 – a few of the loops have not been included as they are not shown in photographs. A note on the second drawing states that several alterations and additions were made to the carriage and slide and refers the reader to the drawing for the Blakely and to a mounted tracing and a full size drawing, which would be very interesting if they both still exist. At the moment no alterations or additions (other than to the loops) have been made to the drawing.

The original drawing of the gun has several notes pointing out the changes made. The cascabel, as noted above, was altered but not the drawing so the only representation found is on the drawing of the carriage. Another note says the gun was turned down at the muzzle because the weight distribution, or preponderance, was found to be wrong. The drawing of the gun, Figure 7, shows both the modifications to the cascable and muzzle, which are also shown in Figure 8 which shows the gun on the carriage and slide.

Notes

1 J D Bulloch, *The Secret Service of the Confederate States in Europe, Volume 1*, Thomas Yoseloff (1959), p251.

2 Ibid, p255.

3 Ibid, p237.

4 Ibid, p 266 and R Semmes, *Memoirs of Service Afloat*, The Blue and Grey Press (1987), p403.

5 R Semmes, *Memoirs of Service Afloat*, The Blue and Grey Press (1987), p407.

6 US National Archives, Washington DC.

7 *North America No3 (1863)*. Correspondence respecting the *Alabama*. Presented to both Houses of Parliament 1863.

8 C G Summersell, *CSS Alabama Builder, Captain and Plans*, University of Alabama Press (1985).

9 J Bacon, *CSS Alabama* in *Model Shipwright No22*. Conway Maritime Press (1977).

ADDENDA TO SWEDISH MONITORS

The article on Swedish monitors that appeared in Warship 1994 *was without drawings due to limitations in space. These drawings are reproduced here as an addenda to the original article. In addition the author, Dan Harris, has provided some further notes on both Swedish and Norwegian coast defence vessels.*

As a result of the March 1862 action between the *Monitor* and the *Virginia*, the Swedish 1862 parliamentary defence committee decided that the navy's vessels were to be steam powered, armoured and built of iron. In June 1862, the Board of Admiralty sent Lieutenants J C d'Ailly and J V Gjerling to Britain and France 'to obtain information about the armoured ships of those two nations' fleets'. Correspondence with John Ericsson, the *Monitor*'s constructor, brought about J C d'Ailly's American visit and in turn resulted in the Norwegian and Swedish monitor construction programme. Part of the cost of the Swedish vessels' construction was to be recovered by the sale of material from scrapped sailing vessels, and obsolete stores. However, the dismantling of the sailing craft was to be unhurried.

In 1863, the Board of Admiralty received 100,000 kronor to test armour plate at the Karlsborg fortress for the new monitors; trials of rifled guns for the new ships taking place at the same time. A committee of three naval gunnery specialists carried out tests in which a 6.5in gun was fired at a British $4^{1}/_{2}$in armour plate, a French plate of similar thickness and built-up armour consisting of five Swedish 1in plates. The British armour plate proved to be the best, the Swedish built-up plates the weakest.

Following the gun and armour trials, the Swedish Board of Admiralty arranged for a meeting of Danish, Norwegian and Swedish naval officers to consider the different types of vessels suitable for their nation's defences. Sweden and Norway chose the American monitor type as the kernel of their naval defences for the 1860s and 1870s but Denmark, with no waters bounded by skerries and denied information of the Ericsson turret by the US Government, ordered the turret ship *Rolf Krake*.[1] In 1864, the Swedish Admiralty board submitted the final drawings for the *John Ericsson* class

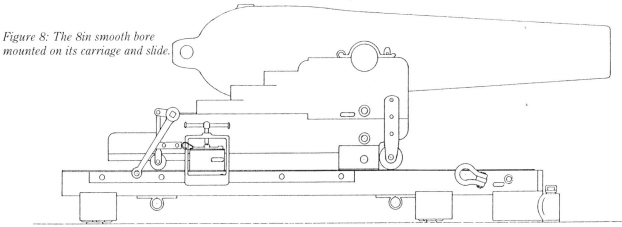

Figure 8: The 8in smooth bore mounted on its carriage and slide.

The fixed turret of the monitor Hildur *viewed from the forecastle; photograph taken in the 1880s or 1890s.* (Gothenburg Maritime Museum)

16–15cm guns, 10–25mm anti-aircraft guns and 6–53cm torpedo tubes. The means of propulsion was to be diesel engines and the maximum speed was to be 10kts. The purpose of the vessel was to defend the Stockholm Skerries but the Chief of Naval Staff rejected all of Bjurner's proposals as out of date and too costly; the fleet was to have an active role at sea, rather than be tied to skerry defence.

The *Thordøn* was not the only vessel of the type to ground during its career. The Norwegian *Mjølner* ran aground at Kragerø in Oslo Fjord on 21 June 1869. The salvage operations required six barges to take off the ammunition, iron ballast and 120 tons of coal after which, on 29 June, tugs were able to pull the vessel off the rocks. The Norwegian navy court of enquiry ordered the commander, D Burchardt, and the pilot to pay for the damages that resulted from their 'carelessness in performance of duties'. The Horten Royal Dockyard had completed the repairs by 7 July 1869 at a cost of about 5,000 kronor. Two years later, the Norwegian parliament released Burchardt and the pilot from their obligation.

The *Mjølner* was laid up in 1898 but was recommissioned in 1905 when difficulties arose during the dissolution of the Norwegian union with Sweden. The vessel rejoined the reserve on the completion of negotiations and was sold for scrap in 1909.

monitors to King Carl XV for his signature of approval. Signing the final profile drawings before dispatch to the shipyards for bids was the Swedish monarchs' standard practice, from the time of Carl XII until the end of Oscar II's reign in 1907.

The delay in the completion of *Loke*,[2] the last *John Ericsson* class monitor, may have been due to manufacturing difficulties encountered by the British supplier of her armour plate.

The *John Ericsson* class monitors that still existed in 1914 were used principally as accommodation ships in the royal dockyards. Personnel lodged in these old vessels found them uncomfortable.

The Ericsson-designed hand-driven

propulsion system for the *Sköld* class monitors was unpopular with the crews. Although Ericsson held the view that crews would be comfortable and protected from shells and weather whilst 'rowing' below decks, the crews had other views – they had not joined the navy to be 'galley slaves'. The fleet's command soon found the hand-operated systems ineffective and had them removed.

In 1945, a Swedish defence committee was set up to determine what types of vessels the navy should have during the ten years 1947–57. The committee's chairman was Admiral Bjurner, one of the old school. Its recommendations included the construction of two 10,000 ton armoured monitors, armed with 3–21cm guns,

Notes

[1] In 1863, prior to delivery, the Danish government had to prove to the British and the US governments that *Rolf Krake* had not been built for the Confederate States. The Danish Government also had to give an undertaking that the vessel would not be sold to the rebellious southern states on arrival in Danish waters. *Rolf Krake* took part in the Danish-Russian war of 1864 and was sold for scrap in 1907.

[2] *Loke* is the name of the mythical giant that was to do battle with the gods at the end of time.

Sources

B Ahland, *Svensk Marin Säkerhets Politik* (Stockholm 1994).

Profile and plan for the John Ericsson *class monitors based on official design drawings held by the Krigsarkivet, Stockholm.* (Drawn by John Roberts)

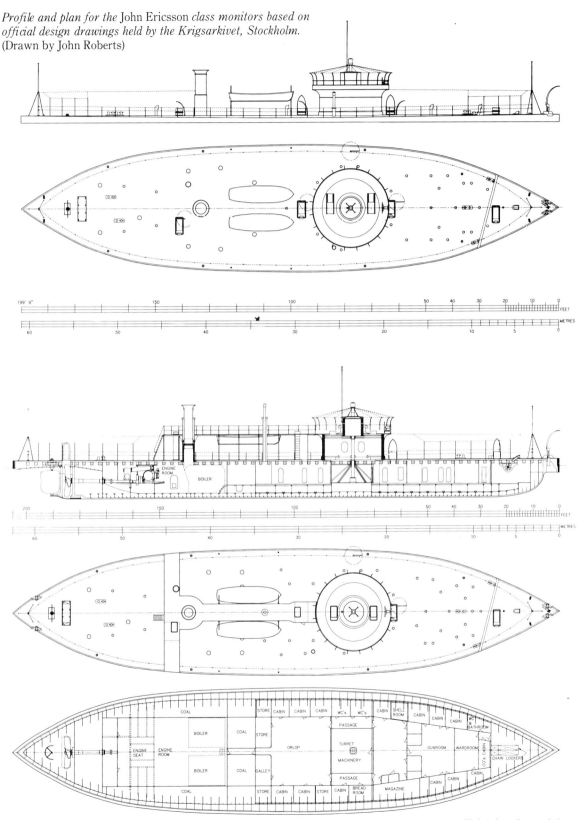

Internal profile on centre line, and weather deck and lower deck plans of the Loke, *based on official drawings of the ship, dated 11 April 1867, held by the Sjöhistoriska Muséet, Stockholm. She differed in dimensions from the other vessels of the* John Ericsson *class in having an additional four frame spaces amidships (which added 6ft to the length of the main hull) but a slightly shorter overhang of the raft body at the stern and a reduced beam.* (Drawn by John Roberts)

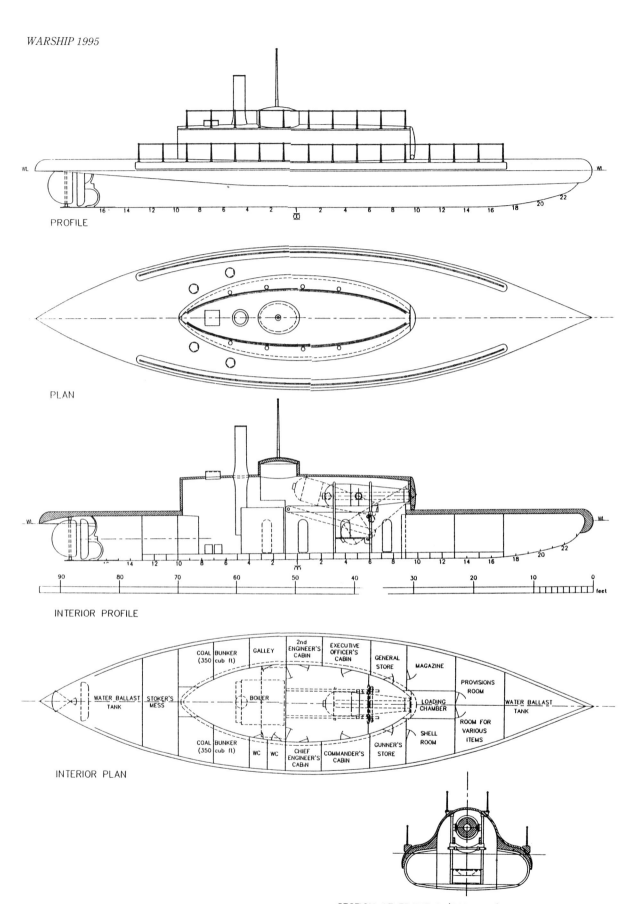

PROFILE

PLAN

INTERIOR PROFILE

| COAL BUNKER (350 cub ft) | GALLEY | 2nd ENGINEER'S CABIN | EXECUTIVE OFFICER'S CABIN | GENERAL STORE | MAGAZINE | | PROVISIONS ROOM | |
| | | | | | | | | |

WATER BALLAST TANK | STOKER'S MESS | BOILER | | LOADING CHAMBER | WATER BALLAST TANK

COAL BUNKER (350 cub ft) | WC | WC | CHIEF ENGINEER'S CABiN | COMMANDER'S CABIN | GUNNER'S STORE | SHELL ROOM | ROOM FOR VARIOUS ITEMS

INTERIOR PLAN

SECTION AT FRAME 6 (FORWARD) LOOKING FORWARD

Plans of Garmer *based on official design drawings, approved on 18 July 1865, held by the Krigsarkivet, Stockholm.*
(Drawn by John Roberts)

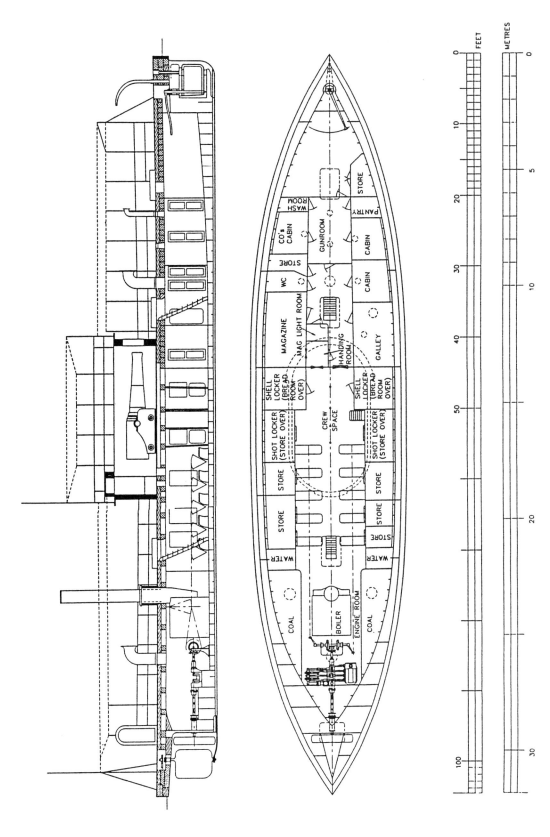

Plan and profile of Fenris *based the design drawings, prepared by D'Ailly and dated 22 December 1869, held by the Krigsarkivet, Stockholm. Note the arrangements for hand propulsion and the general layout of the machinery which differed from that in her sister vessel* Sköld. *(Drawn by John Roberts)*

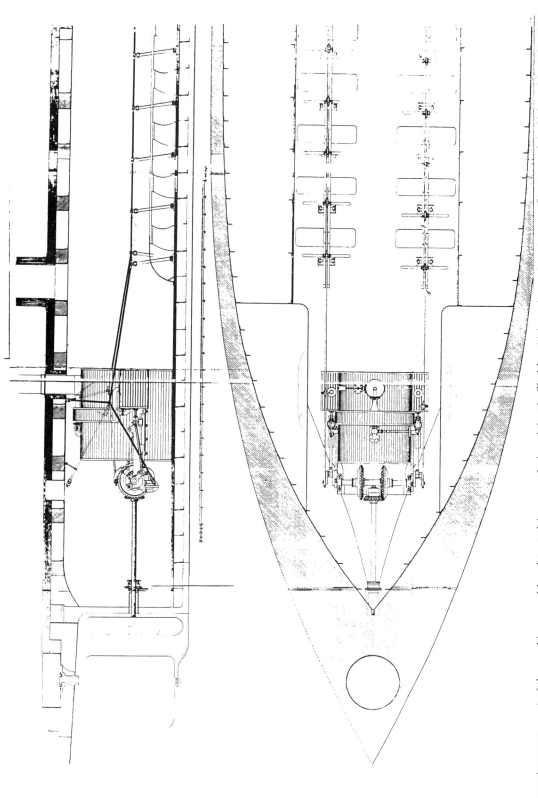

General arrangement of the machinery and hand-propulsion gear designed for the Sköld – thickness' are given in mm. (Courtesy of the Krigsarkivet, Stockholm)

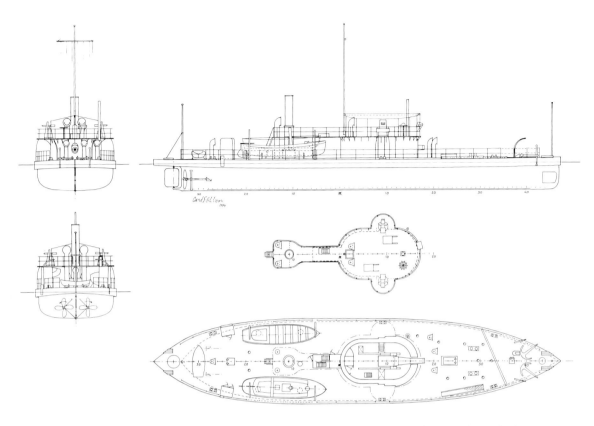

General arrangement drawings of the Sölve *as built. Note the bow rudder, and the machine guns in the bridge wings. The numbers refer to the frames.* (Drawn by C S Ohlsson, P Eng, Gothenburg Maritime Centre)

M Hammar, *Överstyrelsen och Vapen Materielen* (Malmo 1977).

S Moen, *Monitoren Horten* (1992).

R S Steensen, *Vore Panserskibe* (Copenhagen 1968).

P Wedin, *Amiralitets Kollegiets Historia, Vol III* (Malmo 1977).

K Westerlund, *Svenska Örlogs Fartyg 1855-1905* (Stockholm 1993).

The 10,200 ton monitor design of 1945. (Drawn by John Roberts)

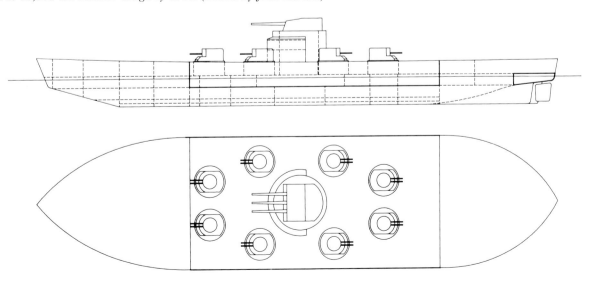

32   32
305   152   152   51

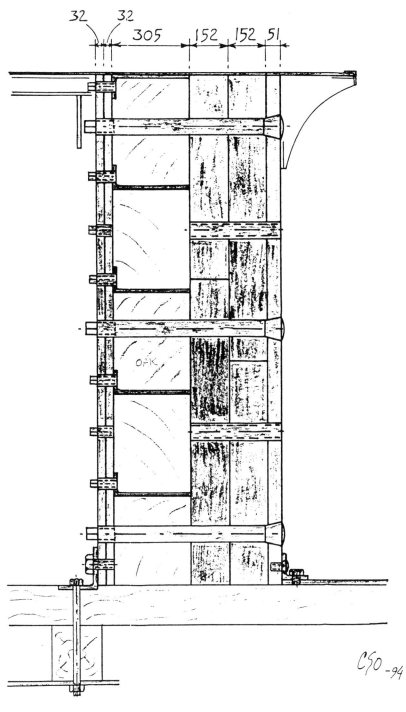

OFK

CSO -94

Section of the face armour of the Sölve's *gunhouse.* (Drawn by C S Ohlsson, P Eng, Gothenburg Maritime Centre)

THE VALUE OF BLIMPS

The use of blimps in the anti-submarine role from the First World War to the 1960s has until recently received little attention despite evidence that they were, at the least, a very effective deterrent. Robert Largess discusses the advantages of these craft in convoy escort and patrol work with particular reference to recent publications on the subject.

Since the invention of lighter-than-air flight, the most significant role of the airship has been anti-submarine warfare. During the course of the First World War, Britain built 225 airships, all but a handful of these non-rigid 'blimps'. They flew a total of 88,000 hours, or more than two million miles, during this war; the operational part of which was almost entirely on anti-submarine patrols or convoy escort. Among the many thousands of merchantmen escorted, they lost, it is claimed, only one to a U-boat. During this war the French Navy built a substantial force of about fifty blimps and claimed to have lost not a single ship sunk under airship escort.

By the Second World War, only the USN retained the airship – barely; but the collection of eight prototypes and relics on hand in 1939 had been expanded by about 165 ships by the end of the war, the largest lighter-than-air fleet in history. These ships operated from Nova Scotia to Brazil, as well as in the Mediterranean and Pacific. In the Atlantic and Pacific theatres combined, 57,710 flights were made, totalling 545,529 hours in the air (or nearly 23,000 days), excluding 280,000 hours flown by training commands. In total 89,000 ships were escorted with no more than one possible loss.

However, in spite of these apparently remarkable achievements, much ambiguity and division over the effectiveness of the airship followed both wars. Actual submarine sinkings were very few. The French blimps claimed more than sixty U-boat sightings during the First World War and British airships sighted forty-nine U-boats and attacked twenty-seven between

June 1916 and October 1918. They claimed damage and possible sinkings in many of these attacks but are actually credited with only three sinkings, all in co-operation with warships. In the Second World War US Navy blimps claimed numerous sightings and attacks but probably assisted in only one U-boat kill, and damaged several others.

Were blimps then a vital ASW weapon, a perfect protection for merchant convoys? Or were they a mere frill, an inessential auxiliary to surface escorts and aeroplanes – the actual sub-killers? The US Navy began ambitious airship development programmes after both World Wars, which produced some remarkable aviation achievements and great technological advances but ultimately petered out and died in the face of criticism or simple disinterest. The British blimp force, on the other hand, was simply shut down and written off overnight, sixty ships being deleted when naval aviation was transferred to the RAF in October 1919.

Evaluating the wartime achievements of the blimp versus the submarine has been made difficult, however, by the fact that they have been almost entirely unknown. Interest in the airship has perennially revolved around the much more impressive rigids – Zeppelins, *Macon, R100, Hindenberg* – with their remarkable achievements and appalling disasters. Practically nothing has been written on the blimps until very recently. In all the military polemics between the wars, only one work, Captain J A Sinclaire's *Airships in Peace and War*, described the anti-submarine activities of the British blimps. One reason was that they were kept secret during the war, like everything else to do with the anti U-boat campaign. A second reason was the astoundingly fatuous but nearly universal attitude after the First World War that the submarine war on trade was an anomaly unlikely ever to recur. Thus, the British blimps disappeared utterly in the face of the RAF's total disinterest in the submarine problem, France kept a single base and skeleton airship force in commission to the eve of the Second World War, and the US Navy transferred blimps to the Army for most of the interwar period while she pursued rigid airship development. After the Second World War on the other hand, the US Navy saw the blimp as very valuable – partly because, for the first time in peace, it perceived anti-submarine warfare as being of critical importance. Much effort was expended on perfecting the ASW blimp and equipping it with advanced technology but, by the end of the 1950s, interest and support had disappeared outside the small lighter-than-air community itself.

How effective were the blimps during the two great U-boat campaigns? What potential did they offer post-war ASW and perhaps still offer today? The amount of published research on these topics is thin but a handful of recent books go some way toward answering these questions.

Robin Higham summarises the achievements of the non-rigids in the First World War in a chapter in *The British Rigid Airship*, the beginning of genuinely scholarly airship history. A few excellent first person accounts exist, such as T B Williams' *Airship Pilot No 28*, and *The British Airship at War 1914–1918* by Patrick Abbott gives an excellent summary of their specifications and operations. Perhaps the best analysis of their anti-submarine tactics and effectiveness was made in Alfred Price's *Aircraft vs Submarine*.

For this was truly the balloon's finest hour, when blimps played a major role in a decisive, successful campaign. The U-boat was defeated by convoy and air cover greatly increased the effectiveness of convoy; only 257 ships were lost from convoys, but only two of these from convoys with air cover. Air cover made it impossible for U-boats to approach convoys on the surface, usually necessary to gain an attack position. Furthermore, blimps had far greater endurance, reliability and weather-worthiness than aeroplanes. Their sorties were normally three times longer, they could stop engines aloft for repairs, refuel from ships or be towed home if disabled. They could take-off in zero visibility, set down on the sea surface, and lift heavy wireless sets when few aeroplanes had them. And this was its most valuable weapon against the submarine – the ability to reveal its position to intelligence and nearby naval forces.

The blimp's deficiencies compared to the aeroplane's were its greater visibility and slower speed. These gave it little chance of catching and bombing a surfaced U-boat, which also occasionally fought back – the US lost K-74 in this way in 1943. French

The US Navy's M-class blimps, largest in existence in the Second World War, were intended to succeed the 134 K-class built during 1938–44. Only four Ms were completed; they served as test beds for the advanced technology incorporated in the new generation of advanced airships of the 1950's. Here M-3 covers the surrender of U858 *to US forces in May 1945. (Courtesy James R Shock)*

M-1 on 13 March 1944 carrying a Piper Cub in what was the last of many experiments with airship-carried aircraft going back to the First World War. (Courtesy Richard Van Treuren)

blimps carried guns of up to 75mm, British blimps tried 2pdr cannon and German Zeppelins torpedo-carrying gliders, in an attempt to solve this problem.

On the other hand the blimp was the ideal platform from which to detect and track a submerged submarine,

M-1 with Piper Cub (with landing gear removed) on 3 March 1944. F9C 'hook-on' fighters based on the rigid Macon *in 1933 operated without conventional landing gear for increased range and speed. This M-1, however, has no means of retrieving the Cub once released. Jas Shock reports the purpose of these tests was to provide the ASW blimp with a standoff weapon to attack a surfaced submarine in the form of a radio-controlled drone, a primitive guided missile.* (Courtesy James R Shock)

visibly, if at all, only within a very small circle directly below an aircraft. Blimps could come to a hover over them, or descend very low for a careful observation of the sea surface. They tracked and bombed U-boats by trails of leaking air and oil bubbles, bottom sediment churned up by their

screws or periscope wakes, and even followed torpedo tracks back to their source. The ability of the blimps to hover enabled them to use primitive dipping hydrophones, pointing the way to the future.

Essentially victory in the first anti U-boat campaign was achieved defensively, by cutting merchant losses, not by sinking submarines. Blimps played a major role in the former; nothing was much good at the latter but blimps demonstrated a unique potential against the submerged submarine, the most difficult part of the problem.

The blimps' performance in the Second World War seems even more impressive, but remains even less studied and more ambiguous. When war broke out in 1941 the USN had four modern anti-submarine blimps operating on the east coast. Amazingly, these four craft were the only modern trained anti-submarine forces on the entire coast in the disastrous opening phases of Operation *Paukenschlag*. They bore the brunt of shipping defence then, operating heavily and reporting numerous U-boat sightings and attacks but, in the absence of convoys, were able only to protect merchant ships in their immediate vicinity. Later, when the US extended a complete blimp, plane and surface coverage over the US coast, the Caribbean and Brazilian waters, U-boats largely avoided these areas.

No one seems better placed to answer the question of their effectiveness and value in the Second World War than J Gordon Vaeth, author of *Blimps and U-Boats*. He was air intelligence officer to the Atlantic Fleet airship command and after the war consulted German naval archives (and Admiral Doenitz personally) in an attempt to answer this question. His book, however, although describing the operations and activities of the blimp force in depth, does not present any final judgement, leaving the reader to make his own conclusions.

The Second World War 'K' class ships represented a substantial advance in capability with non-inflammable helium gas, a normal endurance of 20 hours, 65kt speeds, roomy enclosed gondolas for the ten-man crews and sufficient range to cross the Atlantic by stopping at the Azores. They were equipped with depth-charges, radar, their newly-invented secret weapon (the magnetic anomaly detector or MAD) and, later, sonobuoys, Hedgehogs and homing torpedoes. The blimps' MAD represented the only aircraft sensor in existence in 1942 able to detect a completely submerged submarine. Although it was very limited in range,

M-3 testing the APS-20 radar probably in 1947. This extremely significant radar, developed in the Second World War, was the first AEW radar and later served as the main means of submarine detection by postwar ASW aircraft; it was ultimately able to pick up a snorkel at 30 miles. APS-20 with an 8ft antenna was carried by many aircraft. M-3 is perhaps the first aircraft to carry this advanced APS-20 with a huge 20ft antenna, and may well be carrying the prototype AEW airborne interception control centre. This huge radar was used by WV-2 Constellations and ZPG-2W blimps for AEW, and EP-3 Orions for radar intelligence gathering. The only vehicles to use this version purely for ASW were the ZPG-2 blimps. (Courtesy James R Shock)

M-1 testing a towed sonar sometime between March 1951 and January 1952. The blimp's ability to operate this sonar at high speeds gave it a unique weapon against the nuclear submarine. Jas Shock says a ZPG-2 exercised with and successfully tracked the Nautilus *in 1955. Blimp towed sonars were tested aboard hydrofoils. (Courtesy James R Shock)*

blimps were occasionally able to detect, track and attack U-boats and thus assisted in the kill of the *U853* in 1945. Blimps maintained the MAD blockade of the Strait of Gibraltar at night. They also played a major role in rescue, locating and even towing home lifeboats, dropping supplies, and picking up survivors by line from the sea surface or by landing in difficult terrain. They also proved valuable in the Mediterranean, charting minefields from the air.

Meanwhile, the aeroplane had become a deadly killer of the surfaced or diving submarine, with its speed, ra-

A crucial element of postwar blimp convoy tactics were extended operations from Commencement Bay *class escort carriers (here the* Mindoro*). Second World War K class ships were extensively modified for carrier landings or refuelling aloft by hose (see also photograph accompanying the article '*Warrior and Magnificent*' showing a US blimp landing on the* Magnificent*). These blimps operated in night and fog, using radar, MAD, sono-buoys, and searchlights detect many submarines successfully in convoy excercises.* (Photo taken from a US Navy film by David B Stillerman)

dar and powerful weapons but it still had little means of tracking the wholly-submerged submarine. The problems posed by the appearance of the snorkel-equipped U-boat revived interest in the low-flying, slow moving blimp, better able to detect the snorkel head, covered by radar-absorbent material, by its wake or exhaust plume. The appearance of the Type XXI U-boat, with high submerged speed and endurance, put ASW warfare back to square one. The victory over the submarine in the Second World War was achieved above all by radar, by denying the U-boat the use of the surface, but the more serious problem, the submerged submarine, was not only far from solved but had made the submarine an even greater threat.

After the war the US Navy saw the submarine threat as perhaps its greatest problem. Tremendous efforts were devoted to many areas of technology – among them the blimp, which seemed to offer great promise. This was the period when the blimp's potential for modern ASW reached its highest level, yet the only works which cover it at all are *Kite Balloons to Airships...The Navy's Lighter-than-*

Air Experience, an official publication edited by J Q Grossnick, William Althoff's *Skyships* and the truly excellent *US Navy Pressure Airships 1915–1962* by James R Shock. None of them offers an analysis of post-war blimp anti-submarine capabilities and tactics but Shock offers much detail on weaponry, sensors and exercises scattered throughout his encyclopaedic history, which summarise the careers of every individual US Navy blimp.

However, unpublished accounts of US Navy convoy escort exercises in the late 1940s show blimps refuelling from escort carriers, operating at low level in night and fog, monitoring and replenishing sonobuoy barriers, spotting periscopes visually, repeatedly locating attacking submarines by MAD and even observing the movements of a submerged submarine by searchlight at night. Fixed-wing aircraft had the APS-20 early warning radar, which could pick up a snorkel at 26 miles but few tools to pursue the submarine under the surface.

A new generation of very large blimps, the ZPG-2s, appeared in the 1950s. They had tremendous range and endurance (one stayed aloft for 11 days while making a unique double

Atlantic crossing unrefuelled, nonstop, in 1957). They possessed all the sensors and weapons of contemporary patrol planes plus towed sonars useable at 50kts. Once the blimp found her quarry, it could track her like a surface ship but at higher speeds, invulnerable to counterattack by torpedoes. Even so, convoy escort seemed a hopeless proposition in the face of the huge Soviet undersea fleet and the appearance of the nuclear submarine. The solution came with the ability of SOSUS – fixed seabed passive arrays – to track submarines at great distances by low frequency sound. Then a long-range high speed fixed-wing aircraft – the turbo-prop P-3 – was needed to prosecute these distant contacts, not the slower blimp.

As their size and capabilities steadily increased, the blimp's numbers steadily decreased – there were only twelve ZPG-2s – and they dwindled down once more to the level of an expensive experiment, no longer a viable force. The last two were decommissioned in 1962.

Yet even today the blimp could serve as the ideal convoy escort – if that were needed. It has the capability to deploy a greater range of anti-submarine sensors than any other vehicle, playing in turn the role of patrol plane, helicopter and surface ship. For the most part, other tools have defeated it but the blimp's unique potential against the submarine led Britain and the US to turn to it at those times when the submarine's technical ascendancy and threat were greatest and it seemed almost unbeatable. In all the history of flight, less than 2000 airships have been built and it can be argued that their most significant role by far was anti-submarine warfare. However, this remains its greatest handicap, if it is to be available for ASW it must be created and developed almost solely for this purpose. Throughout its history the blimp has very nearly disappeared over and over again, only to be called back into being when a new submarine threat has arisen.

THE VICKERS GUN MOUNTING PLAN COLLECTION

David Hughes describes the rare and valuable collection of naval gun mounting drawings held at the Cumbria Record Office, Barrow-in-Furness, and his work toward making the collection more accessible.

The Vickers Gun Mounting Plan Collection was deposited at the Cumbria Record Office on behalf of the present Vickers Shipbuilding and Engineering Company. The collection of drawings and associated material represents many aspects of the work of Vickers, under the various company names, during the period 1897–1950.[1] The holdings at Barrow consist of material from the Department of Naval Architecture and the Armament Design Office – drawings of gun mountings predominate. Deposited with the drawings are twenty-six volumes of drawing issue books which act as a

useful index to the original output. The numbered drawings recorded in the books run from 200 to 45309 but one volume, covering numbers 5359 to 8580, is missing. The drawing issue books contain the drawing number, the date of issue, title, name of draughtsman and remarks showing to which departments copies were sent and when.

The greater part of the collection consists of the drawings from the Gun Mounting Department; these relate to guns, mountings and other equipment such as control towers etc, supplied to vessels constructed in the Barrow Yard. In addition a proportion of the collection concerns gun mountings and other work carried out on contract to other yards and the Admiralty, etc in the UK and abroad.

The collection contains no ship drawings except a series generally illustrating HMS *Cerberus*, a breastwork monitor constructed by Palmers of Jarrow and completed in 1870. The plans show a proposed change in the main armament from 10in MLR to 8in BL.[2]

The collection was summarily listed on arrival at the Cumbria Record Office after a certain amount of weeding, which reduced the volume of material by an estimated one third. All early material from 1897 to December 1899 was retained. Thereafter, detailed drawings were discarded in most cases, leaving the remaining general and sub-arrangement drawings. The exceptions to this rule are drawings relating to HIJMS *Mikasa*, HIJMS *Kongo* and to HMS *Dreadnought*[3] where all remaining drawings were retained. Comparing the original collection as first deposited with the en-

A view of the large erecting shop of the Naval Gun Mounting Department at Barrow-in-Furness. The largest of three, the shop was over 1000ft long and could assemble up to twelve battleship gun mountings at a time. The photograph dates from c1903 and shows 12in mountings in various stages of construction in the gun pits. (Cumbria Record Office)

tries in the drawing issue books, it is clear that many drawings had already been lost or disposed of by Vickers over the years. My own rough estimate of the number of drawings remaining stored in the Cumbria Record Office is around 26,000 – of which the great majority are on waxed linen sheet which has generally remained in good condition.

To access the collection the searcher must presently use the original list compiled by the archivist together with the manuscript drawing issue books. The archive list available to searchers is only outline in nature and gives only a rough guide to the plan rolls. The re-

The gun slide department, one of the smaller shops, was used for bench work and making small fittings. A 20 ton electric crane serves the shop together with side mounted gantry cranes. The sections of armour plate stacked in the left foreground were destined for the battleship, HMS Exmouth. *(Cumbria Record Office)*

searcher may have to search through many bundles of plans in order to find any relevant information.

The problem was clearly a practical one of devising a better method of access to the information buried within the collection. I proposed a comprehensive scheme to list the plans based on a modern computer database and funded by the Kirby Archive Trust. The aim was to fully explore the Vickers Plan Collection as it related to naval ordnance and to encourage the use of this unique historical resource. Approval was given by the trustees and a start was made for an experimental six-month period in October 1994.

The database chosen for the scheme was Microsoft Access. After a few initial problems the processing of the drawing collection and the drawing issue books started. Each plan is examined individually together with the relevant entry in the drawing book. The information added to the database occupies nineteen fields or categories. The key fields are the plan number, the name or class of the ves-

sel, the primary title which gives the gun type and the secondary title which reveals the detailed subject of the drawing. From the contract number and by using the drawing issue books the name or class of the vessel is established. The database also records the draughtsman or section leader and the date provided by the Drawing Issue Book. Necessary repairs to drawings and all general arrangements of complete turret mountings are identified.

The database programme is flexible enough to allow the future addition of new fields as different information emerges. It allows the Record Office to produce lists of all drawings relating to a certain class of vessel, or by gun calibre or those executed by a particular draughtsman.

At the time of writing, work has been ongoing for nearly five months with the result that approximately 5,500 drawings have been processed and plan number 16,500 reached. The dates of this material run from 1897 (the time of the take-over of the Bar-

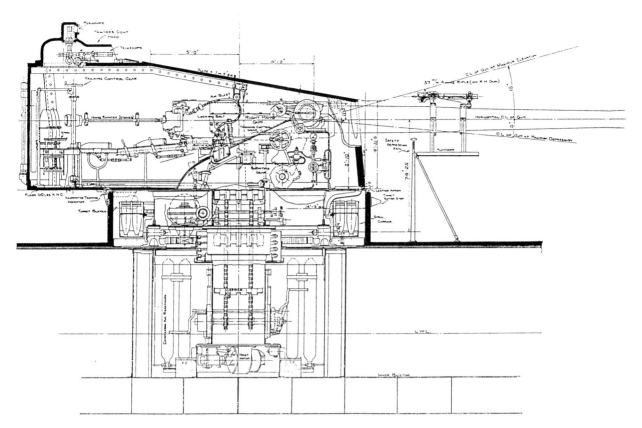

Profile of a 6in twin mounting from plan No 16749. An early twin turret designed for the Brazilian monitors Javery, Solimoes and Madeira. *The design of the mounting was unique and only three were produced. The design overcame the difficulties of accomodating turntable and hoists within such a shallow draught. The vessels were taken over by the Royal Navy at the outbreak of the First World War as* Humber, Severn *and* Mersey *and variously served off the Belgian coast, in the Dardenelles and in East Africa. The very short externally mounted 37mm aiming rifle was an interesting feature of the weapon.* (Cumbria Record Office)

row Yard of the Naval Construction & Armaments Company), to around 1913, covering one of the most productive periods of UK warship design and construction. The gun calibre's represented by the plans run from 6in to 15in. The 6in are twin mountings which were constructed for the County class armoured cruisers *Monmouth, Bedford, Kent, Essex, Cornwall* and *Suffolk*. Later mountings for the three Brazilian River Monitors are

also twins.[4] The Department concentrated on the design and construction of more complex mountings leaving single pedestal mountings to others. Lesser calibres from 12pdr down to 37mm are illustrated in the collection but only when they are part of a larger gun mounting design, for example the turret top mountings prevalent on battleships and battlecruisers prior to the First World War. The 37mm guns were mounted as aiming rifles, directly on to the barrels of the twin 6in mountings of the Brazilian River Monitors.[4]

The identification of the individual contracts and ships have been made possible by the research carried out in Vickers to produce a list of contract numbers. From this research and the drawing books it has been possible to identify the ship(s) and ship classes to which each of the plans refer. Many of the orders apply to material ordered for the Barrow built vessels and often to class sisters constructed elsewhere and in certain cases to ship classes built entirely elsewhere.

The first plan in the collection is numbered 200. It is one of 259 plans remaining from the construction of the battleship HMS *Vengeance*. The

battleship *Vengeance* was an important ship for Barrow-in-Furness and the newly arrived Vickers, Sons & Maxim Limited. The vessel was the first battleship built in the Yard and the first in the world to have all major components (*ie* gun mountings, hull and engines) constructed within one company. The *Vengeance* was the sixth and last of the *Canopus* class. She differed from her sisters in the design of her gun mountings which ended the fashion for curved turret fronts with flat sides replacing them with angled flat plates.

Foreign orders are well represented within the collection – especially mountings constructed for Italy, Japan, Russia and Turkey. The earliest so far discovered is a collection of drawings of single 9.2in mountings for the Turkish warship *Messudijeh*. Barrow also supplied sets of 10in and 7.5in mountings to Orlando of Italy for armoured cruisers.

The period 1899 to 1913 saw Vickers, Sons & Maxim become major constructors for the Imperial Japanese Navy. Three major vessels were built at Barrow, together with orders for heavy gun mountings. The ships HIJMS *Mikasa, Katori* and *Kongo* are all represented in the collection. The *Katori* is particularly well covered with a total of almost 600 drawings for her 12in and 10in gun mountings. These include complete general arrangement views of the mountings for both calibres. Three hundred and four drawings represent the battlecruiser *Kongo* including a partial set of general arrangements for her Type 43, 14in mountings. Disappointingly only eight minor drawings remain for the *Mikasa*. Vickers, Sons & Maxim also constructed two twin 12in/50cal gun mountings for the battleships of the *Kawatchi* class. A comprehensive set of turret general arrangements have survived together with trial results from the Eskmeals firing range. The number of drawings for Japanese vessels so far listed within the collection is 1055.

I was interested to note the number of drawings originating from Armstrong Whitworth & Co. This suggests a strong co-operation between the two companies long prior to the Vickers acquisition of Armstrong.[1] Vickers occasionally constructed mountings to Armstrong designs. HMS *Vanguard*, launched at Barrow in 1909, carried the BIX mounting for the 12in/50cal gun – 134 drawings remain from the *Vanguard* of which two thirds have been traced from original Armstrong Whitworth sources. HMS *Princess Royal* launched at Barrow in 1911 provides the collection with fifty-six drawings of the 13.5in MkII mounting – all of which originate from Armstrong Whitworth. In the case of both ships the general arrangement drawings of the barbette mounting have survived.

With one exception all the mountings recorded so far have been single or twin. The exception is the triple 304cm mounting produced for the Italian battleship *Andrea Doria*. Both the triple and twin mountings for this vessel are well illustrated by 251 drawings, including general arrangements of both mountings.

The part of the collection so far recorded is a major resource for researchers, but much work remains to be done before the collection can be said to be comprehensively available for use. The trial first six months of the project is almost over, with efforts being made to extend the scheme. Future discoveries within the collection are waiting to be made. As I examine the initial listing for the unprocessed part of the collection it emphasises the comprehensive and central role of the Vickers Company in the design and construction of gun mountings. The mention of 14in, 16in, 16.5in and 18in mountings together with representative names from many of the major British warship classes underlines the importance and unique character of the collection and the exciting discoveries to come. (If any reader is interested in obtaining information about the collection, or copies of the drawings, they should contact the Cumbria Record Office, 140 Duke Street, Barrow-in-Furness, Cumbria, LA14 1XW, UK – Ed.)

Notes

[1] Vickers came to Barrow in 1896 with the purchase of the Naval Construction and Armaments Company. In 1897 they became Vickers, Sons and Maxim Ltd on the acquisition of the Maxim Nordenfeldt Gun Company. In 1911 the name was simplified to Vickers Ltd and in 1928 the company bought the Walker Yard and Elswick Works from Armstrong Whitworth and Co to become Vickers Armstrongs Ltd.

[2] The drawings of the *Cerberus* show the vessel in plan and section with specific views of the gun mountings as carried and as proposed. The drawings are undated and may be earlier than the rest of the collection, possibly being contemporary with the conversion to 8in BL of her sister *Magdala*.

[3] With some minor variations, the 12in mountings for *Dreadnought* were of the same design as those for *Agamemnon* and *Lord Nelson* whose guns and mountings had been ordered shortly before those of the *Dreadnought*. In order to expedite the *Dreadnought* order the contracts were effectively transposed, any work already under way for *Agamemnon* and *Lord Nelson* being transferred to the new ship. There are a considerable number of drawings for *Agamemnon* in the collection the majority of which are common to *Dreadnought*.

[4] All launched in 1913, the three monitors were originally built for Brazil as *Javery*, *Solimoes* and *Madeira*. On the outbreak of war in 1914 they were acquired for the Royal Navy as *Humber*, *Severn* and *Mersey*.

ADDENDA TO GERMAN TORPEDO BOATS AT WAR

Pierre Hervieux has written with the following additional information to his article 'War Operations of the Types 35 and 37 Torpedo Boats' which appeared in *Warship 1994*. On 4 January 1945, off Danzig, the German torpedo boat *T3* rammed, and then depth-charged and sank, the Soviet submarine *S4* (Captain Klyushkin). This information supersedes that given on page 130 of *Warship 1994* which assumed the Soviet submarine concerned was *S13* and that it survived. In addition it should be noted that in the description of this incident in *Warship 1994* the *T3* is incorrectly identified as *T13* for which the editor apologises.

NAVAL BOOKS OF THE YEAR

The year has been a rather poor one for naval technical publications, with the notable exception of a substantial number of new books from the French publisher *Marines Édition et Réalisations*. An overall introduction to the series produced by this publisher has been provided by John Jordan, followed by the reviews of the books themselves as a group. The remainder of the section follows the usual pattern with reviews proper followed by short descriptive notices and a list of books announced but not received. In all sections, place of publication is London unless otherwise specified.

The past two years have seen the appearance of a remarkable series of French-language books on major warship types of the interwar *Marine Nationale* published by *Marines Édition et Réalisations* (Bourg en Bresse, France). These fall into three distinct sub-groups: two small monographs on the *escorteur d'escadre Maillé Brézé* and the cruiser *Colbert* of postwar vintage; a larger-format series which already covers many of the most interesting classes of surface warship of the prewar *Marine Nationale*, together with the submarines of the period; and a similar series entitled *Les Ports Français 1939–45*, which aims to give a written and photographic account of the activities of the French naval bases and dockyards during the Second World War.

Each book has been authored by a recognised authority in the field, with extensive use of primary sources. The text is lavishly illustrated by high-quality and often unusual photographs and, where appropriate, by line drawings. The warship books are divided into two sections: one gives a detailed technical analysis of the design, broken down into sub-sections on hull, armour, propulsion, arma-

ment, etc; the other a blow-by-blow service history, detailing every deployment from training exercises and port visits to war action.

Inevitably in a series this ambitious – and being produced within a remarkably short timescale – there are rough edges; not all of the authors are as skilful at using their chosen photographs to illustrate the text, and the quality of the line drawings is particularly uneven, varying from the very good down to the fairly crude. Nevertheless, for those of us who for years have struggled to extract detailed and accurate information about French warships of the period from the 'broad-brush' writings of authorities such as the late Henri le Masson, the hard-headed approach to technical detail exemplified by this new series is to be welcomed. There has been nothing quite like these books published in France before.

Jean Lassaque, Les C.T. de 2400 tonnes du type Jaguar, *published by Marines Édition et Réalisations (Bourg en Bresse, 1994).*
215 × 276mm, 144 pages, 144 photographs, numerous plans and line drawings.
ISBN 2 909675 11 4. 295F

Jean Lassaque's book on the *Jaguar* class is a study of the first French *contre-torpilleurs*. Given the novelty of the *contre-torpilleur* as a type it is perhaps disappointing that the author accords so little attention to its philosophical origins, which are dealt with in an almost peremptory manner in a brief two-page introduction. It also strikes this reviewer as odd to place the full service history of the ships before the technical study (thereby reversing the order established in earlier books in the series). This means that the persistent turbine machinery problems experienced with the so-called 'industrie B' ships, *Léopard* and *Lynx*, are recounted at length before we get to read about the design of the Laval-Bréguet turbines which were largely responsible.

Since these ships saw relatively little war service, the service history section is largely an account of port visits, refits and exercises. Nevertheless, it provides a valuable picture of the operational organisation of the pre-war *Marine Nationale*, and a revealing insight into the premature ageing of these ships, brought about by driving them too hard on trials and by over-use early in their careers in order to impress important visitors.

The technical section is most interesting for its revelations of the full extent of the topweight problems which plagued these ships throughout their service lives. These problems were to be responsible for: suppression of the elaborate fire control system originally to have been fitted, which would have incorporated a light cruiser-style DCT; the abandonment of proposals to rearm the ships with the more powerful 138.6mm/40 Model 1923 guns fitted in later classes (thirty of these had been ordered in 1925 for this specific purpose); the disembarkation of A/S mortars, depth-charges and torpedoes in peacetime; and even a proposal to shorten the anchor chains! Finally it was recognised that the only solution was a radical reconstruction of the ships, but this did not materialise before the outbreak of war in 1939, at which point most of the weaponry previously disembarked was hurriedly re-installed, to the detriment of the ships' sea-keeping performance.

Photographically the book is excellent, surpassing others of the series not only in the range and quality of the photographs but also in their use to illustrate the text. The line drawings by Lucien Gassier are well-executed and comprehensive, and are complemented by the reproduction of numerous official plans.

John Jordan

Jean Lassaque, Le croiseur Emile Bertin, *published by Marines Édition et Réalisations (Bourg en Bresse, 1994).*
215 x 276mm, 103 pages, 80 photographs, numerous plans and line drawings.
ISBN 2-909675-04-1 285F.

This slim volume follows the same format as the author's book on the contre-torpilleurs of the *Jaguar* class (*qv*). It has the same strengths and the same minor blemishes, which are generally in the form of missed opportunities.

Considering that the *Emile Bertin* owed so little to her immediate predecessors, the light cruisers of the *Doguay Trouin* class and the minelayer *Pluton*, and that her design was so influential on subsequent French cruiser construction, the two-page introduction on the origins of the type seems unduly compressed. However, the technical section (again placed second) is excellent, and is well-illustrated with data tables and official drawings, with many close-up photos of weaponry and electronics. The drawings by Lucien Gassier detail the ship's appearance throughout her service life; the profile drawings are of a high standard, but the plan views are somewhat rudimentary, and the interior profile drawing is of limited value because labelling is restricted to the major machinery compartments.

The account of the ship's service history is exceptionally thorough, as is the case with all the books of this series. Although spared the traumatic events at Mers-el-Kebir, Casablanca and Dakar in mid-/late-1940, *Emile Bertin* spent a very uncomfortable two years at Fort-de-France in the French West Indies; with relatively primitive basing and maintenance facilities, and a serious fuel shortage engineered by the Americans which prevented her from crossing the Atlantic to rejoin the naval forces in French North Africa, it was difficult to sustain morale. However, the ship's career was revived following her extensive refit at Philadelphia in late 1943, and *Emile Bertin* subsequently participated in Allied operations in

the Mediterranean, entering Toulon as flagship of the French fleet of liberation on 13 September 1944.

Emile Bertin was the fastest of France's prewar cruisers, attaining 40.2kts on her first speed trials in August 1934. As was common for the period, this speed was achieved before much of her armament had been installed: only the three guns of 'A' turret and the main fire control director were embarked. Nevertheless, *Emile Bertin* could comfortably sustain 33–35kts in service.

The lightness of her construction brought the usual problems. There was substantial working of the hull just forward of 'A' turret in a head sea, and the hull had to be strengthened in 1935 to permit salvo firing. However, by far the most serious of her problems was cavitation at high speeds, which resulted in a rapid and serious erosion of the propeller blades initially fitted. *Emile Bertin* was the classic French design of the pre-war period, built for high-speed sweeps in narrow waters, and Jean Lassaque, although clearly struck with admiration for this daring, racy vessel, is never blind to her all-too-evident faults.

John Jordon

Claude Huan, Les Sous-Marins Français 1918–45, *published by Marines Édition et Réalisations (Bourg en Bresse, 1995).*
215 x 276mm, 260 pages, 250 illustrations.
ISBN 2 909675 12 2 390F.

Claude Huan's weighty volume on French submarines of the interwar period has finally arrived, after a substantial delay stated by the publishers to be the result of the author's wish to include a greater wealth of detail culled from the French official archives. Unfortunately the book shows some evidence of these production difficulties, being somewhat uneven in quality and not always well organised.

The first section, an account of French submarine development from

1918 to 1939, is particularly confusing. There are some interesting insights into some of the early post-war projects, which included large submersible 'cruiser' submarines armed with 305mm (12in) and 240mm (9.4in) guns similar in conception to the British 'M' class. However, the drawings of the various projects tend to be scattered around like confetti, and the tables detailing these projects and the construction programmes would have been better employed to enhance and explain the text rather than being shunted into a block at the end of the section. As it is, the narrative tends to make unwarranted assumptions regarding the familiarity of the reader with the various classes and sub-groups, at the expense of clarity.

The more substantial sections on the operational history of the submarines during the Second World War, which account for about 70 per cent of the text, are much better. They also offer a clear insight into why the French submarine arm, regarded by many as the primary strength of the prewar *Marine Nationale*, failed to achieve any appreciable successes in combat. The unreliability of the diesels, the fragility of the batteries, the constant breakdowns of the electrically-powered control surfaces and the inadequacy of the torpedo gyros became quickly apparent once the submarines were exposed to arduous wartime patrols. Mistaken tactical procedures, which continued to see the submarine force as an extension of the battle fleet, and the larger fleet submarines of the 1500-tonnes group as submersible *torpilleurs*, operating by four-boat division in advance of the battle-line, were responsible for other inadequacies: underwater sensors were underdeveloped, and their performance was all but cancelled out by the noise from the boats' own rigidly-mounted machinery. When the remaining French submarines were sent for extensive refitting in the United States during the latter part of the war, the refits were subject to alarming delays because of the difficulties encountered with non-standardisation of equipment, orders for which had been placed with a multitude of private subcontractors and shipyards throughout the inter-war period.

Photographically the book is excellent. Unfortunately, the same cannot be said about the drawings, many of which are crude and reproduced at too small a scale to be of any great value; they often lack proper explanatory captions and are unlabelled. Those at the back of the book are clearly intended to provide a comprehensive reference, but they are reproduced out of sequence, 'paper' and production designs are mixed up together, and the proliferation of drawings of the 1500-tonnes series, all virtually identical, is puzzling to say the least.

John Jordan

Jean Moulin, Les Destroyers d'Escorte en France,
published by Marines Édition et Réalisations (Bourg en Bresse, 1994).
215 x 276mm, 152 pages, 160 photographs, numerous plans and line drawings.
ISBN 2-909675-08-4. 310F.

This book by Jean Moulin, who has been responsible for a number of other books in this series, will probably be of less interest to Anglo-Saxon readers. The warbuilt US Destroyer Escort (DE) has been the subject of various detailed English-language studies, and there is little new material here.

For all that, it is a well-written book, well-illustrated and with a wealth of technical detail. Its primary subject is the fourteen DEs transferred to the *Marine Nationale*: six in 1944, and the other eight in 1950–52 following France's signing of the North Atlantic Treaty.

There is an extensive introduction, which not only deals with the origins and general service history of the type, but which makes comparisons with other contemporary escort designs and details transfers to other countries and postwar modifications.

The central section of the book covers the service history of each of the fourteen ships which served in the *Marine Nationale*. The photographs are excellent and the profile line drawings, although not of the highest quality, illustrate the overall appearance of the ships at the various stages of their careers.

The final section focuses on ship characteristics, and in particular on the performance of the weapons and radars carried. There are useful labelled plan and profile drawings showing the various armament configurations.

John Jordan

Jean Moulin, L'Escorteur Maillé Brézé.
160 x 220mm, 106 pages, 96 photographs, numerous plans and line drawings.
ISBN 2-909675-07-6. 150F.

Jean Moulin, Le Croiseur Colbert.
160 x 220mm, 106 pages, 98 photographs, numerous plans and line drawings. ISBN 2-909675-09-2. 140F.
Both published by Marines Édition et Réalisations (Bourg en Bresse, 1994).

The stimulus for these two paperback monographs was provided by the decision to preserve the two ships concerned for public exhibition. The *Maillé Brézé* has been on display at Nantes since July 1988; The *Colbert* since June 1993 at Bordeaux.

Apart from brief sections at the back of each book relating to the current status of these two ships, and detailing the arrangements and minor modifications made to enable them to receive the public, the format follows that of the larger series on the inter-war classes, for which Jean Moulin has also written. There is a lengthy account of the technical development of the ships throughout their service lives, followed by a history of the ships in service. Both are impressively detailed, with numerous data tables giving the performance of weapons and machinery. Line drawings by the author illustrate the external appearance of the ships at the various stages of their respective careers. These are fairly basic, and are reproduced at a small scale corresponding to the format of the book, but there are also useful schematic diagrams and interior profiles, together with labelled drawings detailing radars and weaponry. Photographically both books are excellent; besides the well-selected general views of the ships there are close-ups of weapons and electronics.

The '30-year rule' which limits access to the archives relating to these ships precludes any startling revelations about their performance. Nevertheless, there is an interesting suggestion that the 127mm dual purpose gun mounting which constituted the main armament of the French AA cruisers and *escorteurs d'escadre* of the postwar era continued to display some of the defects of its prewar counterparts, and was less robust and reliable than its US 5in and British 4.5in counterparts.

Between them these two vessels carried virtually every major weapon system and electronic antenna operated by the *Marine Nationale* during the period 1955 to 1990. All of these are described in detail by Jean Moulin, and the clarity of his writing is such that his account of their operation would be readily understood by the amateur naval enthusiast; *Warship* readers will be more than satisfied by the level of technical information provided.

John Jordan

Yves Buffetaut, Les ports de l'Atlantique 1939–45, *published by Marines Édition et Réalisations (Bourg en Bresse, 1994).*
215 x 276mm, 164 pages,
200 photographs. ISBN
2-909675-14-9. 295F.

This is the first of a series of books which chronicle the history of the French ports during the Second World War. It focuses on the Atlantic ports of Brest, Lorient, St Nazaire, La Rochelle, La Pallice and Bordeaux, all of which were occupied by the Germans from June 1940 until the Liberation.

The history divides naturally into three distinct phases, all of which receive comprehensive coverage: the contribution made by these ports to the Allied war effort in 1939–40; the German occupation, and the ports' subsequent use as the primary forward bases of the Kriegsmarine for the Battle of the Atlantic; and the Liberation, during which stubborn garrisons of German troops fiercely resisted Allied efforts to reduce the Atlantic 'pockets'.

This is a well-written (and often moving) account, written from the perspective of the ports themselves, and backed by eye-witness accounts and official French and German reports of the period. The feeling of confusion and helplessness at the approach of the Panzers, generally opposed only by a handful of scratch naval units with a few small-calibre anti-tank guns, is powerfully communicated, as is the determination shown by the French in salvaging everything that could float.

The photographs, culled from a variety of French and German archive sources, are excellent. There are striking photos of the German surface units under camouflage in Brest, and the coverage of U-Boat operations from the purpose-built concrete pens with which the Germans lined the Atlantic coast is exceptionally complete. There are also useful maps to illustrate particular parts of the narrative.

This is essentially a history book, in which the military forces involved play a secondary rôle to the ports, their inhabitants, and those attached to them during the period. It makes fascinating reading, and serves as an important reminder of the crucial contribution made by infrastructure to naval power.

John Jordan

Marc Sailbène, Les Cuirasses, Redoubtable, Dévastation, Courbet. Programme de 1872, *published by Marines Édition et Réalisations (Bourg en Bresse, 1995).*
280 x 220mm, 112 pages, 75 photographs.
ISBN 2-909675-16-5. 295F.

This book records most if not all of the data known about the above three ships.

Though of peculiar appearance by the standards of the present century, they were a notable advance on their predecessors in the French navy in having steel hulls whereas, of the four previous large central-battery ships, the *Richelieu*, *Colbert* and *Trident* had wooden hulls and the *Friedland* wrought iron. In point of fact some use was made of wrought iron (pages 21, 22) in the structure of the *Redoubtable* type. The material of the heavy armour plate does not appear to be noted but was, in fact, still wrought iron though, according to British information, 30cm steel plates replaced the wooden backing round the battery ports in *Courbet*. There is an interesting photograph on page 13 showing *Redoubtable* and her immediate predecessor *Trident*, which contrasts the unusual appearance of the latter with the forward and aft tumblehome of *Redoubtable* and her quay-like central battery. This is also shown on page 79 in a photograph of *Courbet* during her 1897 refit. The intention of this was to give more effective ahead and astern fire but it would be interesting to know what damage would have been done to the hull if the 34cm guns in *Dévastation* and *Courbet*, the heaviest ever mounted in a central battery, were fired axially. The complicated changes in armament are recorded but the replacement of the 34cm M1875 in *Dévastation* by the less powerful 32cm M70–81 is not explained. The 34cm M1875 was of complicated structure, probably on the limits of French gun construction abilities, and after a notorious accident in the *Admiral Duperré* it was largely replaced. The 34cm M1881 in *Courbet* was of simpler construction and more reliable.

There are some unfortunate errors in the *Etude Comparative* on pages 86 and 87. The armament of *Dreadnought* was four 31.75cm (12.5in) not 30cm, that of *Alexandra* two 28cm and ten 25cm and of *Neptune* four 31.75cm and two 23cm.

In spite of the above criticisms, this is an informative and useful book for anyone who is interested in the ships of the period and does not object to the French text which contains some naval terms not frequently used nowadays. The photographs are, in general, excellent.

John Campbell

Paul G Halpern, A Naval History of World War I, *published by UCL Press, 1994. 260 x 180mm, 624 pages, 26 maps. ISBN 1 85728 295 7, £25.00*

This single but nevertheless substantial volume from the Professor of History at Florida State University is a general survey of the naval side of the 1914–18 war. One could be forgiven for thinking this has all been done before, but Professor Halpern has added new perspective to what should by now be an old story. The advantage of his work is to be found in the fact that he covers *all* aspects of the naval war thoroughly and, unlike earlier histories, does not concentrate on the North Sea or the Anglo-German conflict to the detriment of other theatres and combatants. Jutland, for example, occupies only nineteen pages from a 450-page narrative – although it should be added that the description is not superficial and the battle is adequately covered. Although this and other sections of the book may lack the detail that more extensive works can provide, no important event is omitted and the reader is provided with a clear and precise understanding of the operations and the events that led to them. Other areas are described in equal or more extensive detail and include coverage of operations in the Baltic, Black Sea, Adriatic, Middle East, Mesopotamia and on the Danube. The defence of trade and the U-boat war occupy more space than any other subject in the book – reflecting the importance of this critical campaign which, like that in the Second World War, lasted throughout the conflict.

The author makes no claims to extensive original research, but he has gathered together a massive amount of material from a multitude of international sources. The select biography runs to twenty-one pages and includes material from Austria-Hungary, France, Italy and Russia as well as the USA, Britain and Germany, in fairly balanced proportions. In addition he has taken care to keep his work up-to-date with the most recent research.

If I had to recommend a single vol-

ume on the naval history of the First World War this would be it. It gives a full and evenly balanced coverage of the war but still contains sufficient detail to make it a highly readable and entertaining account.

John Roberts

Bernd Langensiepen and Ahmet Güleryüz (translated and edited by James Cooper), The Ottoman Steam Navy 1828–1923, *published by Conway Maritime Press 1995. 295 x 248mm, 192 pages, over 300 illustrations. ISBN 0 85177 610 8. £35.00.*

There are few books which can confidently be described as definitive works but *The Ottoman Steam Navy 1828–1923* certainly fits this description. Although it has to be admitted that the likelihood of another such publication appearing is extremely remote, and hence it could hardly fail to be *the* book on the subject, it would be difficult for another author to substantially improve on the quality of information and illustration provided. The authors, one German and one Turkish, were given unprecedented access to Turkish naval archives and the book is, for the most part, based on original research.

The first part of the book, giving a history of the Ottoman navy from 1828–1923, is similar in style to that of the English translation of Rohwer and Hümelchen's *Chronology of the War at Sea* but is slightly more detailed and gives much wider coverage to the political and strategic background. It has the great advantage of providing a view of the naval history of the Levant from a Turkish standpoint: something which, in the West at least, has not previously been available. This is particularly valuable in making judgements as to the intent of Turkish naval policy and provides a better understanding of such events as Turkey's involvement in the First World War and the Dardanelles campaign.

The second section of the book consists of a large collection of photo-

graphs – it should be mentioned that this does not represent the entire photographic coverage as there are many more in the other sections. These are for the most part of high quality and include some rare and unusual views most of which have not been published before. Besides the standard portrait views of ships, there are a number of detailed shots of parts of ships and their equipment; the majority of the photographs are dated, often to the month and occasionally to the day.

The third section of the book provides a ships' listing which gives details of all the steam-ships of the Ottoman navy for the period covered, from battleships down to harbour craft, and includes non-completed and acquired vessels. The particulars presented include such useful information as displacements and armaments at different dates, trial speeds and powers and a basic history of each vessel. This section also contains a number of technical drawings based on the official drawings of the ships. Besides the usual plan and profile these often show internal arrangements, sections and, occasionally lines and other details. A few would have benefited from being reproduced at a larger scale but on the whole they are clear and of acceptable size.

The book is completed with several useful appendices covering fleet organisation and dispositions, translations of various Turkish terms and several other items of interest. *The Ottoman Steam Navy 1828–1923* has been very well produced and should be regarded as an essential addition to any library of international naval technical history.

John Roberts

J N Westwood, Russian Naval Construction 1905–45, *published by The Macmillan Press in association with the University of Birmingham (Basingstoke, 1994). 263 pages, 37 illustrations. ISBN 0 333 55553 8. £45.*

This fascinating book describes the design and building of Russian warships between the Russo-Japanese war and the First World War, which came to an end with the revolution, and the later period from the revolution until the end of the Second World War. As the author says it is naval history with the 'exciting bits left out'. The background is Russia's perceived need to be strong in three widely separated seas, the Baltic to protect St Petersburg, the Black Sea for defence against Turkey and, possibly, to achieve the dream of access to the Mediterranean, and the Far East where many naval officers still thought of revenge against Japan. Since there could never be sufficient resources for three great fleets, the building programme and the design of individual classes was often driven by what was possible rather than what was needed.

The first task in 1905 was to rebuild the fleet after the disastrous losses of the war with Japan, a task complicated by the dreadnought revolution. The lessons drawn from that war by the Russian staff, led by the defeated Rozhestvenskii, were very different from those drawn by Japan and by the British observers at the battles in that they thought the destruction of their fleet was caused by a large number of medium-sized shells. In consequence, the first Russian dreadnoughts of the *Gangut* class were given a very large area of armour of moderate thickness rather than the smaller, thicker belt of most navies. They were powerfully armed and faster than many contemporary battleships.

A very large number of design studies were invited from foreign yards, Russian organisations and even from individuals. The final design was a mix of what was seen by the Russian staff and design department as the best features of the various submissions. Before the war, the Russians developed some very fast and powerful destroyers from the *Novik* onwards. The author relies to a great extent on Russian sources and his claims for 'firsts' need to be taken with care. *Novik* was not the first destroyer with oil-fired steam turbines (this honour belongs to the British *Acorn* class of the 1909 programme) and neither was Russia the first to use diesels in submarines (the British *D1* of the 1906 programme). However,

they were well ahead of most navies in these respects and only marginally behind the RN. The desire to use innovative technology in a country which was industrially backward is commendable but they probably overreached themselves, accounting for late completion, high cost and the unreliability of Russian ships throughout the period of the book.

The revolution inflicted great damage on the design teams with many leaving the country and others dying in the chaotic conditions. By 1930, just as some capability was being restored, the first of the purges began to take out key men, a problem which got much worse in the bigger purges of 1937. There are amazing accounts of design offices run by the secret police as the whole team was under arrest and of designers being released from prison to help put right problems revealed during trials. Over the whole period, personal relationships within design teams seem to have been poor, with far more feuding than in most countries. Outsiders usually fail to realise the extent of differences within a team but, in a well-run organization, these differences can be good-tempered. The need to retain expertise, at all levels, within a design team is an important lesson for today in the light of staff cuts in-house, lack of competition in industry and very limited building programmes.

These bad relationships, together with lack of continuing experience, probably account for the problems with almost all the designs of the thirties such as the *Kirov* and the Type 7 destroyers. In particular, weight growth was usually the result of changes during building. In at least one case the draught marks were moved to conceal the extent to which it was overweight (a trick played more recently in the *Moskva* class). It is also interesting to learn that Stalin took a very close personal interest in the main features of designs, particularly for bigger ships.

Understandably, the author says that he has avoided some technical terms but in some cases he uses phrases which seem to be literal translations of the Russian and are meaningless – e.g. what is a 'theoretical drawing' referred to several times and to which he attaches con-

siderable importance? The illustrations are unfamiliar, interesting and relevant.

There is so much of interest in this book that, though expensive, it is essential reading for everyone interested in warships of the period. The Russian approach was usually different and, though often wrong, their ideas are well worth studying as a contrast to those of other navies.

D K Brown, RCNC

H W Wilson, Battleships in Action, *published by Conway Maritime Press 1995. 230 x 150mm, 2 volumes, 352 and 398 pages, 100 illustrations. ISBN 0 85177 6426. £50.*

This is a handsome two-volume reprint of a recognised naval classic, originally published in the mid-'twenties. That is, after most of the official histories and memoirs had been published, and it was possible to stand back and take a cool look at the naval side of what was then called 'The Great War' and the many lesser wars which had taken place since the coming of the iron and ironclad warship. Much more technical and intelligence information has been published later but Wilson clearly had the main picture right.

Volume 1 extends from 1854 to the Russo-Japanese War and up to 1914, Volume 2 is devoted to what we now call the First World War. The author had been in the forefront of naval journalism and had many contacts with senior naval officers, naval architects and others. He could speak at almost first hand of the ships, navies and leaders of an era now vanished – though Admiral of the Fleet 'Tug' Wilson evidently proved crusty. The author was a 'Beatty man' over Jutland; most writers have seen things from Jellicoe's point of view. One can sense how slow and ponderous the movements of a seven-mile battle-line must have seemed to those whose experience was with a fairly small force of 25kt ships.

Bearing in mind the date of publication and the vast field covered, the high standard of accuracy and judgement is remarkable. There are plenty of nits to be picked, if one is so minded, but the general picture is comprehensive and accurate. There is a slight remnant of the Victorian tendency to regard Britain – or rather England – and its inhabitants as perfect, but in general it is remarkably fair-minded.

The many earlier wars had been thoroughly written up for the most part and could be discussed almost entirely in 'hardware' terms, in marked contrast with the war of 1914–18. In comparison with the latter, even the Russo-Japanese War was 'simple'. Nevertheless, the description of it is clear, as are the diagrams of some complex actions, where the author's system of using different type to distinguish ships of different navies is extremely useful.

Wilson had been a leading advocate of a naval staff, and he tended to attribute all the Royal Navy's weaknesses to the creation of such a staff having been delayed until shortly before 1914. At times, he used the term 'Staff' as the equivalent of 'High Command'. The mere formation of a staff was not a panacea and its effectiveness depended on the quality of the organisation and its members; even the German General Staff managed to lose a war or two.

Despite its title, the book gives extensive coverage to the operations of lesser warship types, especially in 1914–18; earlier wars tended to centre around the work of the heaviest ships involved. The mine war is a little under-represented; the work of minelayers and minesweepers always tends to be regarded as routine. Wilson says a lot about night action – especially in connection with Jutland – but apparently he did not realise just how specialised its techniques were, or just how short a distance the 'Mark 1 Eyeball' could see at night. The Royal Navy likewise tended to ignore the problem. The author could not foresee how much difference air power would make, but he realised that it *was* going to make a difference.

There are not many histories of technical subjects which can be read usefully two generations after publication, but this is one of them.

K D McBride

SHORT NOTICES

Rear Admiral R O Morris, CB, Charts and Surveys in Peace and War, The History of the RN Hydrographic Service 1919–1970, *published by HMSO, 1995.*
254 x 195mm, 280 pages, 54 illustrations, maps.
ISBN 0 11 772456 4. £35.

This work brings up to 1970 the official history of the Royal Navy's hydrographic service. The previous works on the subject were published in 1885 and 1967 and covered the story of the service up to 1919. although primarily concerned with continuing the earlier narrative, the first two chapters of Rear Admiral Morris's history provide background coverage for those without access to the earlier works; chapter one covering the period 1795–1914 and chapter two the First World War.

The format of the remainder follows the same basic pattern for each period (very roughly a decade for each chapter) beginning with a general history of the development of the service, its operations, personnel and ships, followed by a list of the principal surveys carried out and biographies of the principal officers of the service at the time. The book ends with several appendices including a complete list of the Royal Navy's survey ships and craft with their basic particulars.

Compared with histories of front-line naval service this may be seen as something of a dry subject but the story is presented in a very readable manner and is much more than a simple translation of facts and figures. The coverage of the Second World War and the important work carried out during the time by the hydrographic service, particularly for the invasion of Normandy, is of special interest. The book, although rather expensive, is well presented and would make an excellent complement to any naval library.

Bob Nicholls, Naval Notations: Warships in the Illustrated London News 1842–1891, *published by the author, 1994.*
296 x 210mm, 60 pages, illustrated.
£10.

A valuable example of desktop publishing, this ring-bound booklet lists all references to warships in the *Illustrated London News*, between its first publication and the replacement of lithographs with photographs. There are 630 ships mentioned, with brief details, plus a further 300 sister ships; appendices deal with ship-type nomenclature and building yards.

The publication is available from the author at: 25 Duke Street, Balmain, NSW 2041, Australia. The above Sterling price (or $AUS 17.00 or $US 13.00) includes airmail postage.

Geoffrey Till (Ed), Seapower, Theory and Practice, *published by Frank Cass 1994.*
220 x 146mm, 206 pages.
ISBN 0 7146 4604 0 (hardback). £27.50
ISBN 0 7146 4122 7 (paperback). £14.00

This publication comprises a series of eight essays on the development of, and influences on, naval strategies in the Twentieth Century. These are not concerned with the detail of naval operations but with the overall picture of naval policy and development. The primary question being, were the teachings of naval theorists and the aims of naval policy at various times in this century correct, in light of subsequent practice, and can this provide guidance as to the future. The first essay provides a general discussion on the relevance of historical records to the formulation of naval policy and strategy, while the remainder take particular naval events or situations and discuss the issues on a more detailed level. The subjects covered range from the Battle of Jutland to the possibilities for naval power in the 21st Century.

BOOKS ANNOUNCED

Max Arthur, The Royal Navy, *published by Hodder and Stoughton, 1995, £19.19.*
The stories of over 200 men and women of the Royal Navy during the period 1914–1995.

Sir Richard Brooks, The Clandestine Sea Lines to France, Clandestine Naval Operations 1940–44, *published by HMSO, 1995, £25.00.*
Describes the sea transport links maintained with German-occupied France from Britain, Gibraltar and (after the landings in North Africa) Algiers during the Second World War.

Bernard Edwards, Salvo, Classic Naval Gun Actions, *published by Arms and Armour Press, 1995, £16.99.*

Peter Elphick, The Pregnable Fortress, *published by Hodder and Stoughton, 1995, £19.19.*
A study of the fall of Singapore based on newly released documents and survivor's stories.

Jeremy Flack, Today's Royal Navy in Colour, *published by Arms and Armour Press, 1995, £19.99.*

Richard Harding, The Evolution of the Sailing Navy 1509–1815, *published by Macmillan, 1995, £35.00 (£9.99 in paperback).*

William Honan (Ed), Great Naval Battles of the Twentieth Century, *published by Robson Books, 1995, £8.99.*

Köhlhagen, Gale and Ellen Heinbach, United States Naval Academy, A Pictorial Celebration of 150 Years, *published by Abrams, 1995, £35.00.*

Edward Stokes Miller, Civil War Sea Battles, *published by Combined Books, 1995, £17.95.*

Sam Morley, 99 Years of Navy, From Victoria to VJ Day through three Pairs of Eyes, *published by Quiller Press, 1995.*
Three stories of the RN published to celebrate VJ Day.

THE NAVAL YEAR IN REVIEW

The events covered by this review stretch from approximately May 1994 to May 1995, with some reference before and after. Compiled by Ian Sturton.

A. INTRODUCTION

In Europe, East-West relations remained cool; Russia objected to NATO military operations in Bosnia and to attempts to expand NATO eastwards, and the West to the prolonged military operations in Chechnya. The Gulf flared up and subsided. Further east, Chinese truculence in offshore areas, particularly the disputed Spratly Islands, increased; active naval conflict may follow the future disengagement of America from the region.

Military spending in the West remained low, with slight further falls forecast; a favoured remedy for an unexpected budget deficit is a raid on defence allocations! ASEAN nations and China continued to spend more on their armed forces, in line with rapidly expanding economies.

The strengths of the major naval powers are listed in Table 1.

B(i). THE STRATEGIC BALANCE

Although the East-West power balance tilted further against Russia, instability in the Kremlin requires constant vigilance from NATO.

The US Navy, as guarantor of the 'pax-Americana', was used to apply pressure in four continents; the modern equivalent of 'send a gunboat' is to dispatch an American Carrier Battle Group (CVBG) or Marine Corps Amphibious Ready Group (ARG). The October Gulf crisis erupted just as the North Korean nuclear difficulties were being resolved. In the Caribbean, thousands of refugees from Haiti and Cuba were rescued; amphibious landings in the former country and in Somalia were unopposed. In former Yugoslavia, the Navy continued to underpin the USAF in Operation 'Deny Flight', and to prepare for future contingencies.

Table 1: *MAJOR WARSHIP TYPES OF PRINCIPAL NAVIES, 1 APRIL 1995*

Type	USA	Russia	UK	France	China	India	Japan	Italy
CV (large)	12	1	–	–	–	–	–	–
CV (medium)	–	1	–	2	–	1	–	–
CV (small)	–	–	3	–	–	1	–	1
Cruiser (helicopter)	–	1	–	1	–	–	–	1
Cruiser (missile)	32	13	–	–	–	–	–	–
Destroyer	56	32	12	15	17	5	42	4
Frigate (fleet)	50	33	23	1	35	9	20	16
(escort)	–	97	–	23	–	9	–	9
SSBN	15	39	4	5	1	–	–	–
SSGN	} 84	19	–	–	–	–	–	–
SSN		51	12	6	5	–	–	–
SS (patrol)	–	c44	–	7	c40	18	17	9
MCMV (ocean and coastal)	18	c165	23	14	c115	12	32	14

An artist's impression of the Vosper Thornycroft 83m 'Vigilance' corvette design, proposed for the 1990 Brunei new construction programme. The order was not confirmed, but Brunei is expected shortly to issue a new Invitation to Tender (ITT) for corvettes. (Vosper Thornycroft)

B(ii). DISARMAMENT

The 1994 Nuclear Posture Review was published by the Defense Department. Assuming full implemention of START I and START II, after 2003 the US Navy will have fourteen ballistic missile submarines, the present ten *Ohio* class D-5 Trident II boats and four converted from C-4 (Trident I) to D-5. Attack submarines will be allowed nuclear-tipped land attack missiles, but surface ships and carrier aircraft only conventional weapons. The US nuclear armoury has already been cut

by around 60 per cent, and Russia has made about one half of the reductions required by START, US nuclear missiles, 'detargeted' from Russia from 30 May, were given aim points in ocean areas.

B(iii). THE ENVIRONMENT

A joint Norwegian and Russian team will inspect nuclear dumping sites on Novaya Zemlya, checking eight old submarine reactors, three still with fuel, for leakage and radiation. The latest plan to deal with radioactivity from the submarine *Komsomolets*, lying at a depth of over 5500ft off the north Norwegian Coast, is to seal the hull in a special concrete casing laid by underwater robots. Serious oil leakages from the battleship *Royal Oak* in Scapa Flow and the cruiser *Blücher* in Oslofjord were reported. Greenpeace, condemning nuclear ac-

tivities at sea, obstructed the launch of a test Trident missile from HMS *Vanguard* and delayed operational patrols. An interim injunction against Greenpeace was obtained after the second patrol was delayed by six hours.

C. BUDGET PROPOSALS AND NEW PROGRAMMES

C (i). USA, NATO and Allies

Major NATO Navies

(a) United States. The defence authorisation bill for FY95, beginning 1 October 1994, was finalised at $263.8b, while the defence appropriations bill, setting exact spending amounts, was for $244.5b. The Defense Department requested $246.0b for FY96, a reduction of 2.4 per cent

Table 2: *USN SHIPBUILDING PROGRAMMES, 1993–1996*

New Construction		Approved (authorised and funded)		Proposed (subject to amendment)
Type	FY93	FY94	FY95	FY96
SSBN	–	–	–	–
SSN 21	–	–	–	SSN 23
CVN	–	*	CVN 76	–
DDG 51	4	3	3	2
MHC	2	–	–	–
LHD	1**	–	–	–
LSD	***	–	–	–

Notes: * *Advance procurement for CVN 76.*
      ** *LHD 6 authorised in FY93 but only partly funded. Remainder of funding in FY94.*
     *** *LSD 52, authorised in FY92, funded in FY93. Conversion of* Inchon *to mine warfare command ship funded in FY94.*
        SSN 23 was initially funded in FY92.

from its FY95 request, the Navy's share being $75.6b; details of shipbuilding programmes are given in Table 2. The planned future force strength is likely to be 350 instead of 330 ships, with 130–135 surface combatants; some *Oliver Hazard Perry* class frigates proposed for early retirement may be kept until 2000. It was believed that major new equipment programmes might have be cut or curtailed to maintain the armed forces in a high state of readiness, but a $25b boost for spending from FY95 through FY01 is proposed to improve military readiness and modernisation, and the procurement request for FY96 was $43.5b, up by $4.1b from FY95, the start of a real 47 per cent increase planned over the next six years.

The Navy proposed building thirty-one nuclear submarines between 1996 and 2014, giving a fifty-five strong SSN force until 2020. The General Accounting Office (GAO) suggested twenty-five submarines instead of thirty-one, which would provide fifty-five submarines until 2013 and forty-five by 2020. Replacing current carriers on a one-for-one basis would cost some $56b through 2035 for nuclear-powered successors, but only around $35b for fossil-fuelled successors.

In the later 1990s, the Navy must be ready for UN non-combat operations alongside the usual combat priorities from the cold war on a reduced scale. Very quiet diesel submarines in coastal waters and improved Russian nuclear boats are problems that require different answers. The Navy has modernised its nuclear deterrent force and, after the demise of the 'Star Wars' programme, is giving high priority to its theatre ballistic missile defence programme.

The carrier *Constellation* will replace the *Independence* as homeported in Yokosuka from 1997. An American request to pre-position six supply ships in Thai waters was rejected by Bangkok.

(b) United Kingdom. The 1995–96 budget was set at £21.7b (S35.0b), a reduction of 6.5 per cent after inflation from the final 1994-95 figure. A return to stability for the UK armed forces was promised, without further major organisational or equipment changes; defence spending is due to level out at 2.8 per cent of GDP in 1997–98.

HMCS Algonquin *after TRUMP modernisation. Canada is purchasing seventy-two Standard SM-2 Block III missiles, with improved warheads and better low-altitude capability, for the modernised 'Tribal' class.* (Maritime Command)

The results of the 'Front Line First' review, announced on 14 July, included the predicted closures of Rosyth naval base and Portland RNAS. Rosyth will be downgraded to a naval support establishment, with 900 civilians retained for the present to keep open the research centre and other establishments; its minehunters and fishery protection ships will be moved to Faslane and Portsmouth. The new construction programmes already announced continued, with orders placed for seven new *Sandown* class SRMH. Tomahawk cruise missiles will be purchased for the *Trafalgar* class. On 1 January 1994 the total of Royal Navy and Royal Marine personnel was 56,339; one year later it was 51,492. The Netherlands Navy is to take over the British submarine commanders' ('perishers') course from the summer of 1995. Bell-bottomed trousers will cease to be an item of uniform from 1997, after 140 years.

Swan Hunter had to give up a proposed £6m refit for *Sir Bedivere* because it provided insufficient work to attract a rescue bid from the French

shipbuilder Soffia/CMN; a purchaser was reported in June 1995. Bids for VSEL from British Aerospace and GEC were referred to the Monopolies Commission, which decided (May 1995) that both companies could go ahead with their offers.

(c) Canada. The 1994–95 budget of $7.9b is planned to fall to $7.0b in 1997–98; this is nominally the same figure as ten years earlier, but with 20 per cent less spending power. The DND will lose an additional $2.0b over the next three years, in addition to the 1994 reduction. The Defence White Paper, the first since 1987, proposed a smaller multipurpose force, placing greater emphasis on international peacekeeping while maintaining existing commitments. Agreement to

Table 3: *New European Frigate Designs*

Country	France/UK/Italy	Germany	Netherlands	Spain
Type	CNGF	Type 124	LCF	F 100
Possible no in class	4/12/4	3	2	4
Builders	Various	Blohm & Voss	Royal Schelde	Bazan
Building dates	c1996–2002	c1996–2003	c1996–2003	c1996–2005
Displacement (max)	6500	4700	4400	4515
L × b × d (max), metres	148.4 × 19.9 × 4.8	138.9 × 16.7 × 4.4	134.8 × 14.6 × 4.6	127.8 × 15.8 × 4.7
Missiles	Aster 15 VLS	Standard SM-2	Standard SM-2	Standard SM-2
	Aster 30 VLS	and ESS	and ESS	and ESS
	2 ILMS	2 RAM		
	8 SSM	8 Harpoon SSM	8 Harpoon SSM	8 Harpoon SSM
Guns	1–5in	1–3in/62	1–3in/62	1–3in/62
	2–30mm	2 light	1 Goalkeeper	1 Meroka
			2–20mm	
ASW torpedo tubes	4	4–12.75in	4–12.75in	4–12.75in
Helicopters	1	1	1	1
Machinery	CODLAG	CODOG	CODOG	CODOG
Max bhp	–	51,000	–	–
Speed (kts)	30	29	28	28

Note: *LCF data is for Royal Schelde design.*

A fine view of HMCS Halifax *at sea. Microscopic cracks discovered in cruise diesel piston rods in at least two of the class were attributed to a design fault, and Pielsteck accepted full responsibility.* (Saint John Shipbuilding)

purchase the four British *Upholder* class submarines announced in August 1995; the proposed new multi-role support ship has been shelved, but the support ship *Provider*, due to pay off in 1996, will be retained. The future naval helicopter is being deliberated.

(d) Germany. The new structure announced for the armed forces included a reduction in naval personnel from 29,000 to 27,200. In the long term, the Bundesmarine will include six submarines, fifteeen frigates, fifteen corvettes (replacing existing fast attack craft) and twenty MCM vessels. The current order list includes the first batch of four Type 212 submarines (cost $1.62b) and three Type 124 air defence frigates; the corvette programme is scheduled for 2004. The

first of three proposed multi-purpose supply ships with a UN support role was shelved because of its effect on other programmes and because if available it 'might generate UN requests which would not otherwise have been forthcoming'. The Bundestag gave the Navy permission to join the UN naval blockade of former Yugoslavia in the Adriatic and on the Danube, 22 July.

(e) Italy's 1994 defence budget was for $16.2b, a 14 per cent increase over 1989, but in the five years spending on equipment fell by 33.4 per cent and on personnel rose. Only about $500m was allocated for naval new construction in 1995.

(f) Netherlands. The incoming coalition government proposed cuts of up to $500m in the 1994-98 defence budget, making the requirements of the 1993 Defence White Paper very difficult to attain. On 4 November, actual cuts of $1.1b in the 1995–98 budget were announced; savings will come mainly from increased efficiency, and a further cut of $300m is required. The integration of the Netherlands and Belgian Navies continued. The new Netherlands Antilles Coastguard will require several new ships.

(g) Turkey. The progress of the latest MEKO frigate order was delayed because German subsidies to German shipyards for Turkish orders were suspended over human rights issues, and Ankara banned Dutch companies, including Signaal, from defence-related business with Turkey's armed forces.

Lesser NATO Navies

Norway announced a 1.7 per cent cut in 1995 defence spending, to $3.5b. A review of all procurement plans is to

The first Canadian Maritime Coast Defence Vessel (MCDV), the future HMCS Kingston, *seen under construction at Halifax Shipyards, is due to commission on October 1995. The name originally selected,* Frontenac, *was changed in mid-1995.* (Maritime Command)

be ready in mid-1995; series production of the proposed new fast attack craft based on the MCM air-cushion catamaran hull may be delayed in favour of a frigate replacement programme. Later plans include the 'Submarine 2000' project to replace the modernised *Kobben* class submarines, while a new anti-ship missile is proposed for the new missile craft, escort vessels and coast defence batteries. Pursuing the ultimate goal of an integrated Benelux fleet, **Belgium** may eventually replace its *Wielingen* class frigates with amphibious transports.

Plan of the Canadian MCDV. These ships will be stationed on both coasts and will combine offshore patrol duties with some MCM capability. (Saint John Shipbuilding)

France and Spain

France and Spain cooperate with NATO but are not full military members

France. The 1995 defence budget totalled $36.6b, up to 3 per cent of which may be frozen to reduce spending. Two such cuts were made in 1994: $450m struck from the total in June to meet 'unexpected government expenses' followed a smaller reduction in March. The six-year military spending programme pledges an annual spending increase of 0.5 per cent; huge outlays will be necessary on the numerous systems, including an indigenous ballistic missile submarine class and an aircraft carrier, coming on line in the next few years. The direct allocation for new equipment was cut by over 5 per cent in 1995, but the armed

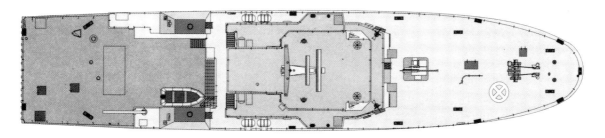

forces were allowed to make up the deficit by using reserves and making economies elsewhere.

Spain. The 1995 defence budget, set in January at $6.3b, was cut by $400m – probably from the new equipment allocation – in a reappraisal just one month later. Defence spending will remain at around 1.3 per cent of GNP for the next three years.

Major US Allies

Japan. The new SDP-led coalition Cabinet agreed an FY95 defence budget of $47.2b, an increase (in yen)

The Chilean Leander *class frigate* Condell *as modernised in 1993 with enlarged flight deck and hanger for Super Puma helicopter, modified stern for line handling etc, and MM40 missile canisters.* (ASMAR)

of 0.86 per cent, the lowest for more than thirty years; the JDF had called for a rise of 2.8 per cent and the Liberal Democrats for 1.95 per cent. The SPD's draft proposals for disarmament and moves towards pacifism seem unlikely to become coal- ition policy.

Australia. The 1995/96 defence budget decreased by about 1.7 per cent to $6.8b, representing 2.1 per cent of estimated GDP and 8 per cent of federal expenditure. The Defence White Paper 'Defending Australia' proposed increasing security rela- tions with Asian nations while retain- ing the vital US defence alliance. The new construction minehunter com- petion was won by ADI, which will build a new facility in the Throsby Basin, near Newcastle, NSW.

The Chilean destroyer Blanco Encalada, *formerly HMS* Fife, *as modernised in 1988 with enlarged flight deck and hanger and in 1993 with the Israeli Barak PDMS. Barak launch canisters are on the former Seacat fire control radar pedestals either side of the second funnel, and the new fire-control radars are fitted fore and aft.* (ASMAR)

C (ii). Other European Nations

(a) Poland. Plans to upgrade the Pol- ish Navy with Western systems are un- realistic because of lack of money and restrictions on technology transfer.

(b) Russia. The 1995 defence request was for RRb115.0tr ($38.4b), but dol- lar equivalents are nominal because of very high inflation; the RRb37.0tr ($19.7b) defence budget voted for 1994 earlier in the year did not completely cover salaries and operations, or pro- curement of new equipment. Defence economies may affect major ongoing programmes, including the latest gen- eration of nuclear-powered attack submarines. Naval fortunes have reached a low ebb; maintenance is ne- glected, morale very poor – over 2000 servicemen died from accidents or crime in 1994 – and only the ballistic missile submarine forces and the soli- tary active carrier seem to be reason- ably efficient.

(c) Sweden. In 1994, Sweden spent about 2.7 per cent of GDP on defence. The next five-year defence plan will now start in 1996, not 1997, and long-term savings of around $550m, about 10 per cent of the budget, are planned by 2001. Marginal increases in spending in the past two years have not improved Sweden's ability on paper to endure a major attack on one front for a limited period – the armed forces are smaller and more modern than in the 1980s, but have been scaled down to the bone.

C (iii). Middle East

Iran. Battery and torpedo problems with the 'Kilo' class submarine purchases have been sorted out; the existence of these boats, and Iran's fortification of the islands in the Straits of Hormuz, has started a naval arms race among the Gulf States. More widespread unease is being caused by alleged Iranian attempts to obtain a nuclear weapon capability. **Kuwait** went to France for new fast patrol craft: eight are to be delivered between 1997 and 2000 at a cost of about $467m. At least twelve shipyards were invited to tender for up to four missile corvettes or light frigates. **Saudi Arabia's** defence and security spending for 1995 was quoted as $12.5b, the lowest figure since 1990, but some defence projects may not be included. The long-awaited order for two modified French *La Fayette* class

The Danish Standard Flex 300 Havkatten, *equipped for the MCM role with two remotely–controlled MCM drones.* (RDanN)

The Colombian frigate Independiente , *last of a class of four completed in 1983 and 1984. Details of a possible modernisation have not been confirmed.* (HDW)

AAW frigates was confirmed. **UAE.** Three shipyards were shortlisted for the new frigate programme, but the offer of two *Perry* class frigates on lease may delay construction. Newport News Shipbuilding is to assist in building a new shipyard in the Emirates.

Israel A dividend of the Middle East peace process has been reduction of the Israeli armed forces to a much 'leaner, meaner' configuration. The third new submarine was approved, and Israel and Germany will each pay half the cost; Germany is paying the full cost of the first two.

C (iv). 'PACRIM' and Indian Ocean

(a) China. The official defence budget for 1995 was announced as $7.5b, an increase of 14.6 per cent before in-

flation. Outside sources estimate real defence spending at two or three times the official figure, but US Intelligence estimates of about $50b seem too high. In July, it was announced that China will spend a further $3.0b on arms from Russia.

Analysts suggest that major submarine and carrier procurement programmes have been approved. According to US Intelligence, China is to buy ten Russian 'Kilo' class submarines, with options on twelve more, but other sources state that only four to six 'Kilos' will be acquired as an

Two views of HMS Illustrious *as modernised between 1992 and 1994. Changes included replacing the Phalanx CIWS with Goalkeeper, a new mainmast, a 13deg ski-ramp and the extension forward of the flight deck on the starboard side.* (DML)

interim purchase while the indigenous *Song* programme gets under way. The Navy intends that a first 48,000t carrier should enter service in the period 2005–2010; HMAS *Melbourne* was scrapped in China, giving some insight into carrier design, while more recently the acquisition of the incomplete *Varyag* at Nikolayev was investigated, and Russian technology is available.

(b) India. The $8.3b FY95–96 defence budget was, after inflation, almost the same as for FY94–95; the navy's share was 14 per cent, too low for adequate funding of existing programmes. India is turning back to Russia and other ex-Soviet countries for military equipment, the spares problem having largely been resolved. Like China, there are nuclear submarine and fossil-fuel carrier programmes in hand, the former taking priority. The land-based test facility for the submarine is complete, and development of the submarine-launched Sagrika cruise missile is nearing completion. Owing to the new carrier programme, the possible purchase of the Russian carrier *Admiral Gorshkov* discussed in the technical press was officially ruled out. Obsolete ex-Soviet submarines may be replaced by improved 'Kilos'.

Lesser Navies

South Korea's requested defence spending for 1995 was $13.8b, an increase from 1994 of 9.9 per cent, and some 3.2 per cent of GNP (1994 figures for North Korea were $6.0b and 30 per

Table 4: *RECENT MINE COUNTERMEASURES VESSEL TYPES*

Country	Australia	Norway	Sweden
Type	Hunter (coastal)	Hunter or Sweeper (coastal)	Sweeper (inshore)
Class	*Huon*	*Oksøy/Alta*	*Styrsö*
No in class	6	9	4
Builder(s)	Intermarine/ADI, Newcastle, NSW	Kvaerner Mandal	KKV
Building dates	1994–2002	1991–97	1994–97
Displacement (max)	720t	375t	175t
L × b × d (max), metres	52.5 × 9.9 × 3.0	55.2 × 13.6 × 2.5	36 × 7.9 × 2.2
Missiles	–	Twin Sadral	–
Guns	1–30mm	1–20mm, 2 MG	2 MG
Machinery	Diesel	Diesel	Diesel
Max bhp	1986	3700	1104
Speed (kts)	14	25	12

cent of GNP). The KDX frigate or destroyer order may be reduced from
nineteen to ten ships, the last seven
perhaps of a larger type. Delivery of
the last submarine is planned for
2001, while Orion maritime patrol aircraft will replace the existing S-2A/F
Trackers. **Taiwan**'s requested defence spending for 1995 was $9.3b, a
fall of 1.2% from the 1994 allocation.
Philippines. The 1995 defence
budget was for $1.1b. The Spratlys
dispute has spurred the very necessary modernisation of the armed
forces, but lack of money prevented
the 1991 order of six fast attack craft
from being confirmed. Coastal patrol
boats are being built in America.

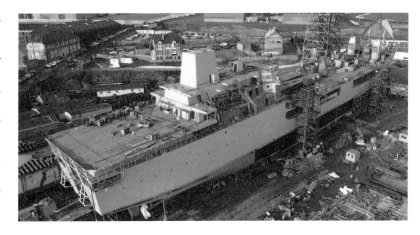

The Royal Fleet Auxiliary Sir Galahad *on the stocks at Swan Hunter's
Tyneside yard in 1986. On 12 June 1995, a successful bid by the Dutch
company THC was accepted by the receivers; at that date, the remaining*

*An Israel Dabur class coastal patrol
craft, intended to counter terrorists
and, more recently, drug smugglers;
rugged and small enough to be
transported by land, they are
presently in service in six navies
although too slow (30kts max) to
catch modern speed-boats.* (Official)

Thailand's major naval build-up is to
protect expanded EEZs and sea lines
of communication. The $600m pro-
gramme for three submarines failed to
get cabinet approval, but will be modified and resubmitted. Thai naval aviation will receive eighteen A-7E Cor-
sair fighters in 1995, and three P-3B
Orion maritime patrol aircraft and six
ASW Seahawk helicopters in 1996.
The **Malaysian** submarine programme is still shelved; invitations to
tender for the first six of twenty-seven
OPVs were issued. **Singapore**'s defence spending for 1994/95 was set at
$2.8b, not more than 6 per cent of
GDP. Recent warship purchase and
construction has been accompanied
by the development of new naval
bases. The **Indonesian** purchase of
thirty-nine former East German ships
proved a controversial drain on
money and manpower. **Myanmar
(Burma)** signed a second major arms
deal with China, for $400m, to include
six additional 'Hainan' class coastal
patrol craft and a number of smaller
vessels. The transfer of at least two
'Jianghu' class frigates is rumoured.
Sri Lanka is in need of new patrol
craft after recent losses. Four from
China were due to be delivered in
early 1995, but the $100m arms deal
with Russia, including a possible two
or three patrol boats, was suspended
during the cease-fire. After the cease-
fire broke down, the purchase of new
equipment was no longer on hold; the
new patrol craft may now come from
Russia or Israel. **Pakistan**'s 1994–95
defence budget allocation was $3.29b,
a real growth of 6.9 per cent if inflation control targets are met. After
much negotiation, including a British
offer of all four *Upholders* for the price
of three new boats, the contract for

Stress fatigue cracks have been discovered in the main deckbeam structure of the Dutch frigates Tromp, *shown here, and* De Ruyter, *under the aft superstructure. Operational restrictions were ordered pending necessary repairs.* (RNethN)

three Agosta 90B submarines was awarded to France (announced 21 September). The first boat will be built in France, the second fabricated in France but assembled in Pakistan and the third is to be almost entirely built locally.

C (v). Latin America

Brazil plans to build a fifth *Tupi* class submarine, and has started the first stretched *Inhauma* class frigate.

C (vi). Africa

South Africa The 1995–96 defence budget fell slightly after inflation to $2.9b, a reduction in real terms of over 50 per cent since 1989. The decision on new patrol corvettes is imminent; the SAN has major equipment problems, with existing strike craft near the end of their active lives and some already experiencing metal fatigue.

D. WARSHIP BUILDING

D(i). New Designs and Principal Orders

Multinational. The two major European air defence frigate programmes gathered momentum, and the first order was placed.

Britain, France, Italy. In July, the Memorandum of Understanding (MoU) for the first phase of 'Project Horizon', the Common New-Generation Frigate (CNGF), was signed, covering design, development and production. The PAAMS anti-air warfare (AAW) system will be developed separately, and

The Dutch frigate Karel Doorman. *It was reported that the class will not be certified for deployment to higher risk areas such as the Adriatic until software limitations in the ships' combat systems are overcome.* (RNethN)

its MoU will come later. The International Joint Venture Company (IJVC), the tripartite company which will be the prime contractor for the CNGF, was set up in London in February 1995.

Germany, Netherlands, Spain. The final baseline review for the looser Tripartite Frigate Co-Operation (TFC) programme was approved, 22 December. The ships will be designed nationally (German Type 124, Dutch LCF, Spanish F100) and are expected to have common AAW missile systems – the long-range Standard SM-2 Block III and the point-defence Evolved Sea Sparrow Missile (ESSM). A MoU to be signed in 1995 will set up the consortium for the command and control systems.

(a) United States. It is hoped to fund the third *Seawolf*, SSN 23, in FY96. After consideration of possible alternatives, the progress of the New Attack Submarine (NAS) was cleared, and the first may be ordered in FY98. It will have interchangeable mission 'modules', with eventually a possible Trident capability, although this is not a current requirement. The cost of the first boat is estimated as $2.3b, not greatly cheaper than the larger *Seawolf* ($2.5b); significant savings would only show in series production, when the cost of each NAS would be $1.5b, of each *Seawolf* $2.1b. $18.1b has been allocated for the programme in the next decade, but programme delays and the very few submarine orders are

The new Dutch fast replenishment ship Amsterdam *on trials, April 1995. The pennant number will be A836.* (RNethN)

A recent photo of the Dutch hydrographic and oceanographic ship Tydemann *, currently conducting sea trials of an active low-frequency variable depth sonar.* (RNethN)

alarming the Electric Boat Division of General Dynamics, the sole US nuclear submarine builder.

The aircraft carriers *Harry S Truman* (CVN–75) and *Ronald Reagan* (CVN–76) will commission in 1998 and 2002 respectively, replacing *Independence* and *Kitty Hawk*. Preliminary steps are in hand for concept exploration of the next surface warfare combatant, designated SC 21. The first orders will be needed about 2004, when the present 57-unit DDG–51 programme is due to be complete.

(b) United Kingdom. During the year, HMS *Vanguard* became fully operational and made the first two Trident patrols. *Victorious*, accepted in January, will become operational in late 1995. The first official step in maintaining Britain's carrier power beyond 2015 was taken when bids were invited for a preliminary feasi-

bility study; cooperation with allied navies is sought. The contest for LPD(R), the assault ship replacement, was aborted because only VSEL was prepared to tender. VSEL was asked to submit a revised non-competitive tender for a probable order by the end of 1995. A £40m contract to build a new ocean survey vessel (OSV) was awarded to BAeSEMA and Appledore Shipbuilders, Bideford.

(c) Canada. The first MCDV will be delivered at the end of 1995, some six months later than originally contracted, but the twelve-ship programme should be complete in

Death of a frigate: KNM Oslo as built and after salvaging. On 25 January 1994, Oslo grounded after massive water contamination of the fuel supply had caused total loss of power; although refloated and taken in tow, the ship sank in shallow water. (RNoN)

mid-1999. The class will restore a limited mine countermeasures capability to Maritime Command: four route survey systems using multi-beam sidescan sonar in a towed vehicle will survey the route generally, with one remotely-operated vehicle for closer inspection and detonation. Two mechanical minesweeping systems will also be acquired.

(d) France. The new carrier *Charles de Gaulle* is now due to enter service in 1999. The cost is estimated as $1.9b for the ship, and overall at $11.5b including the Rafaele M aircraft, research and development for ship and aircraft, and two Hawkeye surveillance aircraft. Design work on the next generation of nuclear-powered attack submarines is to begin in 1995, with full-scale development to start in 1997 and construction in 2005, when the last new ballistic missile submarine should be complete and the first of the older SSN might be withdrawn.

(e) Japan. The MSDF has purchased a second Stirling V4-275R AIP engine from Kockums; Japanese submarines would probably need four engines each, with liquid oxygen tanks and other equipment in a self-contained 'plug-in' system.

(f) Australia. Six minehunters of modified *Gaeta* class were ordered at a cost of about $740m for delivery between 1998 and 2002.

(g) Russia. The pace of warship construction remains very slow; the latest type of nuclear submarine, the *Severodvinsk*, will be superior to present Western submarines in many respects.

(h) Iran. Only three Russian 'Kilo' class submarines will be acquired; five Chinese *Hegu* class FAC out of ten ordered in 1992 were delivered without missiles.

(j) China. The Type 093 ballistic missile submarine, a follow-on to the Type 092 (*Xia*) class fitted with the new CSS-NX-4 missile, is expected in service after 2000; more 'Han' class or a new nuclear-powered attack submarine class will also be built. The first Type 039 (*Song*) class diesel submarine (US designation 'Wuhan-C'), launched in May, is thought to be the follow-on to the *Ming* class. Israeli assistance with the Type 039 and with a *Ming* upgrade programme is reported, and the improved 'Kilo' class boats being delivered may supply further technical input for the Type 039; it is believed that there will be no indigenous 'Kilo' production.

(k) South Korea. The initial order for six submarines is now almost complete; Daewoo will build three more for delivery through 2001. The second and third KDX destroyers or frigates were ordered.

(l) Pakistan. The AIP system for the new submarines will be fitted in the

Two excellent views of the new Norwegian minehunter KNM Oksøy, *commissioned in August 1994. The GRP catamaran hull, of glass-reinforced plastics, produces an air-cushion effect. A tenth ship of the class was not confirmed.* (RNoN)

The launch of the 83m corvette Qahir al Amwaj *for Oman at Vosper Thornycroft's Woolston yard, 21 September 1994.* (Vosper Thornycroft)

The 56m Qatari missile-armed fast attack craft Barzan, *photographed after launch at Vosper Thornycroft's Portchester yard, 1 April 1995.* (Vosper Thornycroft)

third unit as delivered, and retrofitted in the first two; the hull length is increased by 15m.

D(ii). Ships Entering Service During the Year

These are listed in Table 5 (the figures for Russia and China are approximate).

D(iii). Reconstructions

(a) United States. The one-year conversion of the LPH *Inchon* into a mine command/control and support ship by Litton, Pascagoula, will enable her to support modern minesweepers and coastal minehunters in the field and operate eight MH-53 MCM helicopters. The propulsion machinery will be renewed and living spaced modified.

Other upgrades announced are listed briefly: Brazil's *Niteroi* class will be modernised by AESN (Italy) at a cost of $160m; India's *Rajput* class may be modernised in Ukraine; the Pakistan Type 21 class will have the Anglo-French ATAS system. Contests for modernising the German Type 122 and the Australian FFG-7 frigates were announced. Several French classes are to have anti-missile self-defence capabilities improved. The Dutch, Belgian and French Tripartite minehunters are to be modernised, and the British 'Hunt' class may be upgraded.

D(iv). Fleet Depletions (decommissionings, transfers, etc)

(a) United States. The four *Iowa* class battleships, in reserve since 1991–92, were removed from the register, for probable preservation as museums. Subject to Congressional app- roval, eight *Perry* class frigates are being offered for transfer in 1995 and 1996 as follows: two to UAE, two to Turkey and one each to Bahrain, Egypt, Greece, and Oman. The actual transfers of *Knox* class frigates between 1992 and 1994 was (numbers in parentheses): Egypt (2), Greece (3), Taiwan (6 + 3 in 1995 and 3 in 1996), Thailand (1 + 1 in 1995), Turkey (8). Proposed transfers to Brazil (4), Morocco (1), Oman (1) and Venezuela (2) did not take place. Transfers or pro- posed transfers of *Newport News* class LSTs are: Argentina (1), Australia (2), Brazil (1), Chile (2), Malaysia (1), Morocco (1), Spain (2), Taiwan (2), Venezuela (2). Four ocean minesweepers went to Taiwan.

(b) United Kingdom. The remaining Polaris submarines continued to patrol alongside the incoming Trident boats; *Repulse* is scheduled to go in 1995, *Renown* in 1996. *Resolution*, due for withdrawal in July 1994, made one extra patrol because of a radiation leak in *Renown*, and survived until October. Attempts continued to sell the four *Upholder* class submarines; in November, *Unicorn* was recommissioned from reserve, perhaps for demonstrating to a potential customer. Canada, Chile and Malaysia had expressed interest in the class, with the first-named the eventual purchaser. The first four Type 22 frigates and three 'River' class minesweepers were sold to Brazil, for a reported $179m, and transfers of both types are to start in 1995; the other four 'Rivers' on the sales list went to Bangladesh. The Batch 3A (Sea Wolf) *Leander* class frigate *Andromeda* will be sold to India, but *Jupiter* and *Hermione* of the same type went for scrap, after being maintained in reserve for eight years at a cost of £33m.

(c) Germany gave two ex-East German *Condor I* minesweepers to Estonia; they will be laid-up until funds permit renovation.

(d) Netherlands. The submarines *Zwaardvis* and *Tijgerhai* are cocooned ashore awaiting a buyer. The frigate *Van Kinsbergen* became the Greek *Navarinon*, the replenishment ship *Poolster* the Pakistani *Moawin*.

(e) Norway donated three *Storm* class fast patrol boats, disarmed and modified for civilian coastguard and customs work, to Lithuania, Latvia and Estonia.

E. NAVAL WEAPON SYSTEMS

E(i). Missiles, including Ballistic Missiles

(a) United States. Funds may not be available to refit more than two C-4 *Ohio* class SSBN boats with D-5 missiles, giving an eventual SSBN total of twelve boats instead of fourteen. A demonstration is planned for 1996 of a substrategic C-4 Trident, with a conventional warhead to attack heavily defended land targets in a non-nuclear war. It should be noted that Trident missile tubes can accommodate Tomahawk cruise missiles – up to seven Tomahawks can be fitted in one D-5 tube.

The air-launched AGM-137 Tri-Service Stand-Off Attack Missile (TSSAM) was cancelled. As an interim measure, the Navy will acquire 600 SLAM-ER land attack missiles while the search for a TSSAM replacement begins. A ship-launched version of SLAM, SeaSLAM, will be demonstrated. 2000 air-, sea- and submarine-launched Block IC Harpoon anti-ship missiles are to be upgraded to Block 1G standard.

(b) United Kingdom. The first British Trident launch took place from *Vanguard* at the US Atlantic test site on 26 May. A substrategic Trident D-5 with a single thermonuclear warhead will replace the RAF's free-fall WE 177 nuclear weapon, which is due to go by the end of 1998. The cost of the Trident support facilities at Faslane and Coalport reached £1.9b ($3.0b), exceeding estimates by 72 per cent,

and attracting criticism from the National Audit Office. Over fifty Tomahawks with conventional warheads for Both Batch I and II *Trafalgar*s will be purchased, but only two or three boats will be fitted at first.

(c) France. The new generation M-45 ballistic missile was successfully test-fired from the submarine *Le Triomphant* off Brittany in February; M-45 missiles were previously tested in 1991 and in 1993.

E(ii). Maritime Aircraft

Multinational. The development of the NH 90 helicopter restarted in August 1994 after being suspended in May; the delay, to try and find ways of cutting costs, was requested by France. An EH 101 prototype crashed in April because the tail rotor moved to full pitch uncommanded – the cause of the 1993 EH 101 crash.

(a) United States. The Joint Advanced Strike Technology (JAST) programme, merged with the ASTOVL programme, is aimed at providing a

Construction and pre-launch photographs of the Swedish submarine Gotland, *first of a class of three and the first submarine type to be designed with an AIP system. The two Stirling V4-275R engines being installed in this class will give a 5-to 7-fold increase in submerged endurance and a speed of about 5kts; space and weight is reserved for two more Stirling engines.* (Kockums)

The Thai frigate Phutthayotfa Chulalok *(ex-*USS Truett, *FF 1095, of the* Knox *Class) transferred on lease in July 1994.* (Royal Thai Navy)

common modular replacement for existing Air Force, Navy and Marine Corps F-16, F/A and AV8-B strike aircraft. The UK is participating in the programme. One proposal put forward was for a navalised F-117A, originally advanced as a contender for the A/F-X programme cancelled in October 1993. The final design of the V-22 Osprey tilt-rotor was 'frozen'; 425 were approved for the Marine Corps, and the first four are to be budgeted in FY97.

(b) United Kingdom. The first FA2 Sea Harriers were deployed aboard *Illustrious* for the Adriatic. The Blue Vixen look-down radar will give the FA2 (formerly FRS2) an 'offensive counter-air capability'; the FA2 is AMRAAM-capable, but the Fleet Air Arm has not yet deployed this weapon. The Buccaneer was replaced in the RAF's maritime strike role by the Tornado GR1b, carrying two Sea Eagle missiles. Trials of the RAF's Harrier GR7 were carried out at sea aboard *Illustrious*; the GR7 might be embarked for the ground attack role, for example in Bosnia.

(c) France. The in-service date for Rafaele M slipped to 2000, in *Foch*; a later variant, the SU-2, will enter service in *Charles de Gaulle* in 2005. The order for two E-2C Hawkeye surveillance aircraft from the USA under Foreign Military Sales (FMS) procedures was confirmed; two more orders are expected later in the decade.

E(iii). Anti-Aircraft and Anti-Missile Warfare (AAW)

Multinational. The Eurosam Aster 15 VLS missile made its first interception of a simulated supersonic sea-skimming missile. The source selection of the ten-nation Evolved Sea Sparrow Missile (ESSM) programme will be made shortly; four RIM-7PTC missiles will fit into one Mk41 VLS tube.

(a) United States. The Navy's proposals for two-tier ballistic missile defence use improved Standard missiles in AEGIS cruisers. Lower-tier protection, to 50km height and 100km range, will involve adding an infra-red seeker to the present semi-active RF mode of SM-2 Block IV missiles, while upper-tier protection, to 300km height and 400km range, will use the Block IVA missile, with new fuse and warhead, and a Lightweight Exo-Atmosphere Projectile (LEAP) and Kinetic Kill Vehicle (KKV) with an IR seeker to detect missiles in space. The Block IV missile was successfully tested in *Lake Erie* against subsonic and supersonic targets at sea-skimming to high altitudes, but three tests of a Block III missiles with a KKV were unsuccess-

Table 5: *NEW SHIPS ENTERING SERVICE, 1 APRIL 1994 TO 31 MARCH 1995 (RUSSIA, CHINA IN 1994)*

Type	USA	Russia	UK	France	China	India	Japan	Italy
CV (large)	–	–	–	–	–	–	–	–
CV (medium)	–	–	–	–	–	–	–	–
CV (small)	–	–	–	–	–	–	–	–
CAH	–	–	–	–	–	–	–	–
CG	1	–	–	–	–	–	–	–
DD	6	–	–	–	1	–	–	2
FF (fleet)	–	–	3	–	2	–	–	2
(escort)	–	–	–	1	–	–	–	–
SSBN	1	–	1	–	–	–	–	–
SSGN	3	1	–	–	–	–	–	–
SSN	–	1	–	–	–	–	–	–
SS (all)	–	3*	–	–	2	1	1	1

Notes: *all for export*

ful, as two launches failed and a third missed the 'Scud'-like ballistic missile target. Short-range defence against ballistic missiles will use an improved AEGIS radar and the Co-Operative Engagement Capability (CEC).

(b) Bofors announced a new family of surface-to-air missiles, with a laser-beam guidance system, suitable for such naval craft as the new Swedish YS 2000 missile corvette.

E(iv). Mine Warfare Systems

United States. New concepts in mine warfare included self-propelled drones that can use built-in sonar to detect and locate mines ahead of the controlling surface ship or submarine, and a gun-fired munition to destroy mines in shallow water. The laser-based Kaman Magic Lantern mine detector works well in a helicopter, but will need some time to be adapted to fast-moving aircraft. The Mk 7 Marine Mammal System (MMS), using specially trained dolphins, retains strong support.

E(v). Other Weapon Systems.

(a) Hughes and Signaal are to develop jointly a laser-based naval CIWS to replace Phalanx and Goalkeeper around 2000-2005.

(b) Russia is reporting to be developing a rocket-powered torpedo, 'Shval', with an underwater speed of 200m

sec^{-1}. A low-pressure gas envelope around the torpedo may reduce water resistance almost to zero.

F. NAVAL EVENTS

F(i) Areas of Conflict and Naval Actions

(a) The Gulf. UN sanctions against Iraq, including the naval blockade and air exclusion zones, remained in force; in August it was announced that US warships on blockade duty in the Gulf of Aqaba would be replaced by Lloyd's of London inspectors.

On 6 October, satellite intelligence

The last active battleships, USS Wisconsin *(BB 64, nearer camera) and* Missouri *(BB 63), taking on supplies from the fast combat support ship* Sacramento *during the Gulf War. All four battleships were removed from the register in early 1995, as too costly to maintain for possible eventual use as fire support ships.* (USN official)

The very expensive, very capable SSN-21 type submarine Seawolf *ready for launch. The* Seawolf *class was intended to restore to the US Navy its former superiority in one to one nuclear submarine combat with Soviet submarines, but the price tag was too high for the post-Cold War era.* (General Dynamics)

A US patrol in a Sea Raider utility craft passing the bow of the command ship La Salle *during Operation 'Desert Shield'.* La Salle *relieved the cruiser* Belknap *as Sixth Fleet flagship in November 1994.* (USN official)

intercepts detected large-scale Iraqi troop movements close to the border with Kuwait. As Kuwait mobilised reserves, the Gulf War allies moved rapidly to contain any possible threat. On 10 October the USS *Eisenhower* CVBG, with the cruiser *Leyte Gulf* and the destroyer *Hewitt*, reached the Red Sea from the Mediterranean, while the four-ship Marine Corps ARG already in the area, carrying 2000 marines and led by USS *Tripoli*, was ordered up the Gulf. Four thousand men were sent from the United States, and other forces alerted. HMS *Cornwall* arrived off Kuwait from Dubai, 9 October, and was joined by the *Cardiff* and the French frigate *Georges Leygues*. Within a week, Iraqi troops pulled back from the border area and the crisis eased. As of 26 October, US forces in the region numbered over 28,000 personnel, 270 combat aircraft and sixteen warships.

(b) The Mediterranean. The so-called UN peace-keeping operations in Bosnia, including the air exclusion zones and the naval blockade enforcing the arms shipments embargo, continued. The United States abandoned enforcement of the arms embargo from 0500 GMT on 13 November; other NATO nations maintained the embargo, without US naval assistance. The major NATO air attack on a Serb-held airfield at Udbina, near Bihac, on 21 November, used land-

based aircraft; six Sea Harriers from *Invincible* helped to provide 'top cover' for the operation. On 22 November, perhaps in retaliation, two Sea Harriers evaded a retaliatory attack by two Serb SA-2 'Guideline' missiles near Banja Luka; on the following day NATO planes hit back at Bosnian Serb missile sites. On 15 December, a RN Sea King from 845 Squadron was hit by small-arms fire and made an emergency landing near Sarajevo, and a Sea Harrier crashed in the Adriatic while returning to HMS *Invincible*, the pilot ejecting safely.

(c) The Atlantic. Spanish fishermen were involved in several fisheries disputes during the year, some requir-

ing naval intervention. Early in August, Cornish fishermen in the Bay of Biscay alleged that they were being intimidated and threatened by the much larger and more numerous Spanish boats, and their gear cut. The fishery protection vessels *Anglesey* and *Alderney*, sent to investigate, became unpopular for enforcing EU directives as well as protecting British trawlers. A detachment from the *Alderney* boarded the British trawler *Charisma*, broke into the wheelhouse and sent it home under naval escort, with nets sealed for measurement ashore. Spanish trawlers were arrested by British and Irish fisheries vessels for using nets with small mesh.

An acrimonious dispute between Spain and Canada began on 9 March with the arrest of the trawler *Estai* just outside the 200-mile limit off Newfoundland, four bursts of fire being directed over the trawler's bow before she was boarded. The patrol vessel *Vigia* was promptly sent to protect Spanish trawlers; the *Serviola* followed, and a frigate was prepared for sailing. The dispute tended towards farce when the *Vigia*, short of fuel and refused permission to take on stocks in St John's, Newfoundland, had to proceed to a US harbour at slow speed, while on the other side the old frigate *Terra Nova* withdrew to Halifax after springing a leak. Nevertheless, Canada treated the affair seriously; at least one submarine was used to monitor and keep track of the Spanish fishing fleet, and Spanish boats alleged harassment and net-cutting by fishery protection vessels in

The Venezuelan survey and research ship Punta Brava, *built by Bazan at Cartagena and completed in 1991, is a multipurpose type developed from the Spanish* Malaspina *class.* (Bazan) p73

fog. An agreement on revised fish quotas and the introduction of independent observers to monitor catches was reached on 16 April.

(d) 'PACRIM' and Indian Ocean.

Suspicions that North Korea was diverting plutonium into a nuclear weapons programme led to strong US pressure; in May 1994, the *Independence* CVBG was ordered to keep within one week's sailing time of Korea, and Washington prepared to seek punitive sanctions at the United Nations. Pyongyang, apparently unimpressed, ordered an improved Silkworm anti-ship missile to be fired into the Sea of Japan; a defensive minefield may have been laid off its coast. The *Kitty Hawk* CVBG, which left the continental United States on 24 June on regular deployment to the western Pacific remained near Korea during the Geneva talks that began in August. American MCM capabilities were improved by the minesweepers *Guardian* and *Patriot*, and the LPD *Juneau* with four MH-53 MCM helicopters. A tense situation was defused by the agreement of 21 October.

An unexpected consequence of the crisis was a Sino-American naval confrontation, kept secret until mid-December. Between 27 and 29 October, the *Kitty Hawk* CVBG tracked a Chinese 'Han' class nuclear submarine in international waters in the Yellow Sea, using ASW aircraft and sonobuoys. As the submarine neared its base at Qingdao (Tsingtau), Chinese fighter aircraft were scrambled and flew near the carrier and within sight of American aircraft. Beijing took a very serious view of the incident, per-

The island bridge structure of the new French nuclear carrier Charles de Gaulle. (Courtesy A Preston)

The French frigate La Fayette. (DCN, courtesy A Preston)

haps because of the carrier's proximity or because her aircraft entered Chinese air space; the USA was warned that Chinese forces would 'shoot to kill' if such an incident recurred.

On 9 February, the Philippines accused China of stationing warships in a part of the Spratly Islands claimed

A computer-generated image of the Anglo-French-Italian Common New Generation Frigate (CNGF). The official estimate of 2002 for the in-service date of the first-of-class will probably slip by three or four years. (Project Horizon)

by Manila, and of detaining Filipino fishermen in the islands. China denied both charges, but the Philippines ordered naval craft and five jet aircraft – reputedly its entire operational air force – to increase surveillance in the area. On 25 March, four Chinese fishing boats were detained by Philippine Navy personnel. On 11 April, China reiterated its claim to the entire Spratly Island group, while declining to discuss the legal basis of the claim. In May, the movements of a Filipino landing ship and patrol vessel near a China-held reef were obstructed by Chinese fishing vessels backed at a distance by two warships. Other navies were active in the disputed archipelago; in March, Taiwan announced it would send a small naval force to enforce its claims, and Taiwanese naval infantry on one of the scattered reefs or islets shelled a Vietnamese cargo ship.

Organised insurrection in Sri Lanka continued. The 330t offshore patrol vessel *Sagarawardene* was sunk near Manner Island, off the north coast, with the loss of twenty-five crew members, on 20 September. Reports indicated that she was rammed by two fishing boats packed with explosives and manned by a suicide squad of five disabled Tamil Tigers, who also died. Tensions eased during a 100-day ceasefire from 8 January 1995, but just two hours after it ended on 19 April, the patrol boats *Sooraya* and *Ranasuru* were destroyed in Trincomalee harbour, apparently by mines. Two other boats were damaged in the blasts; eleven crew members and four Tamil Tigers were killed and twenty two crew members injured. Two Tamil Tiger boats were sunk by the Sri Lankan Navy off Jaffna, 20 April.

(e) Africa. At the end of February, over 2000 US and Italian Marines staged an unopposed landing at Mogadishu to cover the departure of the last UN peace-keeping troops from Somalia. The rearguard was safely evacuated on 2 March.

A profile of the indicative design of the CNGF. Details are speculative, and complete commonality of weaponry unlikely. (Project Horizon)

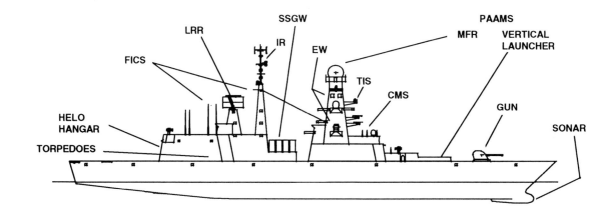

LENGTH OVERALL	149 m	DRAUGHT	5 m
LENGTH WATERLINE	140 m	DEEP DISPLACEMENT	6,000 tonnes approx
BEAM MAXIMUM	20 m	SPEED MAXIMUM	30 kts approx
BEAM WATERLINE	18 m	AVAILABLE ACCOMMODATION	235

A military coup took place in Gambia during the visit of USS *La Moure County* to Banjul, the Gambian President taking refuge on the US warship, 22 July. Joint exercises with the local Defence Forces, with the armoury open and transport provided, facilitated the coup; permission for the US Marines aboard *La Moure County* to intervene ashore was withheld by Washington.

(f) Caribbean. During the summer of 1994, international pressure for intervention in Haiti increased; the UN blockade, although widened in May, was ineffective, and the only consequence of stricter sanctions seemed to be more refugees. A Marine Corps ARG, comprising the *Inchon, Trenton, Portland* and *Spantanburg County* joined USS *Wasp* off Haiti in July, bringing the American warship total in the area to thirteen. By late July, Combined Joint Task Force 120 (CJTF 120) consisted of the flagship *Mount Whitney*, the ARG with about 2300 Marines, the *Wasp* with another 2000, and one US destroyer, six frigates (four US, one Canadian and one Argentine), two US coastal patrol craft and the USNS *Big Horn* on blockade duty. The UN approved military intervention in Haiti on 30 July, but hopes of a negotiated settlement delayed action. As talks dragged on, the carriers *America* and *George Washington*, with additional troops and special forces, were ordered to the Car-

An artist's impression of LPD (R), the projected replacement for the Royal Navy's Fearless *and* Intrepid.

ibbean (13 September), and HMS *Broadsword* and RFA *Oakleaf* were offered for use in a support role. In the event, the threat of overwhelming force was sufficient; the planned invasion was aborted and on 19 September Haiti was taken without a shot by 15,000 US troops. The UN took over from the USA, 31 March 1995.

The Haiti intervention was sidetracked for some weeks by an exodus of refugees from Cuba in August and early September. The US deployed naval and coastguard craft, and surveillance aircraft, to prevent the narrow strait to Florida being crossed by small boats and makeshift rafts. Eight of the American ships off Haiti were diverted, and new refugee camps set up at Guantanamo Bay Naval Base

and in West Indian islands. The crisis was ended by a Cuban clampdown on refugees, 12 September.

F(ii). Major Accidents and Incidents at Sea, 1 April 1994 to 31 March 1995

(a) In May, the crew of HMS *Valiant* was checked for radioactive contamination after a leak was found at Devonport during machinery repairs. *Valiant* was taken out of service several weeks earlier than expected because of the reactor fault.

(b) The Indonesian LST KRI *Teluk Lampug*, on the way to D-Day celebrations, was damaged by a storm in the Bay of Biscay, 3 June; all fifty-seven crew members were taken off by helicopter.

(c) Two crew members died in June when the Indian carrier *Vikrant* was slightly damaged by fire.

(d) The accidental discharge of a marine sound signal on board RMAS *Newton*, off the Florida coast, killed one crew member and injured three scientists, 16 July.

(e) HMS *Brazen*, which ran aground in the Canales Patagonicos, off the Chilean coast near Cape Horn, just after midnight on 11–12 September while returning home from a Falklands deployment, was refloated on 15 September with Chilean assistance. The frigate's commanding officer accepted

An artist's impression of HMS Scott, *the Royal Navy's future Ocean Survey Vessel (OSV). (BAe SEMA)*

An artist's impression of the Japanese destroyer Murasame *, under construction at Ishikawajima-Harima's Tokyo yard.* Murasame *is due to commission in early 1996.* (Ishikawajima-Harima)

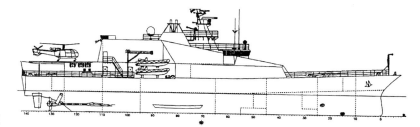

the blame for a series of navigational errors.

(f) HMS *Battleaxe* collided with *U-14* during night exercises in the English Channel, 25 January. Both ships received hull damage but returned to Portland unaided; there were no casualties.

(g) The Portuguese submarine *Barracuda* was slightly damaged by a merchant ship while surfacing in the English Channel, about 13km from Portland.

The futuristic profile of the 75m, 1350 tonne offshore patrol vessel being built by ASMAR in Chile for Mauritius. The vessel was designed in Canada. (ASMAR)

Elevations of the three national designs for the German-Netherlands-Spanish Tripartite AAW frigate.
a) *A Royal Schelde scheme for the Dutch LCF, which will replace the* Tromp *and* De Ruyter. (Royal Schelde)
b) *The German Type 124, based on the* Brandenberg *(Type 123) hull.*
c) *The Spanish F100* (Spanish Navy)

F(iii). Footnotes

(a) The deaths were announced during the year of:

i) Vice-Admiral Henri Rousselot, wartime commander of the Free French submarine *Rubis*, aged 82.

ii) Rear-Admiral Godfrey Place, VC, commander of *X7* in the September 1943 midget submarine attack on the *Tirpitz*, aged 73.

iii) Yohai Bin-Nun, the Israeli commander who led three war-surplus Italian one-man assault craft in the 1948 attack that sank the Egyptian sloop *El Amir Farouk* off Gaza and damaged a minesweeper, aged 69.

(b) Five sunken submarines were discovered or investigated:

i) The remains of the Confederate submarine torpedo-boat *H L Hunley*

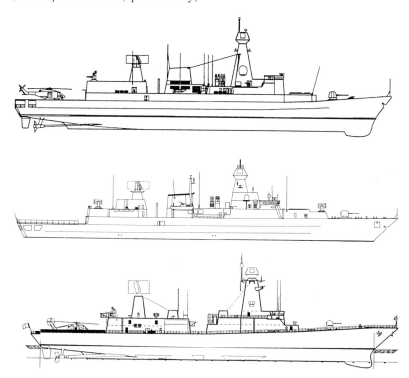

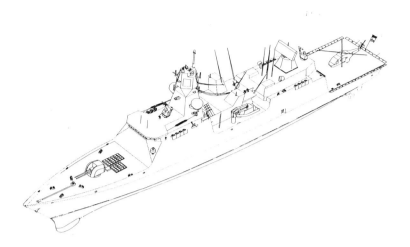

*The latest official Netherlands Navy drawing of the LCF frigate; the gun armament proposed is still 2-4.7in DP, turrets ex-*Tromp *and* De Ruyter.

were found off Charleston, S Carolina.

ii) The remains of HM submarine *E3*, torpedoed and sunk by *U-27* off the Northern Dutch coast on 18 October 1914, were located by a local divers' group.

iii) The remains of HM submarine *Vandal*, lost with all hands on a wartime exercise off Arran, were located and declared an official war grave.

iv) The French submarine *Protée*, sunk in the Mediterranean in late 1943, was located, with the remains of crew members aboard.

An artist's impression of the Dutch amphibious transport Rotterdam. *(RNethN)*

v) *U 534*, raised 23 August 1993, was brought to Jutland for restoration before going on show.

(c) The future of HMS *Caroline*, believed to be the last survivor of the British Grand Fleet at Jutland, and since 1924 the HQ ship for the Ulster RNVR in Belfast, is in doubt because of defence cuts. If surplus to requirements, she may be preserved as a museum.

(d) As part of the celebrations to mark the 50th anniversary of D-Day, an international fleet of warships was reviewed off Portsmouth, 5 June. Merchant ships present included the

last original, operational Liberty ship, the *Jeremiah O'Brien*.

(e) The release of Cabinet papers for 1964 under the 30-year rule showed that the Conservative government's decision to build a fifth Polaris nuclear submarine (February 1964) was taken against Treasury opposition. The government admitted privately that Polaris as purchased hardly provided Britain with a satisfactory independent nuclear deterrent. The fifth boat was cancelled by the incoming Labour administration.

(f) Details were also released of proposed bombing raids on Indonesia in 1964 to destroy air and naval capabilities if Djakarta's confrontation with Malaysia had escalated. Strike aircraft from carriers in the Indian Ocean and South China Sea would have complemented land-based attacks from Malaysia and Australia.

(g) Argentine stated officially that it considered the sinking of the *General Belgrano* outside the Falklands Islands exclusion zone in May 1982 'a legal act of war'.

G. MISCELLANEOUS

The US Navy's nuclear-powered deep-diving vessel *NR 1* is to be used in mid-1995 to search the Carthage-Rome trade route for the wrecks of ancient ships.

The 'Scimitar' frigate, one version of the Canadian patrol frigate submitted to Riyadh in response to Saudi interest; however, in November 1994, the order for smalerl, less capable La Fayette *class frigates was confirmed.* (Saint John Shipbuilding)

The F 3000 S, a variant of the French La Fayette *class frigate for Saudi Arabia.* (DCN)

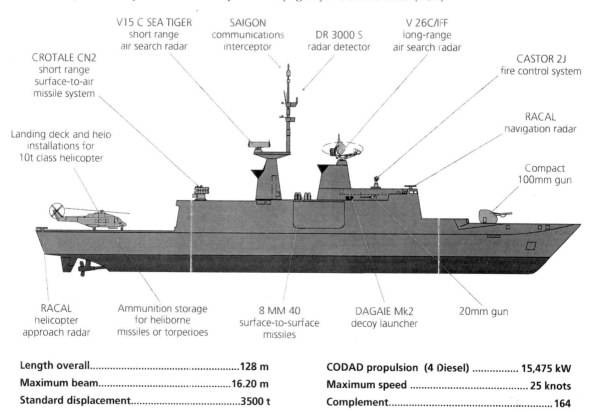

Length overall.......................................128 m	CODAD propulsion (4 Diesel) .... 15,475 kW	
Maximum beam...16.20 m	Maximum speed .... 25 knots	
Standard displacement.............................3500 t	Complement.. 164	

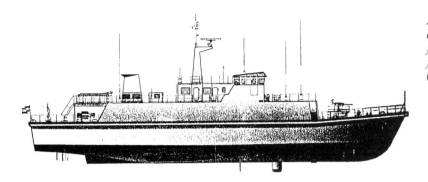

A drawing of the Spanish CME coastal minehunter. The class of four was authorised in 1993 and the first is to be laid down in June 1995. (Bazan)

Keyed cut-away drawing of the Swedish submarine Gotland. (Kockums)

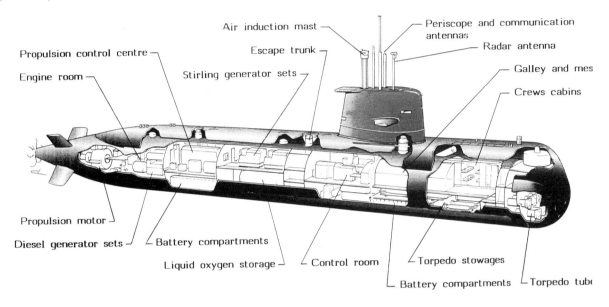

Air induction mast

Periscope and communication antennas

Radar antenna

Propulsion control centre

Escape trunk

Engine room

Stirling generator sets

Galley and mes

Crews cabins

Propulsion motor

Diesel generator sets

Battery compartments

Liquid oxygen storage

Control room

Torpedo stowages

Battery compartments

Torpedo tube

An elevation of the Swedish inshore minesweeper Styrsö *being built by Karlskronavarvet.* (KKV)

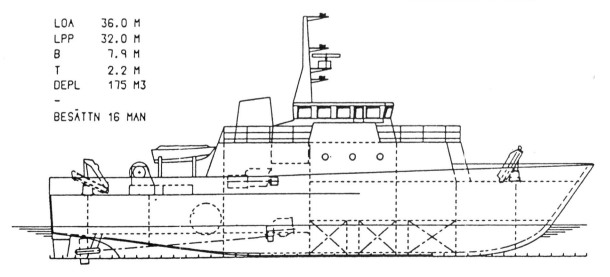

LOA	36.0 M
LPP	32.0 M
B	7.9 M
T	2.2 M
DEPL	175 M3
-	
BESÄTTN 16 MAN	

SAK 57 Mk 3
Gun system

* Stealth design
* 120 rounds in the gun
* Programmable 3P-ammunition
* Multi-purpose
* Integrated fire control computer
* Automatic reloading
* Access to gun from below
* High growth potential
* Easy to install
  – limited space requirement below deck
  – fixed hoists and ship magazines

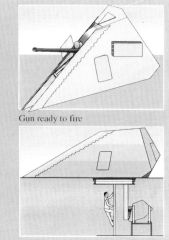

Gun ready to fire

Gun in Stealth position

The Mk3 version of the Bofors 57mm gun includes stealth technology: when not in use, the gun can be retracted into the cupola to reduce the radar signature. The 57mm Mk3 is planned for the Swedish 'YS 2000' missile corvette class. (Bofors)

The Italian fleet patrol ship Aviere *(ex Iraqi* Thi Qar*), one of four* Lupo *class frigates purchased in 1993, as commissioned in January 1995 with provisional weapon and sensor outfit. Full system changes will be made during the year.* (Italian Navy)

The new Italian destroyer Luigi Durand de la Penne *(ex-* Animoso *). The replacement of four Otomat SSMs with a Milas launcher for four ASW missiles with torpedo payloads is being investigated.* (Italian Navy)

INDEX

Page numbers in italics refer to illustrations, and those in bold to tables